Barn Owls
in Britain

Barn Owls in Britain

phantoms of the farmyard

Jeff Martin

with illustrations by Kevin Baker

Whittet Books

For Tina

First published 2008
Text © 2008 by Jeff Martin
Illustrations @2008 by Kevin Baker
Whittet Books Ltd, Yatesbury Manor South, Yatesbury, Wiltshire
SN11 8YE
www.whittetbooks.com
e mail: Annabel@whittet.dircon.co.uk

Cataloguing in Publication Data

A catalogue record for this title is available from the British Library
ISBN-13 978-1-873580-75-2

Printed by Cromwell Press, Trowbridge, Wiltshire. BA14 0XB

'A Barn-Owl was sitting alone and silent as usual in his hayloft hideaway one morning when a talkative jay dropped in for a visit. The jay began sharing his collection of gossip at once, not even pausing for the owl to comment, and kept on with his chatter for an hour or more. When he finally left – still without any remarks from his host – he told all the other barnyard birds he'd never shared a more interesting and enjoyable conversation.'

James Northcote, London

6 barn owls in Britain

CONTENTS

FOREWORD BY
DEREK BUNN

When seen on the wing at a distance the barn, or white, owl's appearance seems almost surreal. This is due to its pale colouring and its buoyant, graceful flight. At close quarters, however, the delicately speckled grey-pencilled plumage of its upper-parts and white facial disc render it exquisitely beautiful. But there is more to this bird than beauty; its ability to approach and pinpoint the exact position of its hidden prey, undetected, and then to catch it in the dark, is truly amazing.

My first sighting of a hunting barn owl occurred when I was a boy. That experience was all that was needed to make me want to see and learn more about this remarkable bird. Sadly though, the species had already become scarce and it was not until fifteen years later, that my ambition was to be realised when I was told about an area not too far from my home where a small population still existed. It was then that my studies commenced. Eventually this interest led to a most enjoyable sharing of information with two fellow enthusiasts who I came to know about - Tony Warburton and Robert Wilson. This collaboration eventually led us to our partnership in writing *The Barn Owl* which, as it transpired, was to be the first of several monographs on the species.

Over the centuries the barn owl has had a chequered history in Britain. Some thousands of years ago, and after the last ice-age, the land was likely to have been too heavily wooded to provide much of its required habitat. However, as large sections of the natural 'wild-wood' were cleared and open areas were created by Man for farming the situation would no doubt have improved. At one time superstitious prejudice was responsible for a certain amount of persecution, but nevertheless it seems that up until some 150 years ago, the species was present and frequently common on virtually every lowland farm in England and Wales. With the advent of game preservation during the 19th century, however, the persecution was greatly intensified and whilst this particular threat did eventually subside, others emerged later, such as in the 20th century when more efficient farming techniques, coupled with a loss of habitat, almost dealt it a terminal blow. Now though, thanks to the efforts of barn owl enthusiasts up and down the country, the bird has a somewhat more optimistic future – at least in some of the least 'busy' areas of Britain.

In writing this new book, Jeff Martin has thoroughly researched the historical and recent literature concerning the barn owl. Besides a description of its biology, he provides the details and discusses the governmental decisions that have affected its welfare. The effects of urbanisation, modern-day farming practices and care of the environment (or lack of it) are well documented, and through this novel approach he has produced a monograph that is refreshingly different from its several predecessors.

Derek Bunn, February 2008

FOREWORD BY ERIC HOSKING

By the late Eric Hosking OBE & Hon. FRPS

(This was written a while ago, when the book was confined to the barn owl in East Anglia. Eric Hosking was a supporter of the project, but died in 1991 and therefore never saw the book in its finished form.)

It was on a lovely, warm evening in June 1930 that George Bird, a well known Ipswich bird photographer and I, were driving towards Staverton Park when we spotted a Barn Owl perched on a post by the road-side. Immediately the car engine was switched off and we coasted, as quietly as we could, towards the bird until we were no more than six yards from it and, at that moment, I lost my heart to the Barn Owl. This happened 60 years ago yet the memory of that lovely bird remains vividly in my mind as though it happened only yesterday. Thus no one could have been more thrilled than I was to hear that Jeff Martin was writing this book, and no one more delighted when he asked me to write this foreword.

Apart from being such a lovely bird the Barn Owl must be one of the most beneficial species in this country, feeding as it does on rats, mice and other rodents. It is, therefore, a tragedy that for years its numbers have steadily declined throughout Britain and there are even fears that it could be exterminated altogether. Fortunately Suffolk is one of its strongholds and the author one of its champions. There can be no doubt that this book will make people aware of the need to help Barn Owls in any way they can – just one way is to put up suitable nesting boxes. So many of the old barns, that provide ideal nesting sites, have been pulled down and ancient trees, with suitable nesting holes, uprooted.

In Staverton Park before the war George Boast, the gamekeeper, and I found nine nests. Today I doubt whether there is more than a single pair left. It is unfortunate that, apart from a shortage of nesting sites, the Barn Owl is at the end of a food chain. Organochlorines, used to destroy insect pests, may eventually find their way into the Barn Owl. Persistent poisons used to kill rats and mice carry on their deadly work when Barn Owls find and eat them.

I therefore welcome this contribution, which so graphically illustrates the problems that Suffolk's Barn owls have endured. However, perhaps more importantly, it shows us the way if we hope to retain this wonderful bird in significant numbers. To those who have an interest in, and a love of birds, I whole-heartedly commend this book.

Introduction

'Plants and animals do not enter into the story merely as part of the environment, as scenery in the theatre of landscape. They are actors in the play; each has its own character, which needs to be understood.'

Oliver Rackham, *The Illustrated History of the Countryside*
(Weidenfeld & Nicolson, 1994)

There is no doubt that the barn owl is one of Britain's best loved birds and the spectacle of one floating across the countryside at dusk is enough to raise the pulse of most observers. With its ghostly, moth-like appearance, a barn owl is indeed a magical sight.

It is sad, therefore, that the British barn owl has been a source of concern to wildlife conservationists for many years; during the course of the 20th century two national surveys were carried out to assess its population. Indeed it is likely that no other bird species in the British Isles has been afforded such attention.

The first survey (in England and Wales) followed a decline of barn owls and was undertaken by George Blaker in 1932. The conservation movement then was not of its present-day stature, and conducting the survey was a major task. It also took place before the post Second World War farming régime of intensification that was to cause so much controversy in the latter part of the 20th century.

A further survey was carried out by Colin Shawyer in 1987, and this time included Scotland. This study revealed in more detail many of the problems that barn owls face in the modern world, some of which did not trouble them in 1932. Both of those surveys were enormous in their complexity and both have been significant milestones in furthering the barn owl's conservation.

My concern for the barn owl was first aroused in the late 1970s when a pair that I had watched for some years in a quiet corner of the East Anglian countryside suddenly disappeared. The reasons for their disappearance were not clear to me at that time and in 1982 I embarked upon the Suffolk Barn Owl Survey. Subsequently, over the course of the next 20 years or so, I was to monitor the barn owl's fortunes and during that period I was to discover the problems that face Britain's modern barn owls. I also came to realise that although some of them, such as the lack of nesting places, can be dealt with relatively easily, others will undoubtedly continue to affect our barn owls, despite the liberal application of human and financial resources.

At present there appears to be a belief in Britain that the troubles for our barn owls are over and that they can look forward to a brighter future. I hope that will be the case but I am of the view that their problems are only just beginning and that this delightful and interesting bird may ultimately struggle to survive in many parts of the British Isles where it is at present a regular inhabitant of the countryside.

However, it is not just in Britain that barn owls are threatened, for across the globe members of the barn owl family are under threat from persecution, poisoning and the destruction of their habitats. On some of the more remote and idyllic holiday destinations several of the island races may be in jeopardy from development and various catastrophes such as hurricanes, tsunamis and volcanic eruptions, whilst worldwide the threat of urbanisation and an escalating amount of traffic on an ever-increasing road network will cause many deaths in the future.

The pioneering work that was carried out in northern England by Messrs. Bunn, Warburton & Wilson in 1982 and the intensive study in Scotland by Iain Taylor in 1994 all focused on barn owls that nested primarily in barns. Most of my observations were carried out in East Anglia and involved barn owls that were nesting in trees, but where appropriate I have included reports, comparisons and notes from elsewhere. It is my view that those barn owls that live in northern and western Britain behave a little differently to those in the south and east, but this may change in the future as more barn owls in southern England begin to use nest-boxes.

Today, barn owls have long gone from many parts of Britain and sadly they will never return. In other places they remain a part of the present day fauna, but their future remains uncertain. In other locations barn owls have only recently departed but with some understanding, assistance and a little patience, they might yet return – to waft their ghostly way at dusk across the countryside. Maintaining self-sustaining populations of barn owls in suitable and stable habitats is the key to their long-term future.

As well as those interested in wildlife conservation, this book is aimed at those who determine how the land is dedicated – the planners – for it is they, perhaps, who most of all hold in their hands the fate of those barn owls that still live out their lives in the quietness of the British countryside. The role of the planners will become increasingly important as the human population continues its relentless colonisation of the countryside.

Yet we cannot assign the barn owl's future solely to the planners. Land-owners and land managers have their roles to play alongside ornithologists, naturalists and conservationists. The bird's future will be helped by the provision of nest-boxes but is also dependent on habitat.

It might be thought that due to the large amount of literature that has been produced on barn owls in recent years there is nothing further to be said, but I hope that the following pages may help to inspire study, enthusiasm, energy and dedication with some future ornithologists, seeking a species upon which to focus their attentions.

The old perception of the owl as 'harbinger of death' has today changed into one of wonder; thankfully the collecting of feathers is no longer practised. Now, more than ever, people from all backgrounds want to see barn owls. Man has had a close affiliation with this creature over many centuries: this may go back to the days when he relied upon predators, such as the barn owl, to control the numbers of rats and mice that threatened to destroy his precious grain. As long as they exist in the British Isles, barn owls will be inextricably linked to our farmlands and we should do all we can to assist our farmers to encourage them.

The barn owl is only one creature on the farmland stage and, whilst its disappearance from many parts of the British countryside is very sad, it has been largely brought about by the decline of those species upon which it depends. It is only by placing the plight of the barn owl within the context of a whole background of wildlife that its story can be told and so I will be including accounts of the lives of voles and other small mammals. I will talk about the barn owl's history, because history usually repeats itself, and we ignore the lessons of history at our peril.

In conclusion, I should like to add that this is not a scientific book, for I am not a scientist. It is a book that has been written by an amateur natural historian who has tried to use a scientific approach to a fascinating subject. If it inspires some younger birdwatchers to take up the study of owls and so further our knowledge of these delightful birds, then it will have achieved its aim.

Alone and warming his five wits,
The white owl in the belfry sits.
'The White Owl', Alfred, Lord Tennyson

1 THE BARN OWL'S WORLD

'World-wide, Barn owls hunt over open farmland, meadows and hillside rough grazing grassland, extending their operations onto commons and moors, and marshland fringes. In many areas they will hunt over broken scrub, and even on the edges of the desert areas of Africa, Asia and Australia, which support good small mammal populations – certainly more than adequate to tempt Barn Owls.'
Eric Hosking, *Eric Hosking's Owls* (Pelham Books, 1982)

Owls are a worldwide family of birds and are placed in the scientific order Strigiformes. Within that classification the owls are divided into two sub-families: the Tytonidae, which consists of the barn, grass and bay owls and the Strigidae, which comprises all of the remaining owls. The Strigidae is by far the largest group, consisting of approximately 124 species, while the Tytonidae consists of 8 species of barn owl and 2 species of bay owl. At present, owl taxonomy is in a state of flux and so a final tally of just how many different owls there are cannot be given until all of the revisions have been processed. For example, in 1976 two scientists discovered a new species, the long whiskered owlet, in the Peruvian Andes, whilst the lack of recent reports regarding some other species leaves us uncertain as to whether they still exist.

ORIGINS

In his review of the world's owls Burton pointed out that the majority of the scientists who were involved in palaeornithology had agreed that the birds originated from the dinosaurs (Theropoda) during the early part of the Jurassic period. In the 4th volume of his *Catalogue of Fossil Birds* (1971) Brodkorb listed 41 species of extinct owl, amongst which there were 11 species of Tytonidae.

It appears that the owls evolved in the Oligocene period, around 36-25 million years ago, but the diurnal raptors evolved around 22-11 million years earlier, in the Lower Eocene. Although they share some similar features with owls, the diurnal raptors are not closely related. On present knowledge, the nearest relatives to the owls appear to be the Caprimulgiformes, which includes the nightjars and frogmouths as well as the oilbird, a species that lives in a limited area of tropical South America and which is placed in the separate sub-order of Steatornithidae.

Bird bones are usually hollow and are liable to disintegrate; so the remains of birds in the fossil records are few, and identification of species is difficult. In southern France some major ornithological fossil finds have been made in the lower deposits of the Miocene period (between 25 to12 million years ago), and it was during this period that two groups of owls made their appearance. They were the Tytoninae (the barn owls) and the Pholodinae (the bay owls). The Pholodinae were found in the lower deposits of the Lower Miocene while the Tytoninae, which are known from deposits in France and also North America, were of the Middle and Lower Miocene.

The evidence of the finds of the Upper Miocene in southern Europe strongly suggested that, at some stage in the past, barn owls of three different size classes must have lived at the same time. The remains of some were 1.5 times the size of present-day barn owls and have been found in cave deposits not only on the Mediterranean islands of Mallorca and Menorca, but from the Caribbean, where they date from the beginning of the Pleistocene period. The Caribbean remains indicate that barn owls of at least the size of present-day eagle owls once existed, and it is possible that even larger barn owls once lived.

THE FAMILY OF BARN OWLS

The Tytonidae is comprised of two genera, the largest of which is the sub-family Tytoninae. This family forms the genus *Tyto* and consists of eight species of barn and grass owls. The smaller of the two genera is the closely related Phodilus and consists of the sub-family of bay owls known as the Phodilinae. This group consists of two species.

The Tytonidae are grouped together because they share the

Fig 1. The skull of a typical owl, Strix aluco, *the tawny owl* (left) *and the skull of the nominate race of the barn* Tyto alba alba.

same physical features that set them apart from the typical owls of the Strigidae. For example, the skull of the Tytonidae is longer than the Strigidae (Fig. 1) and the bill is larger and finer. The orbits, or eye-sockets, are smaller in relation to the size of the skull than those of typical owls, and the inter-orbital septum, that is the interior bone dividing the eye sockets, is also wider.

Other skeletal differences concern the sternum, which in the Strigidae has two notches, while in the Tytonidae there is only one. In addition, the sternum of the Tytonidae, unlike that of the typical owls, is fused to the furcula or wishbone.

An owl's foot is comprised of four toes, of which the fourth faces backwards. In typical owls the inner toe of the three forward-facing toes is much shorter than the third, but in barn owls they are of the same length while the third, or outer toe, is very mobile and can be reversed. This is a unique foot adaptation amongst the owls and it enables barn owls to grasp their prey efficiently.

An additional feature that separates barn owls from typical owls is that the second, or inner talon, has a raised flange with a comb-like, serrated edge. This is not particularly noticeable on young birds but develops with age. It is the only known owl to have this characteristic although some other birds, such as nightjars and herons, have similar features.

Eventually it might be possible to separate the skeletons of young owls from older ones by the developing size and shape of the skull. It could be that the line of the sagittal suture on the central longitudinal line of the skull becomes more obvious as the animal matures and the brain develops. On the skulls of some tawny owls, for example, the suture is more evident on those that have a narrower bridge between the eye-sockets than those that have a wider bridge. It may be that as the brain grows and develops, then the skull changes in thickness and shape. Work is still going on with this theory and eventually it might well be better supported with barn owls because the third talon may be used, alongside the skull, as a guide to age. Typical owls, as it has already been explained, do not have pectinated, or serrated, talons.

Experiments using egg proteins have aligned the owls with the nightjars, oilbirds and other species of the order Caprimulgiformes rather than with the day-flying falcons, but in 1960 Professor C.G. Sibley, an American scientist, proposed the interesting theory that barn owls are more closely related to the falcons than to the other owls. Sibley's hypothesis was based on trials using egg-whites which he considered a more reliable method of ascertaining the evolutionary relationships between families and orders.

With so many species and races of barn owls distributed around the world, it is not surprising that many have evolved to suit their environments. In a study of the nominate race *T.a.alba* in Scotland, the average wing length of both the males and females was 293mm while another study made it 289mm for males and 290mm for females (but those measurements were based upon museum skins and there would have been some shrinkage during drying). The tail lengths in both studies, and for both genders, matched at 115mm.

In the United States the average wing length of the much larger *T.a.pratincola* was 327mm in males and 328mm in the females, while the tail lengths were 139mm and 141mm respectively. The sub-species *T.a.javanica*, a race that lives in the Far East and which weighs considerably more (males 555g, females 612g) than *T.a.pratincola* (474g and 566g respectively), has a wing length of only 300mm in both genders. Clearly there is much variation within the barn owl family.

Apart from the differences in weights and measurements, all barn owls possess a heart-shaped and quite distinctive facial disc and all have the distinctive 'knock-kneed' appearance when perched. In addition to this, the plumage of each race is distinctive and unusually marked. Compared with other owl species, the eyes are small in relation to the size of the body.

THE DISTRIBUTION OF BARN OWLS

The barn owl (*Tyto alba*) is probably the world's most widely distributed species of land bird, and races, sometimes referred to as sub-species, are distributed throughout five continents. However, they are absent from most of China, the greater part of Russia, the desert regions of North Africa, the Polar Regions, the Philippines, Borneo, the Hawaiian Islands and New Zealand, although several races are to be found in Australasia. A full list of the known barn owl species and their races is given in Table 1.

No one knows for certain how many races of the barn owl *T.alba* there are, although a consensus of opinion would suggest that there are around 36. Little is known about many of the island barn owls and it is unclear whether they all still exist.

There certainly cause for concern for *T. soumagnei*, the Madagascar red owl, which is endangered. It was observed in 1929 and has only once been reported since then (in 1973); it is thought to be nearing extinction. A further five barn owls are endangered in various parts of the world: the first of these, *T. nigrobrunnea*, the endemic Taliabu owl of Taliabu in the Sula Islands, is known only from a single specimen that was collected in 1938 and it has not been seen since that time. There is a possibility, however, that this single example might have been an individual of the Minihassa owl, *T. inexspectata*, which is endemic to Sulawesi in Indonesia and is also considered to be a rare species.

On Buru and the Tanimbar Islands of Indonesia, the lesser masked owl, *T. sororcula*, which is often referred to as a race of the species *T. novaehollandiae*, is known from only a few specimens and has never been observed in the field, while on neighbouring New Britain, Papua New Guinea, the rare species *T. aurantia*, the golden owl, has only twice been seen and that was in 1978 and 1984. The late Sir Peter Scott recorded that when he landed at Banz, New Guinea, on December 14th, 1956, he was welcomed by the natives some of whom were wearing head-dresses made of barn-owl feathers.

The large and powerful race of barn owls, *T.a.affinis*, dominates the continent of Africa. It gained notoriety when individuals of this sub-species were introduced to the Seychelles to control the population of brown rats that were threatening the existence of the white, or fairy, tern which is indigenous to those and a few other nearby islands. As well as eating the rats, the barn owls set about devouring the terns and eventually the owls had to be eradicated.

Africa is also home to the common grass owl, *T. capensis*. Apart from its wide distribution in Africa, *capensis* is also found in India, Australia and elsewhere in the Far East, although some think that the *capensis* species in Africa is a distinct and separate species from those elsewhere in that region. Where this view is applied then the remaining owls are separated into a full species of their own, *T. longimembris*. The problems are further compounded by the division of *T.longimembris* into a number of sub-species including *T.l.papuensis,* a race of south-east New Guinea and other races such as *T.l.mella* and *T.l.chinensis* of south-east China and *T.l.walleri,* which includes a group of closely related forms of barn owls. This uncertain description of barn owls in the tropics means that there is a great deal of work to be undertaken on the species and races of barn owls in this, and other parts of the world.

In the tropics many of the barn owls are forest-dwellers and it is unclear what precise effect forest clearance might be having upon

Table 1 A check-list of the species and races of known barn owls

Genus Tyto

Species	**Races**	**Distribution**
Tyto alba		
	T. a. alba (Scop.)	Western & southern Europe
	T. a. guttata	Eastern & northern Europe
	T. a. schmitzi	Madeira
	T. a. gracilirostris	Canary Islands
	T. a. ernesti	Corsica and Sardinia
	T. a. detorta	Cape Verde Island
	T. a. thomensis	Sao Tome
	T. a. erlangeri	Middle East (S.Arabia, Gulf, Syria etc)
	T. a. stertens	India, Pakistan, Nepal, Burma, Sri Lanka
	T. a. affinis	Africa, south of the Sahara
	T. a. hypermetra	Comoros Island
	T. a. javanica	Thailand, Burma, Malasia, Indonesia
	T. a. deseopstorfii	Andaman Island
	T. a. sumbaensis	Sumbe Island
	T. a. everetti	Savu Island
	T. a. kuehni	Lesser Sunda Islands
	T. a. meeki	S.E. New Guinea, Vulvan & Dampier Is
	T. a. deliculata	Australia & Solomon Islands
	T. a. crassirostris	Boang Is.,Tanga Islands, Bismark Arc
	T. a. interposita	Santa Cruz Is., Banks Is., New Hebrid.
	T. a. lulu	Fiji, Tonga, Samoa, New Caledonia
	T. a. pratincola	North & Central America
	T. a. guatemalae	Guatemala and to Panama

	T. a. lucayana	Bahama Islands
	T. a. furcata	Cuba
	T. a. niveicauda	Island of Pines & Cuba
	T. a. bondi	Bay Island
	T. a. glaucops	Tortuga and Hispaniola, West Indies
	T. a. nigrescens	Dominica, West Indies
	T. a. insularis	Lesser Antilles
	T. a. bargei	Curacao Islands
	T. a. contempta	Columbia, Peru, Ecuador, Venezuela
	T. a. subandeana	Columbia, Ecuador
	T. a. hellmayri	Guianas to Amazon
	T. a. tuidara	Brazil,south of Amazon, Chile, Argentina
	T. a. punctatissima	Galapagos Islands
T. aurantia		New Britain Island
T. rosenbergii		The Celebes Islands
T. inexpectata		North Celebes
T. novaehollandiae	*T. novaehollandiae*	Australia, parts of Tasmania
	T .n castinops	Tasmania, New Guinea
	T. n. perplexa	South-west Australia
	T. n. kimberli	New Guinea
	T. n. manusi	Isle of Manus
	T. n. cayeli	Isle of Baru
	T. n. sorocula	Tanimber Island
T. soumagnei		Madagascar
T. tenebricosa	*T. tenebricosa*	Eastern Australia
	T. t. multipunctata	Northern Australia, a race of the species *tenebricosa*
T. capensis	*T.capensis*	Africa
	T. longimembris	is the name used for *capensis* from India through to Australia

Sub-species of
T.longimembris

	T. l. walleri	Australia, Phillipines, Celebes, Kalidupa and Fiji Islands
"	*T. l. papuensis*	New Guinea
"	*T. l. melli*	South eastern China
"	*T. l. chinensis*	South-eastern China

Genus: Phodilus

P. badius	*P. b. badius*	Eastern & central Burma, Borneo & Java
	P. b. saturatus	Northern Burma & northern India
	P .b. assimilis	Ceylon
	P. b. parus	Belitung Island
	P .b. arixathus	Bunguran Island
P. prigoginei	*P. p. prigoginei*	Zaire & Burundi

Sources: *Working Bibliography of Owls of the World*; Clark, R.J., Smith, D.G. & Kelso, L.H. (Natural Wildlife Federation, Washington,1978); *Owls of the World*, Burton, J.A. (Peter Lowe, London, 1984)

them, although it seems likely that barn owls may well benefit as they did when Britain's forests were cleared. In some places oil palm has been planted after the rain forests have been cleared and in consequence of this the plantations of Malaysia, for example, have become attractive to rats, which in turn have attracted barn owls. In southern Africa it is thought that barn owls exist in greater numbers where there is a combination of crops and open savannah, and where scattered buildings may provide nest-sites. It seems likely, therefore, that in the absence of development, road traffic and poisons, barn owl numbers may well increase in places such as these.

Closer to the British Isles there are 9 races of barn owls to be found in the Western Palearctic, but only 2 of these are of prime concern to us. They are the 'dark-breasted barn owl', *Tyto alba guttata*, which I describe later (p. 133) and which lives in the Netherlands, Germany, eastern and northern France, Denmark, Poland, western Russia, Austria, Hungary, Bulgaria and also in southern Sweden, where its existence is precarious. Indeed it may now be extinct in Sweden, although it is possible that global warming might aid its survival.

The 'white-breasted barn owl', *Tyto alba alba*, is the nominate race and inhabits the British Isles, Ireland, the Channel Islands, western and southern France, the Iberian Peninsula, Italy, Switzerland, parts of North Africa, Cyprus, Sicily and Malta, although it now appears that barn owls have gone from that island. Once there were 10 pairs of barn owls on Malta and their disappearance is thought to be due to persecution.

Colin Shawyer was of the opinion that temperature plays an important role in the distribution of *guttata* and *alba* in Europe. He stated that barn owls of the dark-breasted race are found east of the line that marks the 3°C mean January temperature, the isotherm, and that the white-breasted race is found to the west of that isotherm because it is less tolerant of the cold. In addition he stated that winter temperature, and the duration of snow-cover, are undoubtedly the most important factors that determine barn owl distribution and abundance in Europe and that because of it, most of the barn owls in Europe are found in the west; they only occupy one third of Continental Europe's land mass. However, it appears that the distribution of Europe's barn owls is unclear at this time for, as Hagemeijer and Blair showed, there are large parts of Europe for which barn owl data does not exist. From time to time there are reports of barn owls being discovered in the eastern parts of Europe, so until we have further information we cannot be sure of this bias. With the enlargement of the European Union (EU) there is now an opportunity to gather more information.

If the 3°C January isotherm does define the separation of *alba* and *guttata*, then it will be interesting to see what happens if global warming continues its course. Barn owls must surely have been subjected to differing climatic conditions on a number of occasions in the past as the temperature cooled and warmed for appreciable periods, and especially after the last ice age. If global warming continues unabated for a long period, then the 3°C January isotherm will retreat and move north, so if Shawyer's theory is correct, then the range of *guttata* will also recede. It should be noted that where the ranges of *guttata* and *alba* overlap then interbreeding may take place and we shall return to this subject.

THE NAMING OF THE BARN OWL

Before 1940, when the owls were re-classified, the barn owl was scientifically named *Strix flammeus* by Linnaeus, the eminent Swedish naturalist. When the owls were re-classified, however, it was named *Tyto alba alba* (Scopoli), after the Italian naturalist Giovanni Scopoli who originally described it. The name is derived from the Greek word *tuto*, meaning 'night owl', and the Latin *albus* meaning 'white'. The common name 'barn owl' was not adopted until 1883, although it took some time for this name to filter through, especially in places where trees were the dominant nesting-site. For example, it was called the 'white owl' in 1834 by the Pagets when reviewing the natural history of north Suffolk, but by 1884 it was being referred to by Churchill Babington as the 'white or barn owl', while later, in 1938, a compromise was arrived at with 'white-breasted barn owl' although previously Ticehurst had named it 'barn owl' in his *Birds of Suffolk*. Yet despite all of these modern names I still hear an older resident of Suffolk occasionally refer to it as the 'white owl'.

In 1984 I was talking to friend of mine, Clarence Aldred of Southwold, who was an old Suffolk gamekeeper. I asked him if there were any barn owls around. 'No', he replied, 'but we've got a few white owls', and I received a similar reply from Harold Alexander, another of Suffolk's older residents, at Cotton in 2005. But this habit was not confined to Suffolk. In Essex a friend of mine, the wildlife photographer and naturalist Alan Parker, recounted how he was carrying out a bird survey at Gobions Farm at Collier Row, Romford, in 1968. During the survey he found tawny, little and barn owls, along with kestrel, all breeding. Upon informing the farmer that these species were present the farmer told Alan that 'his brother, who ran an adjoining farm just across the A12 (road), had a pair of white owls there too.'

It has been suggested that the name barn owl originated from an old country name of 'barn-door owl', a name that was sporadically used in parts of Europe, because it was customary to nail a barn owl or part of one to a barn door to ward off evil spirits, although in some western areas of Britain other birds and creatures were also used. It was a custom that might have its origins in Roman times although the practice was not confined to barn doors. The door leading to a child's nursery would sometimes be adorned in this manner to protect the child within from evil. It is possible the barn owl obtained its name this way but I think it more likely that the name came about during the Enclosure Period. Before then the name 'barn owl' or 'barn-door owl' seems not to appear in the literature. It was always the 'white owl'.

'White owl' was also used in other counties of Britain and especially those in the south, although I do not know of anywhere in Britain where it was so consistently used and in such a widespread manner as it was in Suffolk. In neighbouring Norfolk, barn owls were seldom referred to as 'white owls'. Rather they revelled in such local names as 'Billy Wix' or 'Billy Wise', 'Madge Howlet' and 'Gill Howter', while in Essex it was called 'Billy Owl', 'grey owl' or 'Willy' according to Miller Christy, although he also referred to it as the 'white owl'. 'White owl' was sometimes used in the United States, having originated with settlers from the Old World.

In Sussex it was called 'Moggy Owl', while in Yorkshire it was known as the 'hissing owl'. From the Midlands of England came some interesting names. For example, in Northamptonshire it was often referred to as the 'hobby owl', and in Leicestershire 'padg' or 'pudge' was occasionally used, while in Nottinghamshire and Worcestershire it was sometimes called the 'padge owlet'. 'Berthuan' is a Cornish name but others, such as 'screech owl', 'scritch owl' or 'scratch owl', reflect the eerie and haunting territorial calls of barn owls which once frequently echoed across most the British countryside, while the name 'roarer', a former common name in southern Scotland and parts of Yorkshire, epitomises, perhaps, the strength of character and the respect this species once had. Apart from 'white owl' perhaps the most frequently used name in the old literature was 'screech owl', so called after its familiar territorial call.

The flat often treeless levels of Somerset are very similar to the polders of the Netherlands; nesting sites for barn owls in both places are scarce. Little wonder then that in Somerset the barn owl was once called the 'church owl' because of its habit of nesting in village church steeples, while in Holland it was also called 'kerkhuile', or 'church owl', for the same reason. In Sweden, where the barn owl is now rare, it was sometimes called 'torn uggla' (tower owl).

In Cheshire, it was once known as the 'monkey owl'; thousands of miles away in the United States, it was once called the 'monkey-faced owl'.

Scottish barn owls had the haunting and wonderful gaelic name of 'Sgriachag' which has its roots in Scandanavia. In Norse, the word 'hag' means witch or evil spirit, and there can be little doubt that in the past there have been few creatures that have excelled barn owls as being the source of so much fear and superstition. Not just in Europe were barn owls once feared: in Madagascar, where the barn owl *T. soumagnei* is an endangered bird, it was once regarded as a bird of evil omen and of harmful influence, and there it was once known – and perhaps still is – as 'vorondulo' or 'ghost bird'. At the Cape of Good Hope it was called 'doodvogel', or the bird of death, and it was dreaded and hated by the natives. The Afrikaans of South Africa named it 'nonnetjie-uil', the 'little nun owl'. Closer to home it is known in some parts of France as 'chouette effraye', the 'alarming or terrifying owl', while in Germany it has the apt and wonderful title of 'schleiereule' - the 'mystery or phantom owl'.

SOURCES USED IN THIS CHAPTER

Babington, C., 1884-86: *Catalogue of the Birds of Suffolk*. Van Voorst, London.

Burton, J.A., 1984: *Owls of the World: their evolution, structure and ecology*. Peter Lowe, London.

Collar, N.J., and Andrew, P., 1988: *Birds to Watch*. International Council for Bird Protection, Cambridge.

Cramp, S. (ed.)., 1985: *The Birds of the Western Palearctic (Vol 4)*. Oxford University Press.

Hagemeijer, W.J.M., and Blair, M.J., 1997: *The EEBC Atlas of European Breeding Birds*. Poyser, London.

Kemp, A., and Calburn, S., 1987: *The Owls of Southern Africa*. Struik Winchester, Cape Town.

Miller Christy, R., 1890: *The Birds of Essex*. Essex Field Club.

Morley, C., 1935: Barn Owl in Kenton. *Trans. Suffolk Nat. Soc., 1:* 75.

O'Neill, J.P., and Graves, G.R., 1977 A new genus and species of owl (Aves: Strigidae) from Peru. *Auk* 94: 409 - 416.

Paget, C.J., & Paget, J., 1834: *Sketch of the Natural History of Yarmouth and its neighbourhood*. Longman, Rees & Co., London.

Parker, A. *Watch the Birdie*. Cerebus Publications Ltd., Walsall

Scott, P., 1983: *Travel Diaries of a Naturalist Volume 1*. Collins, London.

Taylor, I.R., 1994: *Barn owls: Predator - prey relationships and conservation*. Cambridge University Press.

Ticehurst, C.B., 1932: *A History of the Birds of Suffolk*. Gurney and Jackson, Edinburgh.

2 DESCRIPTION, PHYSICAL FEATURES AND BEHAVIOUR

'Of all the owls the White or Barn-Owl is the best known, for it is more frequently associated with human habitations than other species. It is often described as white, the under parts being most noticeable when, with desultory flight, it reels and wavers through the dusk. Crepuscular and nocturnal in its habits, it eludes observation; it appears, a noiseless shadow, and vanishes at once, for its soft pinions make no sound.'

T.A.Coward, *The Birds of the British Isles* (Warne, 1920)

As we have seen earlier, around the world barn owls appear in a variety of sizes and colours, and between them they have adapted to living in a range of habitats. From now onwards, however, we are largely concerned with the nominate race of the barn owls, *Tyto alba alba*, the white breasted barn owl. It is an owl that is very much at home in lightly wooded but open countryside with a mixture of habitats, including rough grassland, although as we shall see later the importance of cultivated farmland with fruiting hedgerows and grassy headlands should not be overlooked. Farmyards, with their associated hayricks, were once also favoured haunts although their importance has now declined.

DESCRIPTION *TYTO ALBA ALBA*

Barn owls are moderately sized birds that stand around 30cm tall and have a wingspan of approximately 85cm, although these measurements will vary depending upon how old the bird is and whether it is a male or female.

In the field they often appear to be white and indeed apart from small amounts of grey flecking and buff suffusions to the chest the undersides are totally white. Iain Taylor pointed out that the most northerly of the barn owls, *T.a.alba,* the subject of this book, has the palest under-parts of all the barn owls, and he pondered that because these barn owls, and especially the males, are often abroad hunting during the hours of daylight, when feeding the females and the young, they have evolved light under-sides to make them less conspicuous to small mammals against the sky, as in the manner of the white under-sides of seabirds and ospreys. This is an interesting theory and poses other questions.

As we shall see later, diurnal hunting by barn owls in the British Isles was, until comparatively recently, not widespread and would appear to have only become common during the last 100 years or so. Indeed Derek Bunn expressed surprise to find just how diurnal the owls were in his study. However, if Iain Taylor's theory is correct, this would suggest that barn owls of the *alba* race might originally have evolved as diurnal hunters and not nocturnal ones. This prompts the question, however, why short-eared owls have not evolved a similar plumage?

The under-sides of a barn owl contrast with the golden brown of the upper plumage, which is interspersed with small and varying amounts of white, grey and dark brown. The pattern on the primary feathers is individual and is unique to each bird. Because of this, the overall patterning can be a useful guide in identifying individual birds in the field, while cast primary feathers that may be found at roost or nest sites may be useful in tracking the movements of individual barn owls. The upper plumage of male barn owls is usually lighter than that of the females, but as they age they also become light in colouring so that old birds of both sexes may have a similar light appearance. This progression, and especially in the males, may account for the sightings of very light, almost silvery coloured barn owls.

Females tend to be darker than males although Bunn et al believed it to be unreliable to try and separate the sexes in the field. Taylor was of the opinion that it was usually easy to distinguish males from females even at a distance, although he considered the most reliable way of sorting captured birds was by the amount of black flecking on the undersides. He found that out of 182 females (98%) had some flecking, but by contrast 95% of males had no markings on the under-body at all and 98% of those had no markings on the under-wings. He also pointed out that few other barn owl sub-species exhibit such clear differences in plumage between the sexes, although he stated that in North America a large proportion of male and female barn owls could be separated in the field using the same method. He also was of the view that the dark-breasted barn owl, guttatta, as well as those in Africa and Australia followed this general trend. Why these differences occur he did not speculate.

Sometimes individuals showing aberrations in plumage are reported and on January 22nd, 1877, a specimen with an all-white tail was killed at Exeter, Devon, and apparently very white birds were 'not infrequently met with'. Bolam in 1912 considered the stuffed barn owls he had seen from old collections to belong to the pale form of barn owl, while many later specimens exhibited speckled plumage similar to the continental form. He considered some had taken up residence in the British Isles because he had seen a few that had been killed in the summer months.

Albinoism appears to be an extremely rare occurrence in barn owls but Whitaker in 1907 mentions a pale variety that he had in his collection with pink eyes that was shot near Newark, Lincolnshire, in the 1880s.

The moult is a complex process with some barn owls having been observed retaining some of their primary feathers for up to three years. It is remarkable that the feathers could sustain so much wear when they are subjected to events such as plunging into thick vegetation when hunting. There is no evidence that tree-nesting barn owls experience more wear than barn-nesting owls but that is likely to be the case.

Although the sequence of feather replacement is approximately the same for barn owls in temperate areas as for those in the tropics, the actual time period in which it takes place is different. Barn owls that live in temperate climates begin their moult in the second calendar year of life, and it takes place over a 4-year period, after which the replacement of the feathers continues over a 2-year period. Barn owls that live in the tropics of Malaysia, however, commence the moult in their first year and complete the replacement of their wing and tail feathers in approximately 7 months. Feather replacement then occurs on an annual basis.

The moult in hen barn owls takes place during the period of May to early June. This is when they are least active, due to the confinement of incubation and the early stages of hatching. With male birds it appears that they place body condition ahead of moult when it comes to the end of a very busy breeding season; after exceptional breeding years, such as the peak vole year of 1981, two males were observed not to shed any feathers at all. Therefore, male barn owls may be in moult from July to September, although usually they defer it until after the breeding season, and during the course of a long breeding season they may not moult at all.

Luminous barn owls have been reported in the past; this has

been variously attributed to bacteria on the feathers, perhaps from decaying wood, or a feather fungus new to science. No evidence for such a fungus has come to light over the years and so it is possible that the luminosity was due to bacteria that had originated from decaying wood.

These barn owls may have been some of the luminous ones that were seen in Norfolk by over 40 different observers during the winter of 1907-8, with a further sighting in February 1909 at Twyford. It seems last recorded instances of luminosity were noted on February 15th, 1921, at Haddiscoe and in January 1922, at Rushall. I am not aware of any further sightings of luminous barn owls anywhere, although Mabey mentions an old report from Norfolk (perhaps one of the aforementioned records) of two luminescent barn owls that were seen hunting over a patch of marshy ground one February afternoon.

The observer stated that one of the birds was quartering a field and came as close as fifty yards from where he was standing and it 'literally lit up the branches of the trees as it flew past'. Mabey considers that the owls had picked up phosphorescence from roosting in a tree infected with honey fungus and that they were eerie enough to produce their own illumination! It appears that only barn owls were subject to luminosity; I can find no records of tawny or little owls being affected in this manner.

There do not appear to have been any further instances of luminosity amongst barn owls after these reports and so the cause of this phenomenon remains a mystery. Neither do there appear to have been any reports from elsewhere other than Norfolk. Perhaps the cause of luminosity was the centipede *Geophilus electra (Linn.)*, which gives off a luminous secretion 'often visible at night in gardens and lives under clods of earth during the day', which Morley reported from Suffolk. Morley stated that the well known Suffolk naturalist William Kirby had commented on 'the light giving Centipede best known as the Electric, which is remarkable for emitting a vivid phosphoric light in the dark; this is produced by a viscid secretion …' and it is possible that the owls in question might have picked up centipedes on their plumage from rotting wood in trees where the owls were either roosting or nesting. They may also have picked up centipedes from the soil or grassland when catching prey.

The thick plumage of a barn owl gives the impression that the body is plump but this is quite deceptive, for beneath the soft feathering the bird is remarkably small. A Scottish study has found an average weight for 361 males was 330g and the average of 445 females was 370g. We do not know whether those barn owls that nest in Scotland, which are at the extreme end of their range in Europe, are heavier than those that nest further to the south but this certainly occurs in some other vole-eating species such as kestrels, for example: thos that live in southern Scotland weigh more than those that live in the farmlands of East Anglia.

In most bird groups the males tend to be larger than the females but in many species of predatory birds the females are larger (called reverse dimporphism). Heimo Mikkola pointed out that reverse dimorphism had been described in many of the diurnal birds of prey but that to his knowledge there had been no detailed study into the relative degree of sexual dimorphism amongst the European owls. Later, however, Taylor presented a detailed analysis of size dimorphism in Scottish barn owls and stated that in his study the females were significantly heavier than the males during the breeding season. Outside of that period, there was little difference in size, although the females tended to be just slightly heavier than the males at all other times. He compared that situation to the subspecies in the Australasian region, where there are wide differences in the morphology of the barn owls there and notably with the masked owl, *T. novaehollandiae*, where body weights range from 520 to 1260g and where there is considerable sexual dimorphism in body size; ie the females are noticeably larger than the males. He also drew attention to the large sooty owl, *T. tenebricosa*, whose body weights range from 500 to 700g in males, and from 750 to 1000g in females.

It is not clear why female owls should be heavier than the males and various reasons have been put forward for this, including the differences in prey selection by both sexes of the same species thus alleviating intersexual competition. When reflecting upon the incubating habits of some northern European owls, Mikkola was of the view that a large body was necessary for the females of species such as the great grey and Tengmalm's owls, who are intensive sitters, in keeping the eggs warm on very cold nights. This sound reason may well be true for some owls of northern Europe, but it does not account for the size differences in some of the more tropical barn owls such as those named above. In Britain it is not clear whether the body weight of the females is adjusted by food intake to meet the size of the clutch, which may vary from year to year, and from habitat to habitat. Perhaps a further study may

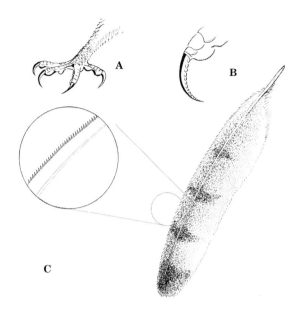

a) A barn owl's foot has four toes of which the fourth, or outer toe, is reversible.

b) At the end of each toe there is a talon, on the third of which there is a serrated, comb-like inside edge. This pectinated flange is unusual in the owl world and is used to groom and clean the facial disc.

c) The 10th primary feather is the primary that meets the air flow over the wing. The leading edge to this feather is serrated (see enlargement) which serves to smooth out the airflow, thus enabling the flight to be silent. Because of this the barn owl's flight is slower and not so efficient as some other bird species, but for a bird that prefers to fly slowly over the ground, then this is not such a handicap; quite the reverse.

reveal this?

The legs of a barn owl are long and retain little feathering. This is a common feature of owls that tend to hunt over grassland and other rank vegetation. In the tropics *T.a.capensis*, the grass owl, a species that not only hunts over grassland but nests and roosts amongst it, has legs that are almost devoid of any feathering.

In relation to the size of the body, a barn owl's wings are long, broad and slightly but distinctly, tapered at the primaries. This is unusual for an owl as the wing tips of most other species are rounded. In addition, the overall wing size is large in relation to the size and weight of the body and so there is little demand on them to support it whilst it is in the air. Consequently the 'wing loading' of a barn owl is very low. A low wing loading ensures effortless flight and allows a barn owl to fly very slowly, so enabling it to scrutinise the ground for prey with great efficiency. Elsewhere in Europe, only Tengmalm's and pygmy owl have similar or lower wing loadings.

Iain Taylor is firm that the barn owl's flight is silent, at least at frequencies audible to the human ear and also at ultra-sonic levels. This, he considered, was to enable an owl to detect small mammals when in flight, without the prey detecting the owl's presence. Three structural adaptations reduce flight noise: the front edges of the flight feathers, and especially the outer primaries, possess a prominent, stiff comb-like fringe, which cuts noise. Secondly, the trailing edge of the wing, the primaries and secondaries, have a soft hair-like fringe which reduces turbulence where air flowing over the top and bottom of the wings meet. Iain Taylor presented remarkable microscopic photography illustrating the long, hair-like extensions of the barbules, and these reduce the noise over the main flight feathers, which would otherwise move over each other thus causing noise. Despite this, there are times, such as when the feathers are worn or wet, or when the primaries are waiting to be moulted, the flight can be quite audible. Phillips was of the view that barn owls could 'switch off' their flight noise and become silent when they wanted to', and according to Alan Parker, you can sometimes hear the swish of the primaries through the air when they take off or land, so, contrary to most descriptions, the flight of a barn owl is not always silent. Derek Bunn on the other hand is clear that a barn owl's flight is not always silent, so the controversy continues. During my survey I received a very interesting observation that was made late one night whilst the observer was at a stable door. Suddenly a barn owl 'swooped out of the small gap above our heads, absolutely noiseless. Quite an experience only to feel the wind as it passed'. Interesting though this report is, the description of the owl swooping out suggests that the owl did not flap its wings but glided out, so the flight would indeed have been silent.

SIGHT

Owls have forward-facing eyes which provide them with binocular vision and which enable them to judge distance more accurately. In common with other birds owls have a third eyelid in addition to the

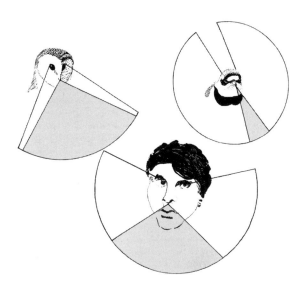

Like humans, barn owls have forward-facing eyes. This gives them binocular vision which allows them to judge distance. However, unlike many bird species, such as the ringed plover for example, this does not give them all-round vision. To allow for this they can turn their heads by nearly 180° in either direction

upper and lower lids. This is known as the nictitating membrane and serves to moisten and clean the eye. Lying underneath the eyelids and on the nasal side of a bird's head, this membrane is normally transparent and is drawn very fast across the eye. With the owls, however, this membrane is opaque and more robust, being drawn across the eye much more slowly and deliberately than most other birds. This nictitating membrane also serves to protect an owl's eye at the point of impact when it is catching prey, a well as being drawn across the eyes when it is feeding itself or the young and when it is preening itself or its mate. Derek Bunn believed that at such times barn owls prefer to protect their eyes and use the bristles around the bill to feel what they are touching. He also thought that because owls have forward-looking vision, their eyes are more susceptible to injury than many other bird species, and so consequently they have developed this sturdy membrane to afford some protection. Despite this, though, some owls do suffer eye injuries and there are examples of semi-blinded barn owls in the literature (see Hosking, 1982, for example).

Although owls cannot see in total darkness, they do have large tubular eyes that enable them to absorb light in very low light conditions. Due to their shape the eyes cannot move in their sockets, so to compensate for this, owls are able to rotate their heads in the most remarkable manner – nearly 180° in each direction. Barn owls have improved their sight by developing an unusually powerful muscle (Crampton's muscle) that allows the cornea, as well as the eye lens, to be adjusted very quickly, thus allowing prey to be kept sharply in focus as the owl drops down on to it. Due to the need to protect the eye from being damaged by its own muscular activity, the barn owl has developed strengthening plates (scleral ossicles) around the periphery of the cornea.

The ability of barn owls to see under low light conditions has been gained at the expense of visual acuity. The photo-receptive cells in the eye, known as rods, are reactive to light but are not very sensitive to colour; a barn owl's eye is 'packed' with rods. The alternative cells, known as cones, are responsible for colour vision and visual acuity. The lower number of cones compared with the number of rods results in a heightened ability to see in low light conditions at the expense of picking out detail. It is possible that they can see better in daylight when their cones are able to function better.

Many observers believe that the sight of barn owls is below the standard of most other owl species and there is evidence to support this view, some of which came to me during the course of my study. One of the most notable records involved 'a very interesting sighting as it (a barn owl) was closely followed by a ring-tail hen harrier for about 15 minutes, finally flying down a path straight at us. The harrier saw us and sheered off but the owl nearly hit our heads.' Other observations such as a barn owl 'flying within arms length' are typical.

For my part I was watching a barn owl one afternoon at 2.30, quartering a meadow only twenty metres away from where I was standing. It only appeared to be aware of my presence when I fired my camera. In contrast, I was observing a barn owl in good light very early one morning in July 1984 when its methodical quartering brought it to approximately 50 metres from me. Being aware of the barn owl's sensitive hearing, I was conscious not to make any sound or movement as I crouched, partly concealed, in my hiding place and yet it had no difficulty in seeing me, for it screeched in alarm and flew off.

There are numerous stories that demonstrate barn owls may fly very close to human beings without being aware of their presence, and the stories of barn owls alighting on people's heads are proof of this. There can be no doubt that barn owls do have great difficulty in identifying stationary objects such as humans, but they are not alone in this: grey swiflets, tropical cave-dwelling birds of the Far East, use a form of echolocation as a means of negotiating their surroundings within their caves; initially, the swiflets may not be able to detect large objects, 'such as a human body', when it is placed in the normal flyway of the cave.

Changes in eye colouration of young barn owls were observed by Bunn et al, and they described the pupils of young birds having a blue blind-looking appearance at day 12. At day 17 the pupils still have a blue appearance, which they begin to lose at day 24, and by day 27 the eyes begin to take on the hazel brown colouring of adult birds. It is not clear why this change takes place although maturing of the pigment cells is likely. The eyes of many people living in the tropics are dark brown, possibly to protect them against the effects of strong sunlight. The barn owl is predominantly a bird of the tropics; is their eye colouration for the same purpose?

It is not clear if a barn owl's eyes continue to develop with age but it is likely they do. The iris of a young barn owl just a few months old has a bright hazel appearance but field observations suggest that those in older birds are darker.

HEARING

The sounds that a barn owl might hear, such as a vole rustling in the grass, are captured by the owl's facial disc and pass through the fine feathering on the disc to the ears. The squarish ear openings covered by flaps of skin are called the operculi, or pre-aural flaps, and these are positioned asymmetrically, one on either side of the head. Looking at the owl face on, the ear opening and the skin flap on the left are set higher than those on the right. Just behind each ear there is a ridge of curved skin from which grows a row of stiff, dense feathers that, due to their solidity, are relatively impervious to sound. These feathers form the ruff, which is a highly developed reflector of high frequency sounds. It appears that the curvature of these feathers is approximately 60°, which Alan Parker has informed me is the same as a parabolic reflector. To draw further attention to the barn owl's highly sophisticated hearing it should be noted that the curvature of the ruff on the left is directed slightly upwards, while on the right the curvature is directed slightly downwards. Through this arrangement a barn owl will obtain information from a single sound source, at different levels and at different intensities, and this enables it to pinpoint the location of small mammals with amazing accuracy.

By contrast to the stiff and impervious feathers of the ruff, the external ears, or conches, are covered in fine feathers that are the opposite in structure to those of the ruff in that they are filamentous, devoid of any barbules and permeable to sound. It is through these feathers that sound reaches the ruff. It is vitally important to a barn owl that these feathers are kept in pristine condition and observations have established that the serrated, or pectinated, second talon is used in the manner of a comb to perform that function. The importance of the facial ruff was demonstrated by Knudsen and Konishi who revealed that when the facial feathers of a barn owl were removed, it was unable to accurately judge the vertical dimension of a sound source and so it was unable to catch prey in the dark.

During the course of his work at Cornell University in the United States, Dr Roger Payne discovered that barn owls could hunt efficiently in extremely low light conditions, although when they were placed in total darkness their hunting efficiency was slightly reduced. Experiments were conducted in a light-proof room that measured 14m x 4m x 2.5m. The floor of the room was covered in dead leaves to a depth of 5cm. Barn owls were introduced to this room and were allowed to acclimatise themselves in low light conditions. When light was excluded from the room barn owls could still catch live deer mice as well as a mouse-sized wad of paper that was pulled across the floor by string. He recorded over 200 successful strikes with very few misses, of which he calculated the worst 5. From these he found that the degree of these misses was very small and that during its flight if an owl was given a further clue to the source of the sound, such as a leaf-rustle, then it was able to adjust its flight and was usually successful in catching moving prey. Following Payne's work a subsequent study carried out by Konishi confirmed his earlier findings: that all a barn owl needs to catch its prey successfully is to hear the rustling sounds it makes on the ground. However, it is important to point out that these experiments were conducted in the relative comfort of a laboratory and that the mice were not able to hide, as they probably would be able to in the wild. They were also not subjected to extraneous noise, such as road traffic for example, as they often are in the wild. Both ears are needed to hear properly and it has been demonstrated that when one ear is plugged barn owls are unable to localise sounds, which means that a barn owl with impaired hearing will probably starve.

The studies by Konishi and others have revealed that barn owls can detect sound levels inaudible to humans, while the human ear is more sensitive to some frequencies than a barn owl's. They have also revealed that they have an amazing ability to distinguish between sound frequencies that differ by minuscule amounts. Consequently there arises, as Taylor mentioned, the distinct possibility that barn owls are not only able to discriminate between prey species but that they are able to separate the age and possibly sex classes within those species!

It might be thought that barn owls only need their hearing when hunting but Taylor was of the view that their sight was important at night, when navigating around obstacles such as tree branches. He also considered that sight is used alongside hearing to locate prey when hunting by daylight. It may be that barn owls use their sight when sound, such as wind for example, precludes them from using their hearing to the full potential when hunting. This might also help to explain why barn owls are occasionally found hunting in the middle of the day, even outside of the breeding season. Observations have revealed that although partially sighted barn owls are capable of living in the wild, such as the one that had lost the sight of one eye that Bunn et al observed, they have great difficulty in catching prey and that they often have to hunt longer and further afield than barn owls with full sight.

Taking into account the results of Payne's research, Bunn doubted that the barn owl's hearing could be bettered but great grey owls also have excellent hearing and are able to hear and catch prey even though it might be under a deep layer of snow. Due to the mortality that barn owls suffer in periods of snowy weather, this is something they do not appear to have mastered, although Iain Taylor has observed barn owls catching unseen prey through a covering of snow. We do not know what depth of snow cover is critical to a barn owl before it loses contact with prey beneath it, and neither do we know whether the sight or hearing of an individual barn owl becomes impaired as its age progresses.

CALLS

It was John of Guildford who first separated the call of the tawny owl from that of the barn owl in 1225 when he wrote his poem 'The Owl and the Nightingale' in which the dialogue mentions that the barn owl 'scrichest' and the tawny owl 'yollest'. Fifteen different calls of the barn owl have been described plus two further sounds, tongue clicking and wing clapping. The call that is best known is the screech, which can be heard in most months of the year but particularly in the autumn and early spring when owls are establishing their territories.

An additional call, not unlike the 'cuk cuk' call made by a moorhen, has been heard when an adult is approaching the nest and may be one that a parent bird uses to alert the young that it is about to alight at the nest entrance. Some other hole-nesting birds, such as great tits, also give a subdued call to their young before entering the nesting chamber. In circumstances where barn owls nest in buildings, then the need to use this call may not arise because the chicks can usually see the parent standing at the entrance hole of the building before it approaches the nest.

Where trees are being used for nesting, this may not be the case and an unexpected visitor to a nest hole could in fact be a predator. If the parents announce themselves as they approach the nest, the chicks can then come safely to the entrance hole to receive food. This is particularly important at night when the owls are at their busiest. In the United States Potter and Gillespie in 1925 noted a flight call of an adult bird resembling 'ick-ick-ick-ick' and they thought this call signified the bringing of food. From South Africa there is further evidence of the existence of this call , with a 'double clicking' note occasionally produced in flight on dark nights.

The late R.B.Warren and the late Eric Hosking confirmed to me separately that they believed this call existed and interestingly Walpole-Bond referred to this call as its repeated 'flight note' – 'somewhat akin to one of the Moor-hen's utterances'. Bob Warren, who was a meticulous and careful recorder, stated that he had heard this call when a barn owl flew very close to him. On May 25th,1987, I heard this call when observing a pair of barn owls that were nesting in a dead elm at Cornard Mere in Suffolk, but efforts to obtain a recording have so far been unsuccessful.

It might be a contact call that is uttered by barn owls which nest in trees; as fewer barn owls now use them, the call might now be more rarely heard.

Is it possible that the 'call' could be a form of echo-location? Experimental studies, coupled with field observations, have shown that oilbirds and cave swiflets can, and do, rely upon their hearing to orientate their flight within the darkness of their cave homes and they can produce short sound pulses (perceived by observers as a train of clicks).However, there is no evidence that echo-location is systematically used by barn owls. No owls in flight have ever been recorded as producing any sounds that could serve in an echo-locatory manner. It might be a contact call that is uttered by barn owls that nest in trees rather than by those that nest in barns. A parent barn owl would not want to draw unwelcome attention from a predator to a nest full of young, but a soft sharp contact call would alert the owlets inside the nesting cavity that a parent was approaching, perhaps with food. The call, therefore, is more likely to be a 'here I come, I'm friendly' call.

Unlike many other owl species, barn owls will often call on the wing, although I have on occasion observed barn owls calling whilst perched in trees and I once saw one calling when it was sat in a bush. Bunn regularly sound-recorded them in barns and other buildings, and these served as interior song-posts but I have no record of barn owls calling from within tree holes. The short-eared owl is a bird of the open countryside and so it usually calls on the wing, because 'song-posts' might not always be available where it lives while the little owl, which often lives in a similar habitat to the barn owl, often calls from a song-post. Nestlings, and occasionally adult birds, hiss and 'snore' when in the nest and these calls may often be heard from a distance.

Many people believe that barn owls hoot and I received a few records of this during my study, although most of the confusion was caused by mis-identification with tawny owls. There are aspects of barn owl behaviour that are similar to other species, notably the nightjars and frogmouths, but more especially to the oilbirds. For example, oilbirds have large eyes and their vision may be similar to that of barn owls; oilbirds, like barn owls, are capable of very slow flight and momentary hovering.

This does not mean that barn owls and oilbirds are directly related, although they do share a common ancestry with the Caprimulgiformes. Rather, they have probably evolved similar behaviour in response to their preferred habitats and their nocturnal way of life, which they may have chosen because their prey has adapted to a nocturnal or semi-nocturnal lifestyle.

RELATIONS WITH OTHER SPECIES

The introduction of alien species into Britain has often had a detrimental effect upon our wildlife, although to date no introduction of any species appears to have caused a problem for our barn owls. Nor do they come into conflict with any indigenous species. Most have been living alongside our barn owls for thousands of years although from time to time there are local problems.

For example, there appears to be no evidence that kestrels are a threat to barn owls even though they both feed mainly on small mammals. Indeed both species have been recorded as breeding in close proximity. During the course of my Suffolk survey barn owls and kestrels were recorded as nesting in the same tree in three different locations, while on four further occasions barn owls and kestrels nested close together in straw-stacks near Halesworth, Rendham and Eye. Kestrels and barn owls have also nested near to each other inside an old aircraft hanger on Orfordness; the barn owls nested inside some piping that was approximately 400mm in diameter while the kestrels nested on a ledge.

There are instances where kestrels have been observed robbing barn owls of their prey and in Suffolk some think that this behaviour is increasing. Whether these are examples of kleptoparasitism or behaviour brought on by a shortage of food is unclear but Andy Village stated that in his study area at Eskdalemuir in Scotland, kestrels often tried to rob short-eared owls of their food, and they experienced a 3% success rate. If kestrels and barn owls are both present in a particular territory, then it is quite possible that a shortage of voles could cause this interaction. However, kestrel will also rob kestrel and one morning in 1996 I witnessed a violent interaction between two kestrels on the outskirts of Ipswich. They ended up rolling around on the road-side verge, talons locked together and totally oblivious of the busy rush hour traffic that was passing.

There is some evidence that kestrels suffer at the hands of barn owls and Mikkola reported three instances of barn owls killing kestrels but no instance of a kestrel killing an owl. On December 15th, 1983, J. H. Woolnough observed a kestrel that was being mobbed by a barn owl at Spexhall in Suffolk, and in 1986 at Rendham, also in Suffolk, the author found the headless corpse of a young kestrel after both species had nested in the same straw-stack, implying that it might have been killed by a barn owl. On October 30th, 1979, a barn owl was seen to strike 'a kestrel that had rose from

Despite some local conflicts, barn owls and kestrels have lived together in the British Isles for thousands of years.

the ground with a small mammal in its talons. The kestrel was on the ground for well over a minute but appears to have recovered'. Clearly, barn owls are capable of looking after themselves where kestrels are involved and there are other examples:

On April 4th, 1947, during the tail end of the very bad winter, a letter appeared in *Country Life* that told the story of an encounter between a barn owl and a 'hawk', which was most likely a kestrel due to the fact that the prey involved was a vole. The correspondent told of how one afternoon a barn owl that lived in a nearby tree left its nest 'as usual to go hunting'. Sometime later she heard a scream and saw the barn owl, with its back to her, tearing at its prey. Thinking it was one of 'her' blackbirds she disturbed the owl only to find that it was tearing at a hawk which was able to fly off when she disturbed the owl. A few days later the owl caught a vole and sat on the ground with it dangling from its beak. At this, a hawk (most likely a kestrel) flew in and sat on the ground about a foot away and opposite the owl. There then ensued a 'sparring match' ending in a fierce fight which the owl won. Apparently a similar incident occurred the next day, although this time the 'hawk' flew off with the vole after an even more ferocious battle.

Following its introduction into Britain during the mid-19th century, the little owl has occasionally been blamed for the decline of the barn owl, although the case for this is thin because the little owl's diet consists largely of small prey such as beetles and worms, and so there is little evidence of food competition. Even so, I once observed a little owl rising from a road with a rat in its talons but it was unclear whether it had killed the rat or whether it was carrion. Little owls do eat small mammals but not on a regular basis.

Competition between barn and little owls may sometimes arise over nesting sites and the decline of the barn owl in south-west Essex has been attributed to competition from the little owl. By 1939 some people thought 'ancient nesting trees' had been taken over by little owls, although that claim proved to be unfounded. On the other hand, M.Packard reckoned that in Shotley, Suffolk, 'the little owl, after being quite common, has ... been lost (as a breeding species)' and that 'the barn owl has made a really wonderful recovery throughout the area after no breeding records for many years'. In Sussex, Walpole-Bond in 1938 was quite firm in his view that a declining barn owl population was due 'to the coming of the Little Owl'. There is no doubt that these two species share very similar habitats in Britain but it is unlikely that the absence of barn owls can be attributed to the presence of little owls.

On a national basis the distributions of both species indicate that in some areas where barn owls are absent little owls are present and *vice versa*. In Europe, there are reports of 7 instances of barn owls killing little owls; including 1 record from Wales and 2 from southern England; there are no reports of little owls killing barn owls.

The most controversial owl species that has been perceived as a threat to the barn owl is the tawny owl, a bird that is usually found in woodland, parkland and gardens with mature trees. According to a number of commentators, the tawny owl increased its numbers during the 20th century and because of this, some ornithologists considered this was a factor in the decline of the barn owl.

Of course, it might be the other way round and that the barn owl's decline, which has been largely been brought about by the destruction of their habitats, has allowed the tawny owl to spread out from its woodland confines and so increase its numbers. In recent years we have once again seen a resurgence in barn owl numbers and it is interesting to note that, talking of tawny owls,

Barn owls may be mobbed by crows or other birds in daytime.

the 'higher levels reached during the early 1970s have not been sustained'. More recently Chris Mead felt there was 'Cause for considerable concern' with regards to the present status of the tawny owl. I think it likely that when barn owl numbers are high, then tawny owls may well stay within their woodland confines, but when barn owl numbers are low then tawny owls may well take the opportunity to increase their range. This factor, together with the matters of woodland management and housing density, particularly in small towns and villages, may well be restricting the number of tawny owls at present.

An examination of the national distributions of these two owls indicates that the ranges of both species strongly overlap. From time to time there may be competition for food or nest-sites but we must be clear that these two owls have lived side by side in the countryside for thousands of years, with each species filling its ecological niche, although there seems little doubt that the barn owl is the dominant species.

During the course of my survey I received several reports of birds mobbing barn owls; most of them related to members of the crow family. On June 1st, 1983, a rook was seen to mob a barn owl at Waldringfield and on May 14th, 1984, six rooks were observed mobbing a flying barn owl at Stonebridge near Capel St Andrew. On February 2nd, 1985, a barn owl was mobbed in flight by magpies at Hasketon, whilst later that year on May 11th, S.Bishop watched a barn owl that was being mobbed by three magpies at mid-day in Culford Park. In 1986 barn owls and magpies were seen to have a number of 'skirmishes' at Reydon Marsh and on March 15th, 1992, a barn owl was watched being mobbed by a magpie at Worlingworth. In February 1989, two black-headed gulls mobbed a barn owl at Rendham during the late afternoon. I can only find one record of mobbing by small birds when one was seen being mobbed by a flock of finches and tits at Hatch Plain Sewerage Farm at 10.15am on February 15th, 1922.

In his survey Taylor found that his Scottish barn owls were rarely mobbed even though they were often observed delivering prey during daylight, whereas in the tropics, and perhaps elsewhere, barn owls that venture out during daylight hours are persistently and aggressively mobbed, which makes hunting a very difficult procedure. In another report of daylight hunting by barn owls: one was seen to receive a 'direct physical attack by a carrion crow which clutched the back of one of the owls twice with its feet, forcing it to the ground'.

The mobbing of barn owls is not a recent phenomenon because on June 13th, 1948, the West Country naturalist E.W.Hendy reported in his nature notes for the *Western Morning News* that he had received a letter from a correspondent reporting on a 'curious account of seagulls attacking a barn owl'. Hendy wrote that he had never seen gulls attack a barn owl but his correspondent later found the lacerated corpse of a dead barn owl in the road and subsequently saw four gulls attacking another barn owl, although the owl escaped when the observer appeared and the gulls departed.

Later, on July 4th, Hendy informed his readers that while he had had no further reports of gulls mobbing barn owls, he had received a note from Woolacombe which informed him that in March, whilst staying in Cornwall, a correspondent had seen 'a barn owl viciously attacked by rooks'. The observer stated that the owl put up a good fight but when the rooks were driven off, the owl was found to be very exhausted. It then flew off and was not seen again.

One of the most unusual records I received during my survey concerned a barn owl that was making 'four or five mock attacks on a dog' near Trimley St Martin on November 2nd, 1985; a more remarkable event took place in Sussex when, in 1985, a barn owl was killed by a dog after it attempted to take one of its newly born pups.

In conclusion, it would appear that barn owls have no enemies that pose a threat to their survival apart from man. There are examples where barn owls have been predated upon, such as one of a pair that nested too close to a pair of peregrine falcons in Galloway; one of a pair of peregrine falcons killed one of a pair of barn owls at a Cambridgeshire sewage farm in 1944, but such occurrences are rare.

At present the goshawk is expanding its range throughout Britain and I surmise that the eagle owl may also be in the process of colonising Britain through migrants from mainland Europe, as well as through successful breeding by escapees that are already established in the wild. These two powerful predators are respectively the most significant diurnal and nocturnal predators of barn owls in Europe, so we should not relax.

SOURCES USED IN THIS CHAPTER

Bircham, P.M.M. 1989: The Birds of Cambridgeshire. Cambridge University Press.

Bolam, G., 1912: *The Birds of Northumberland and the Eastern Borders*. Henry Hunter Blair, Alnwick.

Bunn, D.S., 1972: Regular daylight hunting by Barn Owls. *British Birds*, 65: 26-30.

Bunn, D.S., Warburton, A.W., and Wilson, A.A.B., 1982: *The Barn Owl*. Poyser,Calton.

Campbell, J.M., 1982: Barn owl bringing down Kestrel. *British Birds*, 11: 536.

Homes, R.C.(ed.) ,1964: *The Birds of the London Area*. Rupert Hart-Davis, London.

Hosking, E., & Flegg, J., 1982: *Eric Hosking's Owls*. Pelham Books Ltd., London.

Jacobs, C.A., and Johnson, R., 2003: Field Note. *Suffolk Birds*, 51: 81.

Knudsen, E.I., & Konishi, M., 1979: Mechanisms of sound localisation in the barn owl (*Tyto alba*). *Journal of Comparative Physiology*, 133: 13-21.

Loyd, L.R.W., 1929: *The Birds of South East Devon*. Witherby, London.

Martin, J.R., 1993: A brief summary of the Eagle Owl's status in Europe and its possible implications for Suffolk and Britain. *Suffolk Birds 1992*, 41: 11-14.

Mead, C., 2000: *The State of the Nations' Birds*. Whittet Books,

Cotton.

Mikkola, H., 1983: *Owls of Europe.* Poyser, Calton.

Morley, C., 1933: Luminous Centipedes. *Trans. Suffolk Nat. Soc.* 2: 99-101.

Payn, W.H., 1978: *The Birds of Suffolk (2nd ed.).* Ancient House Publishing, Ipswich.

Potter, J.K. & Gillespie, J.A. 1925: Observations on the domestic behaviour of the barn owl *Tyto pratincola. Auk*, 42: 177-192.

Ratcliffe, D. 1980: *The Peregrine Falcon.* Poyser, Calton.

Sparks, J., & Soper, T., 1985: *Owls: Their natural and unnatural history.* David & Charles, Newton Abbot.

Taylor, I.R., 1994:   *Barn owls; predator prey relationships.* Cambridge University Press.

Village, A., 1990: *The Kestrel.* Poyser, London.

Walpole-Bond, J. ,1938: *A History of Sussex Birds, Vol. 2.* Witherby, London.

Whitaker, J., 1907: *Notes on the Birds of Nottinghamshire.* Black & Co., Nottingham.

3 The food of the barn owl

'It is really wonderful how little they are seen even when they are fairly plentiful, and I feel great pleasure when, with beautiful floating flight, they glide past me, twisting round the gable of the barn, then along the stack sides, swooping down on some unfortunate mouse and departing like a shadow'.

'White or Barn Owl', J. Whitaker, 1907. *Notes on the Birds of Nottinghamshire* (Black & Co., Nottingham)

The barn owl is one of Europe's most familiar birds and its habitual lifestyle, involving an intense fidelity to its nest and roosting site, has allowed it to be extensively studied in many countries. Provided it is not disturbed, a barn owl nest or roost site may be studied for many years, thus allowing a considerable amount of information to be collected. Despite this the barn owl remains to some degree a bird of mystery, living, as it sometimes does, in close proximity to man without him knowing.

Methods and habits of hunting

The abundance of food is critical to a pair of adult barn owls if they are to survive the rigours of life and successfully raise a family. Each parent requires around 7-8 good-sized voles or mice per day whilst half-grown owlets need 3-4. Consequently, when prey is scarce, or when chicks grow large and demand more food, barn owls will hunt further afield in efforts to find adequate prey, and they will do this at any time of the year. In times of prey abundance, they will have no need to wander far from the nesting and roosting area and so this behaviour might help to explain why a barn owl may suddenly appear in a locality for a while and then disappear.

When hunting on the wing, barn owls will often fly low, scrutinising the ground for prey; where perches are available, such as the tops of fence-posts, they will sometimes choose to use these. Occasionally barn owls will perch on overhead wires. From the research carried out on the barn owl's hearing Iain Taylor estimated that the optimum hunting height for European barn owls is around

Wherever they live, barn owls are usually hunters of the open countryside.

3m and he was able to corroborate this with field observations. Interestingly he found that the optimum hunting height for the larger North American barn owls is around 6m although they do not normally drop onto prey from that height, rather they drop to a lower height to obtain a more precise fix on the prey.

A perched barn owl will, when hunting, direct its facial disc at the source of the sound made by the prey. If the vole or mouse is stationary, then the sound of grass, etc, being chewed will indicate its presence; if the prey is moving then, after evaluating the direction in which the prey is travelling, the owl will launch itself at it. Photography has shown that at the moment of impact, the head, which is on a collision course with the prey, is thrown back to make room for the feet which are then slung forward in front of its face. Although hunting on the wing is a slightly more complicated matter, a barn owl's low wing loading allows it to fly very slowly in order to locate prey before plunging into the vegetation after it. In open country and in the absence of a perch, hovering is often employed.

During the course of hunting the usefulness of the reversible third, or outer, front toe is brought into play. During the course of Dr Roger Payne's work at the Cornell University in North America, he discovered that at the point of impact a barn owl's talons are spread in such a manner as to enable a barn owl the greatest chance of successfully capturing its prey. By reversing the third toe a barn owl is then able to grasp its prey by using two talons from each foot on either side of the prey's body, thus enabling it to utilise a considerable spread of talons which covers an area, as calculated by Payne, of approximately 60cm^2. The prey is then usually squeezed to death by the talons, although if the prey continues to move, then the skull is given a nip, and this no doubt accounts for skulls with holes in that are sometimes found when dissecting pellets.

TIMES OF HUNTING

Barn owls are considered to be nocturnal throughout many parts of the world but in Britain diurnal hunting appears to have increased over the past century. Although this may be an indication of food shortage, it is not the sole reason.

In his forest study area Derek Bunn found that hunting times varied greatly between the dozen or so individuals under observation. Some of his correspondents considered daylight activity to be normal, whilst others expressed surprise at seeing barn owls abroad in daylight. Because of this, he concluded that there are barn owls all over the country that habitually hunt diurnally and others that are almost or entirely nocturnal, the proportions of which he did not know. He had originally thought that barn owls were primarily nocturnal creatures that will hunt by day only in times of food shortage or when the demand for food is increased, such as when feeding young or in bad winter weather, but he found that many of his study owls regularly hunted diurnally throughout the year. Perhaps most barn owls had no objection to being about in daylight in the absence of mobbing. However, in my Suffolk study barn owls were often abroad during daylight even though they were sometimes mobbed.

It seems that diurnal activity by barn owls caused some interest in the early part of the 20th century when after a heavy fall of snow on January 28th, 1910, a barn owl was seen hunting at 3pm on the following day. This was followed by another sighting in a neighbouring locality the next day. A further report later that year stated 'here in the extreme north of Lancashire we see the Barn Owl flying all year during the winter months and I am inclined to

Barn owl taking prey.

attribute this purely to a lack of sufficient food supply'.

In a letter to the *Field* on August 31st, 1946, Leslie L. Turner of Lancashire wrote, 'Earlier in the year it was quite a common sight to see up to a dozen barn owls hunting for food at any time of the day, whether the light be dull or brilliantly sunny'. He considered that a scarcity of food might be the reason for daylight hunting, although the weather had 'not been unduly hard'. He then compared this to the winter of 1939-40 ('a harsh winter') when 'these birds were abroad during late afternoon'.

Charles Waterton in the 19th century remarked that 'If this useful bird caught its food by day instead of hunting for it by night, mankind would have ocular demonstration of its utility in thinning the country of mice, and it would be protected and encouraged everywhere...'

During the course of my study I found that barn owls were quite often about during daylight throughout the year, with a peak of activity during the winter months. The reasons for this are not abundantly clear, although it seems likely that the activity patterns of field voles determine this. Although voles may be active throughout the day they do have periods of activity at sunrise and sunset. It may also be that because a barn owl's sight is more efficient during daytime, some owls actually choose to hunt then, particularly if the locality where they are hunting is noisy and they cannot rely upon their hearing. This seems reasonable where barn owls are dependent upon field voles. Mice and rats, however, tend to be nocturnal and it is logical, therefore, that where they feature more highly in the diet of barn owls, the owls hunt nocturnally. It is in those localities that they are likely to go largely unnoticed. An increasing dependence of many British barn owls upon field voles over the last century or so, as suggested by the amount of information now available, would mean that barn owls would have to synchronise their hunting to coincide with peaks of vole activity, particularly if there is competition from other predators such as stoats, weasels, foxes and kestrels, all of which also feed on field voles. The presence of short-eared owls would add further pressure for food.

In the United States barn owls often feed on voles, but shrews and other rodents also feature in the diet, with the owls starting to hunt at dusk. This is probably to take advantage of the crepuscular habits of the voles, although in some instances barn owls begin hunting well before dusk. In some areas the presence of great horned owls, which are significant predators of barn owls, might restrict their diurnal activities; this might also apply to other predators, such as goshawks, which will also kill and eat barn owls.

The barn owls of southern Syria are largely nocturnal because most of their prey is nocturnal species such as the house mouse, which forms a large part of the diet (47.17%), grey hamster (8.85%), the gerbil Tristram's jird (5.65%), brown-toothed field mouse (5.16%) and brown rat (4.42%). The more diurnal social vole contributes 12.78%, so clearly the barn owls of Syria show a preference for rodents that tend to emerge at night. In the agricultural lands of Central Greece, where numbers of barn owls are probably at their highest density in the country, they feed largely on small mammals and the dominant prey species are the western house mouse, the bi-coloured white-toothed shrew and the wood mouse, with each species contributing 26.7%, 25.4% and 15.5% to the diet respectively. These species are largely nocturnal and correspondingly the barn owls in Central Greece are also nocturnal. In Usta Muhammad, Pakistan, barn owls also feed on small nocturnal mammals, of which the most frequently found in their study were the soft-furred field rat (46.3%), house mouse (33.5%), black rat (5.1%), shrews (4.7%); birds (3.3%) and various other species make up the remainder. In Spain, where barn owls are nocturnal, nearly 60% of the barn owl's diet consists of mice, with shrews forming just over 17% of the food and voles, notably the pine vole which is nocturnal, accounting for 12% of the prey. The field vole is absent on the Iberian Peninsula. Frogs and lizards are also taken in Spain and some of the 119 lizard species are diurnally active, thus confirming that Spanish barn owls may sometimes hunt in the daytime.

In Britain it may be useful to correlate diet with diurnal activity to establish whether those barn owls that are active by day are more dependent upon field voles than those that are predominantly active at night and whether this trend is increasing and what are the long-term implications for Britain's barn owls. Might the barn owls in the British Isles eventually become largely dependant upon a diet of field voles? If they do then the repercussions for this trend need to be taken into consideration. Perhaps this was the case with the short-eared owl, a species that will wander far in search of voles in Europe, but which is not so dependent upon voles elsewhere. In a recent study in Pakistan, short-eared owls were found to feed on mice (91.9%), shrews (2.0%), bats (1.3%) and birds (5.0%) but in Europe and North America voles are the predominant prey. It may

Table 2 Analysis of 188 barn owl pellet samples collected in Britain and Ireland. The numbers of vertebrate prey items are listed and expressed in percentages of total prey eaten.

Mole	88	0.2	Water vole	85	0.2
Common shrew	12.229	25.6	Wood mouse	5640	11.8
Pygmy shrew	2567	5.4	Harvest mouse	248	0.5
Water shrew	574	1.2	House mouse	648	1.4
Bank vole	1876	3.9	Brown rat	944	2.0
Field vole	21906	45.8	Birds	958	2.0

Total vertebrate items 47,865 of this study include other vertebrate tems which were taken in very small numbers but are not shown here (from Glue, 1974)

be that if present trends continue, barn owls will in time adopt, as it seems short-eared owls have, a nomadic way of life in search of food.

FEEDING

When returning to the nest with food, barn owls usually carry prey in their talons. Should the nest be sited in a tree, they usually transfer the food from their talons to their beaks in flight as they approach the nest; this enables them to land at the entrance hole unhindered. Where barn owls nest in buildings, then they often have the opportunity to alight at the entrance to the nesting area and transfer the food there to the beak before flying to the nest-site within it. If a perch is available, then tree-nesting barn owls will sometimes rest there before entering the nest chamber. In Hampshire, Kelsall & Munn in 1905 remarked how Gilbert White had also noted that barn owls carried their prey in their talons but that they 'constantly perch first on the roof of the chancel, and shift the mouse from their claws to their bill, that the feet might be at liberty to take hold of the plate on the wall as they are rising under

Table 3 Barn owl prey in east Norfolk. Results are expressed as a percentage of prey items in relation to the total number of prey species.

Mole	0.2	Water vole	0.4
Common shrew	23.7	Wood mouse	6.2
Pygmy shrew	4.7	Harvest mouse	3.2
Water shrew	1.3	House mouse	0.7
Bats	< 0.1	Brown rat	3.2
Rabbit	< 0.1	Weasel	< 0.1
Bank vole	3.3	Bird	2.3
Field vole	50.7	Frog	0.1

From Buckley & Goldsmith (1972)

the eaves'.

Although it is generally accepted that barn owls deliver their prey directly to the nest-site, a remarkable piece of behaviour was noted near Sudbourne in Suffolk on July 3rd, 1987, when a barn owl passed food to another barn owl while they were both in flight; this was not an isolated incident because it was observed in the same area two years later.

When feeding, barn owls usually swallow prey whole and head first, although this does depend upon the age of the owl and the size of the prey. Very young owlets require their food to be torn up and fed to them in small pieces although even owlets of just a few weeks old are able to swallow quite large prey items whole. It is unusual for a full-grown barn owl to eat small prey piece-meal but on the afternoon of November 22nd, 1991, a barn owl was seen tearing up and eating a small mammal whilst it was perched in a tree near Kelsale, Saxmundham, in Suffolk. During the 1962/63 winter, a barn owl corpse was submitted to a veterinary laboratory for analysis and was found to have swallowed a house sparrow tail first.

When owls locate an abundance of prey they will often gorge themselves by killing and eating as many small mammals as they

Prey is usually swallowed whole and head first.

can. In 1985 Lilford recounted how he witnessed a young half-grown barn owl swallow 9 full-grown mice, one after the other, until the tail of the last creature hung out of the owl's mouth, and I once saw a short-eared owl perform a similar feat in very cold weather at Reydon Marsh, Suffolk, in December 1986. The owl, which was only some 50-60 yards away from where I was quietly standing, eventually flew off with the tail of a rodent hanging from its beak. Other species, such as starlings, for example, do not possess crops either, and they will gorge themselves for the same reason when they find an abundance of food, thus gaining a reputation as greedy.

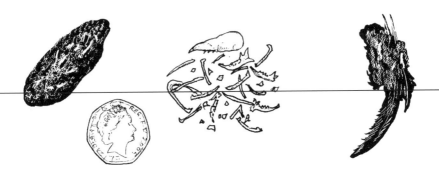

Barn owl pellets are usually dark but slightly glossy. They usually contain the remains of small mammals, but occasionally bird and other remains turn up. The pellet on the right contains a bird feather.

PELLETS

Owls do not possess a crop, so when they swallow food it goes straight to the stomach. A barn owl's stomach has a higher pH (it is less acidic) than many of the diurnal raptors. The significance of this is that unlike the diurnal birds of prey, the bones of an owl's prey remain largely intact during digestion, during which the waste matter from the prey – the fur, feathers and teeth, together with the bones – are bound together into a compact pellet that the owl later regurgitates as a conscious action rather than a reflex one. Depending upon whether there is something to regurgitate, a barn owl may eject a pellet at will. Observations on captive barn owls suggest that they will produce a pellet when they believe that another meal is imminent. They can be stimulated to produce a pellet, either by offering them more food, or allowing them to see live prey outside of their cages. In one case, a researcher found that due to the desire by his captive barn owls to obtain a further meal when he carried out his food rounds, some barn owls would regurgitate half-digested meat.

Studies have demonstrated that 6.5 hours is the minimum period before food is digested and pellets can be egested following food intake; this is of paramount importance when carrying out any food study as is the inhibiting effect of small, regular intakes of food. Some studies believe a maximum of four pellets per 24 hours can be ejected but this is in exceptional circumstances. The usual number is two, of which only one is usually recovered at the roost, the other being deposited elsewhere when the bird is out hunting;

however, barn owls usually hunt for a while before returning to their roost for a rest, so there remains the distinct possibility that barn owls may indeed deposit more pellets at their roost than is claimed. Iain Taylor carried out a number of experiments including a continuous photographic study over several nights, which found that the number of prey items delivered to four nests virtually matched the contents of the pellets that were collected at the roost. This demonstrated that after the consumption of the food, the subsequent pellets were not being deposited elsewhere and few, if any, of the bones were being broken down in the stomach as they are in the diurnal birds of prey. European barn owl pellets display a considerable variation in size and are slightly glossy black in appearance; in Syria they are green. They vary in length from 29-74mm. Due to the habit of barn owls not only using the same roost site but also the same perch, their pellets may be collected and the contents analysed to see what they are eating. Through this analysis, a great deal of information can be obtained which enables the recorder to monitor changes in diet. If a number of pellet studies were put together over a period of time, it might be possible to use the analyses as a tool to draw up a barn owl conservation plan.

Diet

Early attempts at highlighting the barn owl's diet were largely instigated in attempts to alleviate them from persecution. In Cheshire in 1910 Coward found that from 143 pellets came the remains of 114 field voles, 110 common shrew, 55 wood mice, 69 sparrows and finches, 32 mouse (spp.), 7 bank vole, 7 water shrew, 9 rats, 3 insectivorous birds, 1 water vole and 3 lesser shrew (pygmy).

Following the first national barn owl survey, an analysis of barn owl pellets from five counties in England was carried out by Claude Ticehurst, who based it on samples that were collected during the course of the survey from one pair of birds only from each of the counties: Wiltshire (26 pellets), Staffordshire (9), Suffolk (30), Norfolk (13) and Essex (44). Pellets were also collected from Kent (43), although the period in which they were collected was unknown. Only 165 pellets were collected but from those there is a suggestion that field voles were not so commonly taken as they are at present, although care must be exercised because we do not know whether field vole numbers were low at that time. Field vole was the most common species in only three of the samples, Norfolk, Essex and Kent, and it was second to brown rat in the Suffolk sample although we should be aware that this came from the dockland area of Lowestoft. In Norfolk the pellet sample came from rural surroundings and rats were the second most commonly taken prey species (20.7%) after field vole.

Recent studies have shown a greater dependency upon field voles than once probably existed. The most important survey in more recent years was carried out by Glue in 1974. He obtained analyses from 188 pellet samples around Britain and Ireland (Table 2). Preceding this, Buckley and Goldsmith carried out a study in east Norfolk, the results of which (Table 3) were incorporated into Glue's study. In addition to these, I collected samples and analyses from 18 sites in Suffolk from 1979 to 1990 (Table 4). My study was not a detailed investigation into the diet of Suffolk's barn owls but an overview as to what species of small mammal Suffolk's barn owls were feeding upon at that time, the collection of those samples at the same time reflecting the broad distribution of the county's barn owls. Most were collected from east Suffolk, but a few were collected from the west of the county. From these three studies and others from around the British Isles, it is clear that small mammals are the most important prey for barn owls.

In addition to ascertaining what barn owls are feeding upon, pellet analysis can perform an important role for the mammalogist in providing a snapshot of the small mammal fauna in a particular area, and they can be especially good for establishing the presence of scarce creatures such as the water shrew. For the student of barn owls, however, then the impact that creatures such as the water shrew have on the diet of a barn owl is relatively small and whilst we must not dismiss any creature that features in barn owl diets, there are some that play a more important role in the conservation of the barn owl than others. The key identification features for those small mammal species are shown on p.62.

THE IDENTIFICATION OF SMALL MAMMALS IN OWL PELLETS

The identification of small mammal remains in barn owl pellets can perform two functions. For the mammal student they may indicate what small mammals there are in a particular locality, while for barn owl conservationists they may provide dietary information over a period of time. It should be remembered that if a barn owl is hunting mainly over grassland, the pellets will contain many vole remains, but if it is hunting over arable farmland the remains are more likely to be of mice.

If detailed information is required, such as whether a pellet contains the remains of insects or worms for example, then dissecting air-dried pellets is probably best. The alternative method is to soak them in a dish of water. This will loosen the pellets, which can then be removed and placed on old newspapers. This method is messier but it does allow the remains to be separated from the matrix a little easier. It is probably the best method for barn owl workers seeking to identify the broad contents.

Working on one pellet at a time, it should be teased apart using a dissecting needle or tweezers. Examination of the remains should be made using a lens such as a jeweller's eye-glass. An identification guide, notebook and pen or pencil are necessary to record the contents. The remains of uncommon or rare species, such as water shrew, harvest mouse, house mouse, water vole and brown rat will be found and they are likely to be of chief concern to mammalogists who may be studying their distribution. Bat and bird remains may also be discovered along with bird rings, which should be forwarded to the BTO. The remains of the brown rat can usually be identified by their large size. There are other species of mammal that may form part of a barn owl's diet and they include mole, weasel and rabbit.

The most common species to be found in barn owl pellets is the field vole whose remains can be separated from the bank vole by inspection of the upper molar teeth. The field vole has a loop on the inside of the second upper molar but bank voles do not have that.

Particular notice should be taken of water vole remains. Great efforts are now being made to conserve this declining species and with so many barn owls choosing to hunt riparian habitats it seems possible that in the future water vole remains may occur more frequently in pellets than at present. The root system of the water vole is similar to that of the field vole, although like the bank vole, the upper second molar of the water vole does not have the characteristic loop at the end.

Shrew skulls are more fragile than those of mice or voles and so it is not uncommon to find that the cranium has partially disintegrated leaving only the jaws and teeth. As with all small mammals the teeth indicate the difference between the species. Both common and pygmy shrews have five unicuspids (the teeth behind the incisors) although on the pygmy shrew the third

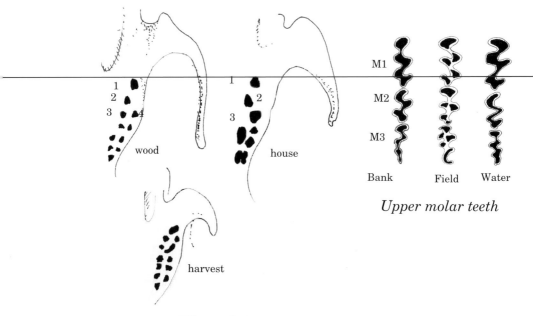

Mice palates

Upper molar teeth

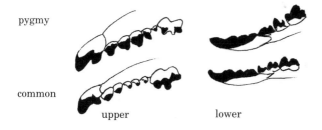

Shrew unicuspids

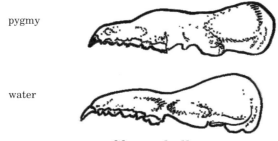

Shrew skulls

unicuspid is larger than the second, while on the common shrew the third uniscupid is smaller than the second. The remains of the uncommon water shrew occasionally turn up in barn owl pellets and adult skulls are easily recognised by their larger size. The water shrew has only four uniscupids. The lower jaw patterns of shrews can be difficult to separate but with care this task is not too difficult. On the pygmy shrew the four cusps of the lower incisors are evenly spaced, while on the common shrew the two front cusps of the lower incisor are grouped together. The incisor of the water shrew's lower jaw is distinct from the other shrew species, although care should be exercised due to the possibility that a worn common shrew lower incisor could be mistakenly identified. The skull of the water shrew has a distinct forehead as opposed to the flatter skulls of pygmy and common shrews.

The most common of the mice species in barn owl pellets is the wood mouse. Its remains may easily be identified by the root system on the first upper molar, which has four roots. Altogether there are eleven roots on the wood mouse compared with seven on the less common house mouse. The harvest mouse sometimes occurs in barn owl pellets although it is uncommon to find intact skulls because they are very fragile. They have an intricate root system comprising no less than twelve. The much rarer dormouse seldom occurs in barn owl pellets, although its remains sometimes turn up in the pellets of the tawny owl.

The most commonly taken species in all of those studies was the field, or short-tailed vole, a creature that lives mainly in rough grassland such as grazing meadows, field margins, road-side verges and other places where they are able to feed on grasses, sedges, green leaves and other succulent vegetation. It is also there that they find sufficient cover amongst the tussock vegetation to create a network of runs and to build their nests that are often deep in the undergrowth. Field voles are prolific breeders so if the conditions are favourable several litters may be produced between spring and autumn. Young that are born in early spring may commence breeding by the latter part of the same year if they survive.

Populations of field voles are usually subject to three to five year cycles and because of this, the barn owl population tracks the highs and lows of this small mammal. Vole cycles tend to be more pronounced in northern parts of Britain than in the south and indeed Taylor found a marked three-year cycle during the course of his Scottish study. When voles are plentiful, the number of eggs

Table 4 Analysis of barn owl pellets in Suffolk (1979-1990) showing numbers of prey items.

Acknowledgements: A number of people kindly assisted to produce these results. I thank Richard Woolnough, Simone Bullion, Tina Martin and Paul Wraneck for their assistance

	No	%		No	%
Common shrew	489	25.44	Wood mouse	168	8.74
Pygmy shrew	83	4.32	Harvest mouse	20	1.04
Water shrew	18	0.94	House mouse	18	0.94
Bank vole	85	4.42	Brown rat	24	1.25
Field vole	968	50.36	Birds	42	2.19
Water vole	7	0.36			

laid will be high and the chances of the young surviving beyond their first autumn are enhanced. When the vole populations are low, however, then the number of eggs laid will also be low and the survival for the young will be less. The size of the clutch will be determined by the amount of food that the male presents to the female before and during egg-laying. At the end of the cycle, when the vole population has reached its peak, it usually crashes, leaving just a small number of voles to re-initiate the cycle. Consequently, if there is a large population of barn owls in a year when the field vole population crashes, there will be a subsequent crash in barn owl numbers because many will not find sufficient food, and then during the course of the autumn and winter, many will starve to death. This is not unusual. The reasons for the fall in field vole numbers at the end of their cycle may include severe weather conditions although as voles are able to live beneath snow cover this seems unlikely. It is more probable that the fall in numbers is brought about by predation, disease and stress within the vole communities.

Occasionally vole numbers may reach plague proportions and when this occurs they can cause great damage to the vegetation.

Table 5 Barn Owl Prey on the Dengie Hundred November 1994-
May 1997 (after R.A. Love).

Species	Prey Items	
	Number	**Percent**
Field vole	4,891	28.2
Bank vole	829	4.8
Water vole	80	0.5
Wood mouse	5,269	30.4
House mouse	245	1.4
Harvest mouse	549	3.2
Brown rat	94	0.5
Common shrew	3,464	20.0
Pygmy shrew	1,672	9.6
Water shrew	42	0.2
Mole	8	0
Pipistrelle bat	2	< 0.1
Brown Long-eared Bat	1	< 0.1
Rabbit	1	< 0.1
Very small bird	25	0.1
Small bird	57	0.3
Medium bird sp.	28	0.2
Large bird sp.	52	0.3
Very large bird	27	0.2
Reptile sp.	13	0.1
Amphibian sp.	3	< 0.1
Total	17,352	
Number of pellets	4,733	

In Essex there was such an occurrence many years ago when in 1903 Johnston reported that field voles had 'suddenly appeared swarming in millions'. Prior to this a substantial vole plague also occurred in the central southern uplands of the Scottish Borders area during the latter years of the nineteenth century and as a consequence of that, vast numbers of short-eared owls (estimates put it between 500 and 2,000 pairs) bred in Dumfriesshire. The common shrew was the second most frequently taken common prey item to occur in the three surveys and for many barn owls it formed nearly a quarter of their diet. This small and very active mammal is found in many habitats but especially grassland, hedgerows and scrub. Common shrews are sometimes found in heather and their populations may also be subject to fluctuations, but these are not cyclical and often occur in the autumn when there may be a marked decrease in its numbers. Whatever the cause, a fall in shrew numbers, occurring at the same time as a vole shortage, will have a severe effect on the chances of barn owls surviving the winter unless there is another food source to turn to. Common shrew featured more highly in two of my Suffolk samples; one was comprised of only a few pellets and so conclusions should not be drawn from that but the other one from Thorpeness came from a site close to heathland with heather; Smith in 1938 was particular to note that 'in the moorlands they may be seen not infrequently 'quartering' the heather in the manner of Short-eared Owls'.

In recent times the pygmy shrew has come in for some attention due to its increased frequency in barn owl pellets and it is now more commonly found in them than common shrew. The pygmy shrew has the oldest fossil record of all the European shrews and is found throughout Britain and Ireland at all altitudes. Unlike common shrews they do not eat earthworms but prefer beetles, woodlice, adult flies, spiders and various other insects. The burrows of other animals, such as field voles, are not necessary for it to find its way around and so pygmy shrews are found in a wide variety of habitats and especially where there is plenty of ground cover. In 1907 Forrest noted that in North Wales that barn owls fed on shrews 'to a much greater extent than any other owl; indeed, in some cases considerably more than half the total consisted of shrew remains, Field and Bank Voles ranking next', while in Cheshire, Coward and Oldham in 1900 noted that while the diet of barn owls at Dunham Park fed predominantly on field voles, those in an outlying covert 'yield long-tailed field mice and common shrews in excess of any other creature'.

The bank vole is a creature of woodland, hedgerows and areas of thick scrub, although in the absence of the field vole it may be found in grassland. It featured in all of the three comparative surveys and in each the importance was approximately the same. However, in a study based upon live-trapping in north Suffolk, the bank vole was found to be the most common species, accounting for 43.6% of the 818 small mammals that were caught. Only 66% of the bank vole catches were in hedges, and the remaining captures were made away from the hedgerows. The field vole ranked only 4th in the order of capture (7%). In Ireland, where the field vole and common shrew are both absent, the bank vole is an increasingly common creature in the open countryside following its recent introduction and it now accounts for between 15 to 22% of the barn owl's diet.

The wood mouse is found in a wide variety of habitats including open fields and hedgerows although more especially in woodland. It is probably the most abundant mammal throughout the British Isles and so it is not surprising to find it in most samples. In arable areas especially, this species migrates between open fields, woodlands and hedgerows at various times of the year but especially during harvest time, thus leaving itself vulnerable to predation. The heathland sample in Suffolk that was mentioned earlier had a particularly high percentage of wood mouse (37%) and it is the only sample in my Suffolk study where the field vole was not the most abundant prey species. In Ireland, where the field vole is absent, the wood mouse is the dominant prey item, accounting for around 50% of prey taken.

Many of the old accounts suggest that in years past the barn owl was a prolific rat-catcher but today this is difficult to believe, although there is evidence that rats were once taken more commonly. In the past many commentators have stated that the barn owl was 'a most useful bird in helping to control rats and other rodents'. Writing in the first half of the 20th century, Ticehurst commented that the brown rat was 'All too common: the rat-ridden hedgerows of some agricultural fields in Suffolk are a disgrace.' These comments, along with many others, provide us with an insight into how much more common rats once were.

As we shall see later, most barn owls now tend to inhabit riparian habitats, such as riverside meadows, fenland and coastal grazing marshes but very few of the typical waterside creatures, i.e. water vole and water shrew, were found in the samples. David

Table 6 Comparative number of samples sites, pellets and prey items from the 1974 survey Glue (1974) and Love et al (2000).

	No sites	No prey items	No pellets
South- west England			
1974	28	7,719	783
1997	2	230	53
Southern England			
1974	14	2,835	689
1997	13	4,577	1,630
Eastern England			
1974	8	3,418	923
1997	32	31,270	8,364
Midlands			
1974	20	3,169	803
1997	7	2,501	748
Northern England			
1974	36	6,640	1,556
1997	5	927	242
Scotland			
1974	21	5,815	1,125
1997	4	4,822	1,385
Wales			
1974	16	4,455	474
1997	18	4,669	1,140
Totals			
1974	143	34,051	6,353
1997	81	4,899	1,356

Thirty-two (39.5%) of the sites surveyed in the 1997 study were located in eastern England, while 8,364 (61.67%) of the total pellets were collected from them

Glue discovered that nationally, the remains of 574 water shrews (1.2%) were found in his survey compared with 1.3% in Norfolk and 1.0% in my Suffolk survey. Water voles were poorly recorded in Glue's study and only slightly more frequent in the two comparative surveys from East Anglia. In a later study, Love (1996) indicated a slightly higher percentage of water voles (0.5%) from the Dengie Peninsula, in Essex. While the study of barn owl pellets can be very useful in helping to draw attention to what barn owls are eating, they can also be very useful in drawing attention to the plight of some mammal species. It is interesting to note that in the Lake District MacPherson in1892 noted, 'An examination of the pellets beneath one of their nesting- places showed that the birds were in the habit of feeding on the Water Shrew, the teeth of that small animal being easily recognised'. It was also in the Lake District that the remains of a dormouse were found just a few years ago in a pellet, thus drawing attention to the fact that dormice were living 100 miles (160 km) further north than was thought at the time.

In the past, barn owls have often been referred to as opportunistic hunters, catching what they can, where and when they can. However, Taylor contested this and was of the opinion that barn owls actively seek out those areas that contain good numbers of field voles because voles are heavier than mice or shrews and are therefore more profitable in terms of nutrition. In the United States similar opinions were expressed regarding short-eared owls. There can be no doubt that when rats were more abundant in the countryside than they are now, they too featured more highly in the diet of some barn owls for the same reason, but we should not dismiss opportunistic behaviour when it comes to barn owls and food.

In a barn owl roost I was studying at Reydon in Suffolk, I would often find many headless corpses of starlings that had been taken by a barn owl from a nearby reed-bed roost in the autumn and winter. Sometimes I would find primary feathers in the numerous pellets that were deposited there, but rarely would I find the skulls. This study unfortunately ceased after the cowshed in which the roost was sited was blown down in the great storm of October 1987. In 1911 Owen described a tree nest with two owlets in which there were 2 decapitated starlings. Two days later there were 14 more starlings and 10 days later there were another 70, all of which had been decapitated. (In his Scottish study Iain Taylor reported that of 614 prey deliveries to the nest that were photographed, none involved headless prey.) Apart from swallowing birds' heads, barn owls will sometimes nip them off and drop them elsewhere.

Another example of opportunistic hunting was noted the Alward oil refinery at Khomaquin, Iraq. A large roost of several hundred house sparrows roosted in oleander bushes surrounding the lawns. The lawns and bushes were floodlit until late at night and each evening, from May until July, one or both of a pair of barn owls would come to feed on the sparrows. The owls would sit quietly in one of the nearby eucalyptus trees before dropping swiftly to the bushes below where they would catch a sparrow and then take it off to a nearby vantage point to eat. Sometimes they would do this for an hour or more and although they would regularly hunt by floodlight, neither of the owls was ever seen by daylight. Closer to home, David Glue reported on a pair of barn owls at a gravel pit in Hampshire that regularly disturbed an autumn roost of house sparrows, starlings and pied wagtails. He discovered that of the 109 bird skulls found in 14 batches of pellets from southern England, the 57 identified skulls were of communal roosting species.

Without doubt larger birds are taken on occasion, for on December 6th, 1982, I found the remains of a water rail at the previously mentioned barn owl roost near Reydon. In 1985 Nuttell witnessed a remarkable sight when he saw a barn owl attacking a wood pigeon that fell to the floor with the owl on top of it. The owl then commenced to pluck the breast. On May 4th, 1952, two barn owls were disturbed from a hole in a tree at Charlecote, Warwickshire, and inside were found the half-eaten remains of a jackdaw. Occasionally pellets reveal surprising items such as the one from Orfordness in Suffolk that produced 'the unlikely find of a dunlin head'; earlier, in 1907, Forrest mentioned the finding of a dunlin skull in a pellet from Anglesey, while in 1983 I was present when the skull of a redshank was found in a pellet sample from Barsham in Suffolk!

Other prey that have been recorded in pellets includes adult and juvenile moorhens, rook, corncrake, dunlin, common snipe, woodcock, woodpigeon and lapwing.

Some observations of barn owls taking birds were reported during my Suffolk survey: on July 24th, 1983, Mrs M. Dyke saw a barn owl 'flying early evening and saw it go down on the hedge. When it got up it had a blackbird. It went off to an oak tree near our house'. On January 26th, 1985, David Bakewell saw a barn owl chasing a blackbird at dusk near Waldringfield and on June

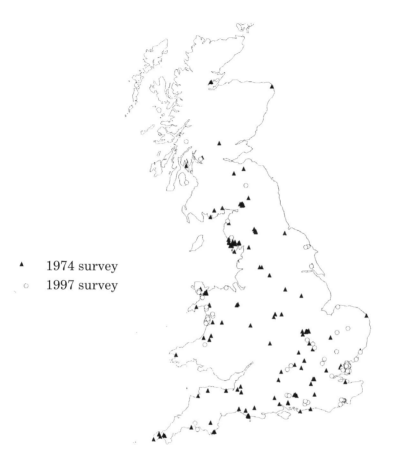

▲ 1974 survey
○ 1997 survey

Fig 2 Distribution of pellet samples (after Love et al 2000).

23rd, 1986, I found the headless corpse of a male blackbird in a barn near Wrentham; later, in July 1992 and July 1995, I found other headless male blackbirds at additional sites near Mildenhall. Presumably the pre-roosting commotion that some male blackbirds give out at dusk occasionally draws unwelcome attention.

Elsewhere I mention the return of the barn owl to Skomer Island, in Pembrokeshire, south-west Wales, and how the barn owls there appear to have adopted the habit of 'commuting' 1km to the mainland to catch and bring back prey to the island to feed their young, but it remains to be seen whether this habit will continue. A study from North America was carried out on a

Table 7 Set-aside trends in England by region 1990 -2003
Figures in hectares

Region	1990	1995	+/- hectares	+/-%	2000	+/-% < 1995	+/-%	2003	+/-% < 2000	+/-%
North-east	2,703	22,527	+19,824	+ 733	21,421	-1,106	- 4.9	26,571	+5,150	+ 24.0
North-west	1,569	9,060	+7,491	+ 477	8,589	-471	- 5.2	12,645	+4,056	+ 47.2
Yorkshire & Humber	4,877	65,974	+61,097	+ 1253	57,323	8,651	- 13.1	69,218	+11,895	+ 20.1
East Midlands	9,166	98,883	+89,717	+ 979	87,224	-11,659	-11.8	108,445	+21,221	+ 24.3
West Midlands	4,036	43,649	+39,613	+ 981	41,128	-2,521	-5.8	50,151	+9,023	+ 21.9
Eastern	16,419	141,745	+125,326	+ 763	118,414	-23,331	-16.5	143,006	+24,592	+ 20.8
London	259	1,105	+846	+ 415	949	-156	-14.1	1,237	+1,081	+ 692.9
South-east	21,206	95,584	+74,378	+ 351	82,408	-13,176	-13.8	100,269	+17,861	+ 21.7
South-west	11,665	65,478	+53,813	+ 464	62,801	-2,677	-4.1	75,537	+12,736	+ 20.3
England	71,890	544,005	+472,115	+ 657	480,257	-63,748	- 11.7	587,079	+106,822	+ 22.2

Source of information: DEFRA June Census Statistics

rocky island off of the coast of Carolina in the 1930s where barn owls were nesting in an old cabin. It seems that four owlets were reared on a diet of Leach's storm petrel from a nearby colony, and that the remains of these birds formed a carpet on the cabin floor 7.5cm deep, so perhaps, in the fullness of time, Skomer's barn owls may themselves turn to feeding upon the seabirds that inhabit the island, thus removing the need to commute to the mainland? Previously, Sutcliffe reported from Skomer on little owls feeding on storm petrels and he considered the little owl to be a factor in the decline of that species on the island. He stated that little owls had previously been deported from Skomer due to the impact that they had had on the island's seabird population, so perhaps the same fate awaits Skomer's newly arrived barn owls?

More recently there has been a pellet analysis from Essex in which it was found that field voles contributed only 28.2% of the diet (Table 5) and that wood mouse contributed a significant 30.4% with common shrew providing 20%. The results from this survey, which was carried out on the Dengie Peninsula, contrast sharply with the findings of the two previous surveys in East Anglia and also with the national survey by David Glue. It was thought that the high number of wood mice found in the two-year study was a reflection of the large quantities of food that were available to the mice at a time when field vole numbers were depressed due to a severe drought in 1995. This produced a reduction in the quantity and quality of grass for field voles and enabled the unusually high numbers of wood mice to disperse across the countryside, thus leaving them open to predation. The high numbers of wood mice were fortunate for the owls at a time when field vole numbers were markedly low. How different things were for Bunn et al in 1982 when, after what promised to be the best breeding season for barn owls on record, many of them died of starvation in the exceptionally hot summer of 1976. This was due to thousands of voles dying because the succulent grass and young shoots that they feed upon had dried up. In Britain this problem may become more prevalent in the future, if the climate is warming. This is because field voles prefer moist, damp grassland to live in and succulent vegetation to feed upon. On mainland Europe, however, the common vole is more important for barn owls because it tends to live in drier habitats, such as short grassland, but also in cereal and some other crops. As a consequence of this, the two voles live side-by-side in the environment, offering a greater choice of food to the owls.

Although field voles are important prey for barn owls in Britain, there is evidence to suggest that they once fed on a greater diversity of prey and in more equal proportions than at present and Glue and Jordan reported on a large find (three sackfuls!) of pellets from a chimney in Hampshire which appears to support this. The building records for the site revealed that the chimney had been capped in October 1913 but due to the warmth of an adjacent chimney that was still in working order, the pellets had remained dry and intact. When they were examined, it was found that their composition differed strikingly from the modern barn owl diet in that it contained a wider spectrum of mammalian prey items. They found the remains of 14 species amongst a total of 813 prey items and they considered that the field vole, wood mouse, bank vole, common shrew and pygmy shrew all comprised virtually one tenth or more towards a more evenly balanced diet than in the present day. From a search of the old literature, and by scanning old maps, it was considered that this was due to a more varied landscape in terms of hedgerows, pastures and the like.

At one nest in Hampshire Phillips in 1939 recorded, 'As the nest was situated in the open it was easy (particularly on moonlight nights) to see exactly what food was being brought to the nest. An examination of the pellets and contents of the nest was also periodically carried out (as well as was possible). The relative quantities of the different types of food were approximately as follows:- Rats 60%, Mice and Voles, 25%, Miscellaneous 15% made up of the following:- Stoats 2, Weasels 1, Slow worms 4, Grass snakes 1, Shrews 2, Young rabbits 1'. In another example from Lancashire a Mr I.Whittaker obtained 40/50 pellets that contained the remains of 20 field voles, 1 bank vole, 11 house mice, 6 wood mice, 15 common shrew, 3 beetles, 21 house sparrows and a brambling/chaffinch. Clearly, although this was just a small sample, at that particular time the bird in question was feeding on a wide range of prey. A study published in 2000 by Love et al compared the present-day situation with that which David Glue had found found. This investigation was more comprehensive than the 1974 survey and so it is beyond the range of this book to describe in detail, but the general thrust of this research was that there had been changes in the percentage intake of some species, notably common shrew, wood mouse, house mouse, pygmy shrew and brown rat, and that these changes were independent of the general habitats but dependent upon region. Efforts were made to ensure a wide geographical distribution of sites from which the pellets were collected but this depended upon the volunteers who were willing to collect them and, more importantly, the presence of owls. Many of the collection sites were from the south and east of England and so naturally a greater amount of data was obtained from there (Fig 2).

The authors considered that the most significant increase in the overall diet was in the percentage of wood mouse and that this was largely due to the set-aside farming scheme. Wood mouse is the species that is most likely to benefit from set-aside and they reported that the increase in wood mouse was greatest from eastern England, where the percentage of rural land that is in set-aside, 7.5%, is greater than the average in England, 4.2%. According to the June agricultural census, as conducted by Defra from 1995-2000 (Table 7), there was an increase in the amount of set-aside, which probably explains some of the changes in diet. Although the eastern region had by far the greatest amount of land put into set-aside, the increase in the amount there was not so great as in Yorkshire and Humber, a region that witnessed a remarkable 1,253% increase in the amount of set-aside, although in the survey only three pellet samples came from there.

Overall, from a modest national figure of 71,890 hectares in 1990, the amount of land put into set-aside rose dramatically during the course of the next five years to a staggering 544,005 hectares (over a million acres), an increase of 472,115 hectares (657%). Since that time the figure has gradually increased so that by the end of 2003 a further 43,079 hectares of land had been included in the scheme.

The authors suggested that the heavier wood mouse might be sought by barn owls in preference to the lighter common shrew but they stated that the decrease in common shrew was not reflected by a widespread increase in wood mouse. What the survey could not explain is why there was such an increase in pygmy shrew, which negates the proposal that wood mice are being taken in favour of the lighter common shrew.

The authors thought that there had been a decline in field voles due to the loss of grassland, which would partly explain why common shrew has also declined. They considered that although there had been a small drop in the percentage of field voles in the overall diet, it was still a more important prey item than it was earlier in the 20th century and that field voles are the most abundant prey species of rough grassland. This is why grassland

is the preferred hunting ground of barn owls; earlier in the 20th century, and probably before then, that might not have been the case because there was an abundance of prey elsewhere, such as along hedgerows, stubble fields and around hayricks. They felt that rats, along with birds such as sparrows and starlings, had also declined as prey because those farmland species had also declined.

A total of 466 rat remains were found amongst the 34,051 prey items in Glue's study, but in this latest survey, which comprised of 48,996 prey items, the remains of only 260 rats were found. The question as to why the brown rat has declined over the years can be summed up in two ways. Farmyards are now much cleaner places than they used to be and poisons are vigorously applied. Compare this to the Middle East where a joint Israeli, Jordanian and Palestinian programme is promoting the use of lesser kestrels and barn owls as biological pest controllers rather than the use of agricultural poisons.

The report by Love et al stressed the 'need for a greater understanding of the effects of habitat changes on small mammal populations, particularly in agricultural landscapes' and concluded that although prey species other than field vole were now playing a greater part in the diet of Britain's barn owls, the actual spectrum of prey had declined further since the 1974 survey and barn owls are now increasingly reliant upon field voles, shrews and wood mice. This survey, which came thirty years after David Glue's important review, did not mention whether the change in diet was against a rising or falling barn owl population, although the authors thought that the changes would have a negative effect upon barn owl numbers. It may be that in the future, it will be useful to align the monitoring of barn owl diet, distribution and perhaps population, with the five-yearly June agricultural census. This could have positive uses for agriculturalist, naturalist and conservationist.

As well as eating small mammals, barn owls also feed very occasionally on carrion. Only one record of this was reported by Cramp in 1985; Shawyer in 1987 also reported carrion feeding; during the course of my study two reliable sightings of this unusual behaviour were reported to me. On January 27th, 1983, a barn owl was seen at Sudbourne feeding on rabbit and on August 22nd, 1990, near Great Glemham another was also seen feeding on rabbit. These sightings of barn owls eating carrion are noteworthy, but an even more remarkable event has recently come to light when I was informed of a barn owl that was seen to carry off a large rabbit one summer's evening in 1988. The observer, Mrs Leonie Golding, was driving home through the lanes between Stow Maries and Woodham Ferrers, in Essex, with her young son after an evening's sailing on the River Blackwater. The lane in question had grass verges with hedges either side and although headlights were in use, it was not yet dark. As the car swung round a sharp bend she saw a rabbit lying stationary across the middle of the road. Standing on top of the rabbit and facing the approaching car was a barn owl, that thrust its head forward and stared in their direction, its wings mantling the rabbit, which the observer believes was dead. The observer slowed the car but allowed it to continue rolling gently forward, whereupon the owl raised its wings and taking hold of the rabbit, managed to just lift it off the ground and carry it to the side of the road. The car then 'rolled on by and left the bird to its supper'.

Barn owls may sometimes take other mammals and on August 14th, 1961, the rear portion of a weasel was found at a barn owl roost-site at Corpusty in Norfolk. Mansel-Pleydell in 1887 recorded a nest in an ash tree containing two young owlets in which the parents had 'stowed away' two nearly full-grown rats, a dozen mice, a couple of young rabbits and three birds. Buckley and Goldsmith recorded rabbit in their study while on more than one occasion Eric Hosking informed me that he saw barn owls bringing young rabbits to nests he was photographing. A most unusual and interesting record comes from Borrer in 1891, who mentioned that while he was watching a barn owl on the branch of an oak tree that was overhanging his pond, he saw that it 'suddenly dropped from a height of some 8 feet and carried off a carp in its claws'. Lilford in 1895 mentioned finding various remains in owl pellets including 'one or two of Bats, and fragments of various fishes', while there are other reports of a barn owl feeding its young on fish', which it had been seen to catch in the most dextrous manner'. There are other historical records of barn owls taking fish dating from the 19th century, as well as a more recent sighting of a barn owl taking a 'good-sized roach' from the River Anholme in Lincolnshire. Insects too have been reported as prey; in 1910 Coward mentions that in the stomach of a barn owl that had been killed were the remains of 'two Long-eared Bats, one Wood Mouse, three beetles and a small weevil – and a large moth', while MacPherson in 1892 recounted that he 'watched a Barn Owl gliding noiselessly along the tops of hedgerows, and also flying around the upper branches of the larger trees, evidently picking off insects'. A naturalist mentioned to me several years ago that one night he had witnessed a barn owl flying in front of his car in the headlights, and he thought that it might have been hawking for moths. However, a few years later this rather fanciful idea was given a little more credence when I had the same experience Langham in Essex, when one night, along a sheltered lane, a barn owl flew in front of my car's headlights for over a hundred metres before it parted company at a bend.

Heimo Mikkola was keen to point out that the amount of insects consumed by barn owls should not be underestimated, even though they appear to form only a small part of the diet. He pointed out that 1973 was a good year for butterflies in southern England, and that a pair of barn owls he studied there had consumed around 34 small tortoiseshell and 24 peacock butterflies, as well as 2 herald moths and various other insects. He also highlighted the study of Buckley & Goldsmith which also found butterfly and moth remains, along with those of a damsel fly.

Close observations of perched hunting barn owls cannot fail to reveal to the observer the erect rictal bristles that can be seen around the margin of the upper mandible and above it. On relaxed barn owls these feathers flatten to the facial disc and are not easily discerned. Nightjars have similar arrangements of bristles growing from around the margin of their upper mandible and these are arranged so they can trap or direct insects towards the open mouth. The sensory properties of the bristles are unknown but it seems unlikely that they would not have some function concerned with feeding. Owls may feel with their bristles, and the wedge down the centre of the facial disc may separate the two visual fields in a similar manner to the nose on the human face.

SOURCES USED IN THIS CHAPTER

Bontzorlus, V.A., Peris, S.J., & Vlachos, C.G., 2005: The diet of the barn owl in the agricultural landscapes of central Greece. *Folia Zool.,* 54: 99-110.

Borrer, W., 1891: *The Birds of Sussex.* Porter, London.

Buckley, J., and Goldsmith, J.G. ,1972: Barn Owls and their prey in East Norfolk. *Trans. Norfolk and Norwich Nat. Soc.,* 22: 320-325.

Bunn, D.S., 1972: Regular daylight hunting by Barn Owls. *British Birds,* 65: 26-30.

Bunn, D.S., Warburton, A.W., and Wilson, A.A.B., 1982: *The Barn Owl.* Poyser, Calton.

Clark, R.J., 1975: A field study of the short-eared owl *Otus flammeus* (Pontopidan) in North America. *Wildl. Monogr.,* 47: 1-67.

Colvin, B.A. ,& Spaulding, S.R., 1983: Winter foraging behaviour of short-eared owls (*Asio flammeus*) in Ohio. *Am. Midl. Nat.,* 110: 124-128.

Coward, T.A., 1910: *The Vertebrate Fauna of Cheshire and Liverpool Bay.* Witherby, London.

Coward, T.A., & Oldham, C., 1900: *The Birds of Cheshire.* Sherratt & Hughes, Manchester.

Cramp, S. (ed.), 1985: *The Birds of the Western Palearctic* (Vol 4). Oxford University Press.

Dunlop, E.B., 1911. The Diurnal Flight of the Barn Owl. *British Birds,* 4: 314-315.

Forrest, H.E., 1907: *The Vertebrate Fauna of North Wales.* Witherby & Co., London.

Glue, D., 1967: Prey taken by the Barn Owl in England and Wales. *Bird Study,* 14: 169-183.

Glue, D., 1974: Food of the Barn Owl in Britain and Ireland. *Bird*

Study, 21: 200-210.

Glue, D., and Jordan, R., 1990: Baked Barn Owl pellet revelations. *BTO News,* 167: 5.

Jacobs, C.A., and Johnson, R., 2003: Field Note. *Suffolk Birds,* 51: 81.

Johnsgard, P.A., *North American Owls: Biology and Natural History.* Smithsonian Institution, Washington.

Johnston, H., 1903: *British Mammals.* Hutchinson, London.

Kelsall, J.E., & Munn, P.W., 1905: *The Birds of Hampshire and the Isle of Wight.* Witherby, London.

Lacey, M.E. ,1990. Food pass by Barn Owl. *British Birds.* 83: 399.

Last, J.M., 1962: Barn Owl apparently killing Weasel. *British Birds,* 55: 87.

Lilford, Lord, 1895: *Notes on the Birds of Northamptonshire and Neighbourhood.* Porter, London.

Lord, J. ,1953: *West Midland Bird Report 19.* Birmingham and West Midland Bird Club.

Love, R.A., 1996. The Analysis of Barn Owl Pellets from the Dengie Hundred. *The Essex Bird Report 1996.* The Essex Birdwatching Society.

Love, R.A., Webbon, C., Glue, D.E., & Harris, S., 2000: Changes in the food of British Barn Owls (*Tyto alba*) between 1974 and 1997. 2000: *Mammal Review.* 30: 107 – 129.

MacPherson, H.A., 1892: *A Vertebrate Fauna of Lakeland.* 1892: David Douglas, Edinburgh.

Mansell-Pleydell, J.C., 1888: *The Birds of Dorsetshire.* R.H.Porter, London.

Mikkola, H. ,1983: *Owls of Europe.* Poyser, Calton.

Mushtaq-Ul-Hassan, M., Ghazi, R.R., & Nisa, N., 2007: Food preference of the Short-Eared Owl (*Asio flammeus*) and Barn Owl (*Tyto alba*) at Usta Muhammad, Baluchistan, Pakistan. *Turk J. Zool.,* 31: 91-94.

Nuttell, A., 1985: Barn Owl attacking and killing adult Wood Pigeon. *British Birds,* 78: 664.

Owen, J.H., 1911: Food of young Barn Owls. *British Birds,* 5: 112-113.

Perrow, M., Peet, N., and Jowitt, A., 1992. The small mammals of drainage ditches - the influence of structure. *Trans. Suffolk Nat. Soc.,* 28: 3-9.

Ratcliffe, D., 2007: *Galloway and the Borders.* Collins, London.

Sage, B.L., 1962: Barn Owls catching sparrows at roost. *British*

Birds, 55: 237-238.

Shawyer, C., 1987: *The Barn Owl in the British Isles – Its Past, Present and Future.* The Hawk Trust, London.

Shehab, A.H., 2005: Food of the Barn Owl *Tyto alba* in Southern Syria. *Acta zoologica cracoviensia,* 48A: 35-42.

Smal, C.M., 1987: The diet of the Barn Owl *Tyto alba* in southern Ireland, with reference to a recently introduced prey species – the Bank Vole *Clethrionomys glareolus. Bird Study.* 34: 113-125.

Smally, F.W., 1911. The Diurnal Flight of the Barn Owl. *British Birds,* 4: 339.

Smith, T., 1938: *The Birds of Staffordshire.* North Staffordshire Field Club.

Sutcliffe, S.J., 1990: The Diet of Little Owls on Skomer. *The Pembrokeshire Bird Report 1989.* The Dyfed Wildlife Trust, Haverfordwest.

Taylor, I.R., 1994: *Barn owls; predator prey relationships.* Cambridge University Press.

Ticehurst, C.B., 1935: On the food of the barn owl and its bearing on barn owl populations. *Ibis,* 13: 329-335.

Ticehurst, C.B., Andrews, H., & Morley, C., 1932: The Mammals of Suffolk. *Trans. Suffolk Nat. Soc.* 2: 13 -33.

PELLET IDENTIFICATION SOURCES

Brown, R., Ferguson, J., Lawrence, M. & Lees, D. 1987. Tracks and Signs of the Birds of Europe: An Identification Guide. Christopher Helm, London.

Corbet, G & Ovenden, D. 1980. The Mammals of Britain & Europe Collins, London.

Glue, D. 1974. Food of the Barn Owl in Britain and Ireland. Bird Study, 21: 200-210.

Lawrence, M.J. & Brown, R.W. 1979. Mammals of Britain: Their Tracks, Trails and Signs (2nd ed.). Blandford Press Ltd., Poole.

Mead, C.J. 1987. Owls. Whittet Books Ltd., London.

Mikkola, H. 1983. Owls of Europe. Poyser, Calton.

Taylor, I. 1994. Barn Owls: predator prey relationships. Cambridge University Press.

Yalden, D. 2003. The Analysis of Owl Pellets (3rd ed.). The Mammal Society, London.

4 ROOSTING, NESTING AND FLEDGING

'In 1839 we read in an opening behind the coat-of arms cut over the portals of the inner court at Drumlanrig, a pair of barn owls have brought forth their young for the last eight years'.

H.S.Gladstone, 1910 *Birds of Dumfriesshire*
(Witherby, London)

The breeding cycle of the barn owl has attracted a great deal of attention over the years and as a consequence there is a large amount of information regarding this aspect of its biology. Most studies have concentrated on barn owls that nest in barns because nests are readily accessible and the opportunities to make detailed observations are greater than in places such as East Anglia where barn owls tend to nest in trees. Even so, it is possible, from time to time, to observe the behaviour of tree-nesting barn owls and to compare it with barn-nesting owls.

TERRITORY

The barn owl may not be as territorial as some other owls, such as the short-eared owl for example, which publicises its territory with raucous calling and by driving away other short-eared owls that encroach upon it. Bunn et al noted that in their study area the barn owls were inclined to be more vocal than barn owls elsewhere due to the high density of barn owls that were present.

They found that a male barn owl usually advertises his ownership of a territory at dusk with territorial screeching, but I hardly ever heard the territorial screeches of barn owls during my nightly vigils; this might have been because barn owls living at low density are much quieter than those living in higher densities. It seems likely that in winter, when the need to feed a young family is no longer important, territorial behaviour changes and the necessity to retain an area for the coming breeding season, combined with the necessity to retain body condition, takes priority. In my view it is uncommon to see barn owls in company with each other, especially during the winter months, and so the behaviour between individual barn owls is difficult to assess, unlike the short-eared owl, for example. These may arrive in southern England from northern Europe during the autumn in reasonable numbers. Once they have arrived, each short-eared owl sorts an individual feeding territory and during 1982, when above average numbers of short-eared owls were reported in south-east England, Moore reported on ten short-eared owls holding winter territories on Old Hall Marshes, in Essex, each one defending its own air-space against other short-eared owls as well as hen harriers and kestrels. At one site in south-west Suffolk that I used to visit during the winter, it was not unusual to see up to six individual short-eared owls in the air at once, all defending their territories in a similar manner and seeing off any intruding short-eared owls. Tawny owls may also set up a winter territory prior to the forthcoming nesting period, but there appears to be no evidence for this amongst barn owls, although the winter foraging flights of barn owls that often take place in the afternoons might be associated with territorial behaviour rather than hunting expeditions.

The reasons for a barn owl to leave its territory were pondered by Bunn et al who expressed caution in reaching the conclusion that a barn owl had left its territory due to its apparent absence: they pointed out that a barn owl will often become elusive, especially after the breeding season and the onset of the moult. However, they also felt that barn owls might leave their territory if the habitat changed or became unsuitable and they stressed that 'excessive and continued disturbance' causes birds to abandon their territory. Where this disturbance takes the form of road traffic, then I am of the view that often the birds will eventually be killed rather than leave their province. They mentioned that one observer in central Wales, Neil Bowman, believed that barn owls vacated their territories in winter and moved to lower ground with the onset of severe winter weather, and that this was probably due to a lack of food but this is unlikely to occur in lowland areas such as East Anglia.

Various estimates have been given for the size of a barn owl's territory and the figure of one pair to 2-4 sq. km is sometimes quoted. This might be the case in areas of quality habitats, but elsewhere it is impossible to define a territory in such certain terms. It is impossible to describe how much land barn owls require because territory size will depend upon the quality of the habitats within it. It may not follow that good hunting territory surrounds the nest-site even though the nest is the focal point of the territory and it may be that in some instances barn owls may have to forage some distance away from the nest-site. Alternatively, if an area is rich in food and nesting places are available, then barn owls may nest in quite close proximity and there are various records in the old literature that illustrate this point. Bunn et al were of the opinion that in young coniferous forest with areas of pasture, barn owls required quite a small territory and they felt that 2.5 km² was perfectly adequate even when vole numbers were low. However, they were of the view that in grazed farmland, where hunting would be largely confined to hedgerows, borders of woods and copses, stream and river banks and farm buildings, then barn owls will need to hunt further afield. Their study, however, does not reflect the situation in arable farmland, such as that found in eastern England, where I found that some barn owls travelled at least one kilometre to find food. In the arable farmlands of north Suffolk Cayford found the size of a barn owl's territory ranged from 1-2km during the nesting period, to 4-5km during the winter time, when foraging became more difficult. The distance that barn owls will travel depends upon prey availability. In the Suffolk Fens, however, where the large number of drainage ditches with their vegetated banks provide plenty of cover for small mammals, I found that when nesting places were available, the density of barn owls could be quite high, and in one area I had three nesting pairs in a 1 km square, but this is unusual.

COURTSHIP AND DISPLAY

Derek Bunn et al reported that some of the pairs they observed remained together throughout the year indulging in activities such as mutual preening and conversation, thus strengthening the pair bond. In many of my nest-sites this would have been difficult due to the actual size of the nesting places and indeed they found that other pairs in their study tended to live apart more frequently and they believed that this was the more common occurrence. This is an important factor to consider in barn owl nest-box schemes, and no doubt explains why many boxes are used, but not for nesting. Sometimes one of a pair moves away and their place is taken by another owl, so that over a period of time the same site might be used but by a varying number of birds. Consequently some sites acquire a long history of nesting barn owls but not necessarily involving the same owls.

Courtship may start early in the year even as soon as February. An increase in the number of daylight sightings is a sure indicator of courtship and this is reflected in my Suffolk study (Fig. 3). Although some of these appearances can be attributed to males establishing their territory, almost certainly much of this increased activity is due to the male hunting to bring food to the female not only to strengthen the pair bond, but also to indicate the abundance of prey that may be available to them during the forthcoming breeding season. These demonstrations also indicate to the female how good her partner is in providing not only her, but also the chicks, with food, which he will have to do during the incubation period and also in the first few weeks after the chicks have hatched. The provision of an abundance of prey by the male to the female will also help to build up the female's reserve for egg-production and also for the time that she will spend on the nest incubating. Iain Taylor found that in his Scottish study clutch size was directly related to the weight of the hen immediately before laying, thus stressing the importance of the male as the meal provider (Fig 3).

Where barn owls are nesting in barns then, as Bunn et al described, the male arrives with prey and 'a self advertising chirrup' which the female answers with an excited snoring which then turns into a high-pitched purr. If she is perched on a beam away from a possible nest site, then she will fly to a dark part of the barn and commences to call the male to her. Upon his arrival he then presents the female with the prey which she then holds in her bill while crouching down and inviting the male to copulate with her which he does immediately. When mating has ceased, she then usually eats the prey, unless she has already eaten, in which case she stores it nearby. This process may happen two or three times per night and during this time the male may bring in more food than the hen requires, in which case the unwanted food often lays around and usually rots. Unmated males usually stock-pile food at an intended nest and one which Taylor was observing contained 136 dead prey items, most of which were decomposing. The reason for the food is that should a newly arrived hen arrive, he has a larder full of food with which to entice her to stay.

I have no idea of the food presentation procedure with tree nesting barn owls, but with many of the tree sites that I have seen it would be difficult for a pair of barn owls to exhibit the type of display described by Bunn et al. With the present day technology it should not be too difficult to carry out observations on barn owls

*Fig 3 Casual sightings of barn owls in Suffolk by month,
1983-1986.*

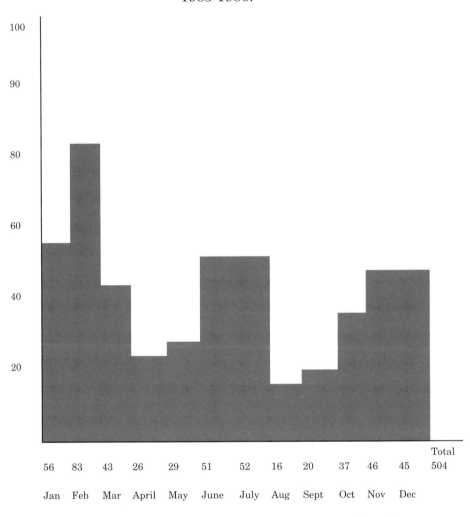

	Jan	Feb	Mar	April	May	June	July	Aug	Sept	Oct	Nov	Dec	Total
	56	83	43	26	29	51	52	16	20	37	46	45	504

These are sightings of barn owls recorded on a casual basis. The records are of
barn owls either seen on the wing, or perched. Nesting and dead barn owls are not
included.

nesting in boxes, although this would entail some lengthy vigils, most of which would need to be carried out at night, as in the manner of Derek Bunn.

The frequent screeching of male barn owls as they fly their territories is another indicator of courtship and as a means of attracting a mate, although I have little information of this from my studies. Bunn et al said that it was not unusual to see the male and female together at night as they begin to indulge in sexual chases that they felt was 'such a feature of Barn Owl courtship'. In this the male follows the female, twisting and turning, all at great speed. During these chases the birds usually screech quite frequently although occasionally their chases are silent. They also described the moth flight of the male, where he hovers at head height in front of the female for up to five seconds, thus exposing his white under-parts and wings. Wing clapping sometimes occurs although they were of the view that this was not a deliberate part of the display as it is with the short-eared and long-eared owls. Taylor also stated that barn owls became more conspicuous in the spring and he was of the view that although the courtship behaviour could not be described as spectacular it 'has a subtle beauty and more than a hint of mystery' about it.

ROOSTING AND NESTING SITES

Until recently the main roosting and nesting sites for barn owls in Britain were buildings and trees, and there can be little doubt that before buildings were constructed, trees were the preferred sites as well as caves, rocky fissures and crevices. Today nest-boxes are becoming more and more important. In Somerset the caves in the Mendip Hills were once frequented by barn and other owls, while there are a several examples in the literature that demonstrate their use elsewhere, and occasional nesting of barn owls in cliffs and rocks continues today. In 1993 I received a record of a barn owl that was observed occupying a hole in a quarry face in Suffolk, although it was unclear whether the hole was being used for nesting.

In 1936 McWilliam reported that barn owls were nesting in cliffs in Dumbartonshire while in 1900 it was reported from Ireland a somnolent barn owl 'has been found asleep in rock-fissures at Malin Head and Mine Head'. On the Isle of Wight barn owls bred at an inland cliff near Shanklin, while cliff nesting in Sussex was confirmed when 'On May 19th, 1919, Colonel C. Smeed made the interesting discovery that this bird was breeding in Rottingdean

Head – a sheer precipice about a hundred feet in height. When he was about five feet from the summit of the cliff – he was descending to a kestrel's eyrie, a Barn-Owl flopped out of an embrasure almost in his face, leaving exposed to view a brace of youngsters and a couple of eggs'.

In Cornwall, nesting and roosting in cliffs have rarely been observed in the county although on August 14th, 1952, an owl was observed to be coming out of a crevice in the cliff at Trevone. Nesting may also have occurred in a bank that was over-hanging water at Carclew, Mylor, while a pair frequented Wiggle cliff, Rame, in January 1969 and was thought to have roosted there throughout the autumn and winter of 1972. In 1931, H.P.O.Cleave wrote that a fissure above the Strangles at St Gennys had been taken over by a pair of tawny owls after being used for many years by a pair of barn owls.

There are a number of records in the old literature that mention barn owls nesting in stone ruins such as castles and this is particularly relevant to the northern and western parts of the British Isles. For example, in 1879 barn owls inhabited Castle Menzies, at Rannoch, in Scotland while elsewhere in Scotland they nested in the cathedral at Dunkeld and a pair once nested in the ruins of Morton Old Castle. They also bred in the cliffs and rocks of St Cyprus and other parts of the coast. From Durham, barn owls historically were 'Breeding in the most inaccessible parts of rocks, towers, and ruins …'; in 1948 and 1949 a pair successfully bred in a tower of Durham Cathedral. A pair also nested in the old tower of Chester Cathedral. Apart from these examples there are a number of others that describe barn owls nesting in rocks, cliffs, crevices and castles.

Examples of nesting in inhabited houses are not unknown; in 1974 barn and tawny owls occupied the opposite ends of a cottage at Tregeseal, St Just, in Cornwall. Elsewhere in Cornwall a pair of barn owls nested in a deserted cottage on Bodmin Moor during the years 1942-44. The birds were using a cupboard, despite the fact that in 1943 the cottage was almost demolished as a result of army manoeuvres. The remains of this cottage, which are sited at an altitude of around 300m (1,000 feet) can still be seen and are an excellent demonstration not only of site fidelity through adversity, but also of how high barn owls once nested in the British Isles. It seems likely, however, that the barn owls departed following the severe winters of 1944/45 and 1947. Borrer in 1891 had

In years past cliff ledges, crevices and the like would have been nesting places for many barn owls.

described how barn owls were destroyed in Sussex on account of them 'disturbing the rest of the lodgers who are now occupying our farmhouses in the summer months'. In Devon provision for barn owls has been incorporated into some recent barn conversions. The resident owls stayed despite the alterations, thus strengthening the view that barn owls will remain faithful to their nesting place despite some disturbance.

TREES VERSUS BARNS

Although, as we shall see later, barn owls have used buildings to nest in for hundreds of years, it is only in the last two to three centuries that buildings have been used to any great degree. According to Bunn et al the percentage of tree nests as a proportion of the total nesting sites of barn owls in Britain had declined (Table 9) since Blaker carried out his study in 1934 (Table 8) ; and Shawyer (1987) reported that tree sites accounted for only 29% of the nest-sites in his survey. In my study county of Suffolk I found that 81.91% of all nests were in trees (Table 10) and this was supported at the time by the nest records for the county held by the BTO (Table 11).

Using the BTO's nest record cards, Osborne found that on a national basis the trend for barn owls to nest in trees was increasing

In 1948 and 1949 a pair of barn owls successfully bred in a tower in Durham cathedral, as well as in the old tower of Chester cathedral. Granite buildings such as these have been favoured places to nest in the past, but not now it seems.

in the south of Britain and decreasing in the north. This seems likely to have been brought about, before they were cleared, by the temporary abundance of tree cavities in elms as the trees died and holes developed (see below). Osborne thought that the percentage increase of tree nests found in southern Britain was of some interest because it had previously been reported from the Netherlands and West Germany that trees were rarely used for nesting. He also pointed out that in Devon many of the available farm buildings were unused, either because they were no longer suitable or there was a lack of prey around the buildings due to modern-day pest control. He also felt the reason for the decline in the use of trees in the north of Britain required explanation, but was unable to offer any. It now seems likely that with the large number of nesting boxes that have been erected over the past few years, the percentage of tree nests is likely to fall throughout the British Isles and here I include Suffolk. There are now a substantial number of nesting boxes in place and many of those are in use, and it may well be that in time the vast majority of barn owls will nest in boxes. The loss of the elms, of which I have to say more about later, and many other trees in the countryside has drastically curbed the availability of natural nesting sites throughout most of Britain, but especially in the lowlands, while the number of suitable farm buildings has been declining for many years and now there are very few available.

THE WET AND DRY DEBATE

There is some misunderstanding as to why barn owls in western Britain prefer to nest in buildings and why those in the east prefer to nest in trees. Shawyer theorised that this was because southern and western Britain receives a greater amount of annual rainfall than eastern Britain and so consequently the barn owls in those parts deliberately choose buildings to nest in because they afford better shelter for the owls and their young. He chose Suffolk in which to try and demonstrate this theory, believing that because Suffolk receives the lowest amount of rainfall in the British Isles, the barn owls there chose to nest in trees because there was not such a need to protect the young from the elements. He stated that over 70% of Suffolk's barn owls nested in trees because of this, although the figure is somewhat higher (Table 10).

During the course of my study I found that buildings have rarely featured in the nesting habits of Suffolk's barn owls. This is because many of the county's barns are of a wooden construction and unsuitable for nesting. They do not have the nesting platforms, such as the tops of walls, that stone-built barns in northern and western parts of Britain do, although the beams within them make wonderful roosting sites. Before the onset of elm disease and hedgerow clearance, the sole reason for most barn owls to nest in trees in Suffolk, Essex, parts of Norfolk and some other places, was due to the abundance of tree nest-holes and a lack of suitable buildings. In the fens of north-west Suffolk, where mature trees with suitable nesting holes are uncommon, I once placed a nesting box in a barn in early spring and three months later there were three owlets inside. In the north-west of Britain most barn owls use buildings for nesting because there are few suitable trees and likewise in Scotland. Derek Bunn informs me that he does not know of a single tree with a suitable hollow for barn owls to nest in, and he does not think he has ever known one in the north-west of England. In Ireland Ussher and Warren in 1900 had reported that

The behaviour of barn nesting barn owls is different from those that nest in trees. Here, the chicks have the opportunity to see an approaching parent before it arrives at the nest-site.

they had known 'a hollow tree to be used by barn owls but a chimney a pigeon-hole a roof or a ruin offer themselves more frequently in this country as breeding places' while in the Isle of Man 'buildings and hollow trees are used almost equally as nest-sites'.

Up until 1990 I was aware of only 9 recorded instances of barn owls nesting in buildings in Suffolk over the past 75 years or so. These were: one at Eyke, where a pair of owls nested in a large basket inside the brick barn in which Eric Hosking took his famous 'Heraldic Barn Owl' picture in 1948; a mill at Chilton Street near Clare in 1927; one in a nest-box at Lound; one in an old water-mill at Barnby; one in a barn at Copdock; and three at Mildenhall, two of which were in nest-boxes in barns and one that was in an old World War II gun emplacement. Finally there was one on Orfordness in an old aircraft hanger. Historical records of barn owls nesting in buildings in East Anglia are uncommon, although in Essex Glegg in 1929 noted 'Buildings and sheds on the outlying marshes generally shelter a pair of these owls' and at Dagenham barn owls had for some years nested in the large disused railway sheds.

OTHER SITES

Trees without holes may also serve as nesting and roost sites although I am not aware of any other instance where barn owls have nested in an open nest since Blaker published his results ; he

Table 8 Nest sites for barn owls in England and Wales, 1932 (after Blaker, 1934).

	no	%
In holes in hollow trees, chiefly oak and elm, but including also beech, ash, willow, sycamore, walnut, apple, horse chestnut, Spanish chestnut and Scots fir	393	42.96
In barns, outhouses and farm buildings, on rafters, piles of hay, in boxes and baskets	308	33.66
In holes in walls, ruins, church towers, chimneys, roofs of houses	121	13.22
In owl boxes and dovecotes, with and without doves as well	55	6.01
In holes in rocks, in cliffs, quarries, mines, etc	26	2.84
In trees, but not in holes, chiefly yew	12	1.31

Table 9 Barn owl nest sites in Britain (after Bunn, Warburton and Wilson, 1982).

	%
Barns (including indoor haystacks and owl boxes in barns)	33.32
Hollow trees	31.72
Old houses	12.90
Outbuildings	10.22
Cliffs	3.23
Holes in walls, etc	2.69
Thatched roofs	1.61
Inhabited houses	1.61
Haystacks in the open	1.08
Dovecotes	0.54
Granaries	0.54
Disused hop kilns	0.54

In lowland Britain open countryside, interspersed with mature trees, is important for nesting.

Table 10 Nest-sites for barn owls in Suffolk, 1982-90.

	No	%
Tree holes	77	81.91
Enclosed building (including those in nest-boxes)	7	7.45
Straw-stacks	10	10.64
	94	
	====	

Table 11 Nest-sites for barn owls in Suffolk from the nest record cards held by the British Trust For Ornithology until 1988.

	No	%
Trees	38	84.44
Buildings	3	6.67
Straw-stacks	4	8.89
	45	
	====	

considered it unusual that a barn owl regularly roosted in the upper branches of a young spruce tree about fifteen feet from the ground. I received one report of a barn owl roosting in a pine tree, and that was at Sutton Common on August 4th, 1983. More recently Derek Bunn informed me in November 2007 that he had found a recently arrived barn owl in his locality that had also taken to roosting in a conifer tree. He informed me that during the course of his lengthy study he found just one example of barn owls roosting in a spruce, but he also found one roosting on the branch of an old oak tree. I have never seen barn owls roosting in conifers although I have seen them roosting in coastal thorn bushes during the autumn, and others have seen them roosting in hawthorns at Carlton Marsh, (Barnsley) and in a hedgerow at Oldbury (Avon).

Ten nests in straw-stacks were reported during my survey and in the arable farmlands of Britain especially, this type of site might well be more important than we realise in providing a dry and warm place for barn owls and their young as well, perhaps, as providing a hiding place for the owls. There has been a report of a nest in Staffordshire that was 'fairly deep-down in a pile of straw in a barn at Sandyford' and in Cornwall, a nest with two downy young that were found in a haystack at Penrose, Helston, on February 4th. (These birds later fledged about the end of March and it was estimated that the eggs had been laid around late December.) I was shown two nests in straw during the course of my Suffolk study. One was at a farm at Rendham, where the owls had used a straw stack for several years. They would nest in different parts of the stack depending upon which part was being used. It seemed that they were more dependent upon the straw than upon the exact same site. Sometimes the nest would be one bale high (one metre) whilst I have known a nest in that same stack to be around 6 metres high. In 1988 Tim Craven drew my attention to a remarkable incident on an industrial estate at Eye in Suffolk. During the course of moving some large bales of straw, a nest containing three young owlets was disturbed. The owls were rescued but by then the stack in which they were living had been demolished. A new stack of around 10 bales was assembled some 20 metres away from the original nest-site and a replica nest was built and the chicks placed in it. I was able to witness this event. Tim Craven returned to watch that evening and around midnight the parents returned and recommenced feeding the chicks in their new nest-site from which they successfully fledged some six weeks later. Unfortunately incidents such as that do not always have a happy ending.

In the Algarve of Portugal, Nazar et al reported on the unusual occurrence of barn owls attempting to nest in a well. At the third attempt they managed to construct the nest and laid eggs, but of the chicks two died and the remaining two had to be hand reared. Barn owls have also been reported as nesting on the spiral steps of an old well, nine metres below ground level.

According to the BTO nest records nest entrance holes are sited at an average height of 4 metres. I found that in Suffolk the average height is 3½ metres but during my study three extremes came to my notice. Nests at Rendham and Eye were just over one metre high while at Butley a pair nested in an oak tree at a height of over 8 metres. There were also several instances of birds nesting at ground level within hollow trees even though the entrance hole was several feet higher. In Buckinghamshire, Mayali in 1920 found three young in a large hole in an elm tree at Eton on November 5th, 1920, and that hole was 30 feet from the ground.

EGG-LAYING

The white, almost round eggs are laid at intervals of two to three days and this has implications that are important for the survival of the brood. Laying usually takes place in April or May. The eggs are usually laid on a bare surface, although sometimes a layer of pellet matter provides a soft bed for them. At one nest I found in a building near Mildenhall in Suffolk, it appeared that the female had formed a shallow, cup-like, depression in the pellet matter that had been deposited on a flat, bare concrete surface. It was reminiscent of the nest formed in nest-boxes by such birds as great and blue tits though, proportionally, the shallow depression was not so deep; once a site has been chosen, then the birds make a slight scrape or depression. In many tree nests, rotten wood fragments and other debris seem to be sufficient matter for the female to incubate on, although no bed appears to be made in straw-stacks.

In common with other owl species barn owl eggs are white, although Taylor reported one exceptional clutch of five eggs that was finely marked with dark brown flecking. Barn owl eggs are not large and are slightly elliptical in shape. The average size is 39.74 x 31.57mm with an average weight of 17.9g at laying. Egg size varies amongst the sub-species; for example it was found that the average size of an egg from a sample of 57 eggs of the race

T. a. guttata measured 41x 32 mm with an average weight of 22g. North American barn owls are larger than those of Europe and their eggs are correspondingly greater; the average size of barn owl eggs there are 43.1 x 33.7mm with an average weight of 26.6g. As the body size of differing female barn owl sub-species increase, so the eggs form a smaller percentage of their bodyweight. Thus in *alba* and *guttata* the percentage is 4.9% but in the heavier North American sub-species *pratincola*, the weight decreases to 4.8%: clearly there is a need for more information on this subject.

Iain Taylor carried out a useful exercise and found that the egg size of *alba*, compared to its bodyweight, was small and that if *alba* females were to lay eggs in the same proportion to their size as other European owls, they would weigh 24.6g instead of the 17.9g that he reported. He further investigated why the size of barn owl eggs was so small and found that based upon body size, the barn owl (*alba*), when compared to other cavity-nesting owls, should actually lay eggs weighing 25.5g. He presented two possibilities: one of which was that egg production by barn owls, compared to other owl species, could be limited by the food that the female consumed during incubation, but he was disinclined to accept this explanation because of the amount of unconsumed fresh prey that may often be found lying around nests at this time. He proposed that small egg size might be an evolutionary strategy: by using the same body reserves, barn owls are able to lay more eggs and rear a greater number of young. If barn owl eggs were of the predicted weight then a clutch of 5 eggs would weigh 125g, which equates to around 7 eggs of the present weight. Therefore, barn owls will only lay more eggs in times of prey abundance or if they have evolved a method of coping with the feeding of larger broods. Because of that they have evolved their egg-laying in such a way that their bodily mechanisms, and a unique approach to egg size, allows them to take advantage of high prey abundance and so rear larger broods when food is plentiful. Similarly they will adjust the size of their broods when food is less plentiful. This unusual evolutionary adaptation has no doubt been an important factor in their successful colonisation of the world.

The plain white colour of owl eggs may be an inherited trait from ancestors that nested in secure holes, where the necessity for camouflaged eggs was less important than the need for eggs that could be seen in the dark confines of the nesting place, which would prevent them being trampled on. Certainly other hole-nesting birds, such as the woodpeckers, swifts and kingfishers, all have white eggs, but this does not explain why other birds such as some geese, ducks and birds of prey, such as the marsh harrier, which are not hole-nesters, also have white or very light-coloured eggs. The fact that many owls have nested in fairly inaccessible places, where there is less need to camouflage the eggs from predators, might have negated any need for the colouring of eggs.

Prey abundance was always regarded as the likely reason for egg laying starting in April; more recently it has been shown that laying dates are affected by weather conditions. The higher the rainfall in the spring then the later the laying date of the first egg. Interestingly, the results from Project Barn Owl, a joint survey that was organised by the BTO and the Hawk and Owl Trust in the 1990s, found that the proportion of occupancy rates of potential nest-sites by barn owls was greater in the west of Britain than in the climatically drier eastern parts of Britain. This may well have been true but there are issues here that might have determined the outcome of those results. In western and northern Britain many barn owls nest in buildings and their nests are often much easier to discover than those in tree holes, as they are in the south and east. I have witnessed, on more than one occasion, the astonishing sight of a barn owl entering a tree hole no greater than 9cm (3½ inches) in diameter. Many observers would deem such holes as inaccessible for barn owls. In addition to this, given the barn owl's propensity to nest in a variety of different sites, it is very difficult to decide what places might suitable. If an assessor determines certain sites potentially suitable for nesting, and others not, then it is likely that only those sites nominated by that surveyor will later be checked for confirmation of breeding. Any that are not considered suitable are likely to be ignored.

CLUTCH SIZE

A number of studies have revealed that clutches number around 4 to 6 eggs although the precise number will depend upon prey availability. In most bird species there is usually very little variance in the number of eggs laid but with barn owls the opposite is true and clutches have been recorded from 2 to 18, but these are exceptional. Taylor found in his study that in good vole years the clutch size averaged around 5 or 6 eggs, but when voles were less abundant, then that number fell to between 3 or 4.

Some earlier commentators have mentioned the barn owl's ability

The behaviour of barn owl chicks brought up in the relatively small confines of tree nests is likely to be different from that of those chicks that are reared in more spacious areas such as barns.

to lay a high number of eggs if sufficient food is available and this may indicate that food was more abundant just over a century ago. In 1885 a nest was found at Laverstoke in Hampshire from which 3 eggs were taken on April 6th. Four days later 2 more were taken and 3 more were taken on June 25th. On August 4th there were 4 young in the nest, the youngest of which was thought to be a day old. Altogether 13 eggs had been laid. On March 25th, 1913, 2 eggs were found in a Berkshire nest and by the 30th there were 4. By the 10th June the nest contained 8 eggs and one young. This was considered to be an unusually large clutch. Even so, at Lode Fen, in Cambridgeshire, a nest containing 2 newly hatched young and 2 eggs was found under the floorboards of a ruined house on May 25th, 1925. By May 26th the young had disappeared and, despite a search of the house, they could not be found. On July 2nd the house was searched again and 2 more newly hatched young were found, along with 7 eggs. More recently, an amazing 12 eggs were laid in a pole-box in the Lincolnshire Fens, from which 9 young fledged.

Iain Taylor found in his study that clutch size tended to be greatest in the areas of young conifer plantation where the strict three-year cyclical lifestyle of the field vole heavily influenced the number of eggs that were laid. They ranged from 6.7 eggs on average in the best vole year (1990) to 3.7 on average for the year when voles were at their lowest (1985). Taylor also found that sheep-walk was quite fruitful in his study although the owls there were not as prolific as those found in conifer plantations. He described sheep-walk as land above 150m, dedicated to sheep production and forestry plantations, with narrow strips of land that may be used as fields for pasture and hay. In these areas there were unenclosed areas of wet rough grassland that were grazed by sheep at low density and strips or patches of coniferous woodland that often had edges of un-grazed long grass. Down in the valleys there were large hardwood trees and old buildings for the owls to nest in. He pointed out that 'sheep-walk' was a traditional Scottish term, but elsewhere it is probably best described as 'hill margin' land. The most productive number in sheep-walk was an average of 6.0 in 1984, which was also a peak vole year, whilst in 1985, a year of declining vole numbers, the average was only 3.1.

In his study areas of lowland farming, clutch sizes were on average smaller than in the two previous habitats, but in those years of low productivity in the sheep-walk habitats, the barn owls that lived in lowland farmland were nearly always more productive, although never as productive as those in conifer plantations. Due to the grazing of livestock, few areas of lowland farmland were capable of supporting rank grassland for voles, especially at the base of hedgerows. The best hedgerows were those found along roads or tracks, or where wheat was grown. However, as Taylor himself pointed out, an important factor to emerge from his study was that there was some evidence that vole cycles in lowland farming areas were not so pronounced as they were in the plantation areas and that the spectrum of prey was wider than that of owls nesting in plantations. When vole and shrew numbers fell, those owls nesting in lowland farming areas could turn their attentions to wood mice. This produced slightly lower clutches overall, but assured a much more even and reliable clutch size on a regular yearly basis, ranging from 3.0 in 1986, a year of increasing vole numbers, to 4.6 in 1991, a year of vole decline when the average in the conifer plantations reached 5.0 and those in sheep-walk 4.4. However, in the previous year, a year of peak vole abundance, the average clutch size even in lowland farmland reached 6.0. Therefore, it would seem from these results that mixed farmland produces a smaller clutch than a predominantly grassland habitat, but year to year the latter generates a more stable clutch size.

In 2004 the BTO expressed concern for the long-term welfare of the barn owl when it added it to its Nest Recording Scheme Concern List, because for the first time they detected a downward trend in average brood size. They considered that the recent spate of wet winters, which had culminated in severe autumn flooding, had deprived many owls of food. The authors hoped that this spell of bad weather was a 'one off' although they still felt that the overall trend was for smaller broods. Interestingly, that other farmland predator of rodents, the kestrel, was placed on the same list in 2006 for precisely the same reason.

INCUBATION AND HATCHING

Female barn owls start to incubate as soon as the first egg is laid and because of this, the owlets will be of different sizes when all of the fertile eggs have hatched. The incubation period varies from 29-34 days, which is a similar period for some of the other races, such as 31 days for *T.a.affinis* in Rhodesia, 30 days for *T.a. pratincola* in America and 30 days for *T.a.guttata* in the Netherlands. The incubation period for barn owls is long compared with other owls in Europe – only the eagle owl has a longer incubation period.

Once incubation has begun, the female barn owl sits tight for long periods, leaving only occasionally to exercise and defecate. During this time she does little or no hunting and is usually fed by her mate. It is due to this inactivity that her weight increases, but she soon loses this when the chicks are around 4 weeks old and she starts helping the male with the hunting. A few days before laying the first egg, the female loses her belly feathers and develops a brood patch of bare skin. Derek Bunn observed that on one occasion a male barn owl appeared to make an attempt at incubation but he was stopped by the hen, who pushed him to one side and immediately sat on the eggs. There are records of male barn owls incubating eggs, but this behaviour is unusual, because the males lack a brood patch.

Females sit tightly during incubation, and by the time the eggs are due to hatch they may prove almost impossible to flush. Taylor said that females are tight sitters and found that some of the older birds had become so used to his regular visits to their nest that they would sit tight and remain on the nest whilst he nudged them aside to check their clutch size. Derek Bunn, on the other hand, believed that this type of intrusion was stressful for the females and that in the early stages of incubation, if disturbed, females tended to fly off silently and leave the vicinity; when hatching is imminent, however, then their parental commitment takes over and they are more likely to sit nearby uttering agitated warning screams.

From early on in the year until the young have hatched, male barn owls tend to spend virtually all of their time with the females and both Bunn and Taylor found that even when the clutch was completed, and the hen was incubating, the male continued to copulate with her on a regular basis, and always when he returned with food. Regular copulation then continues until the young hatch out and until they are around eight days old, after which it is usual, but not certain, to stop. After copulation the male may screech as he leaves the nest. However, after the first week of hatching, most males fall silent and screeching does not resume until the eldest owlet's seventh week, when courtship may resume.

Bunn et al meticulously described the hatching of the chicks and demonstrated how the female is aware of the imminent hatching of the eggs due to the owlet of the first-laid egg calling from inside, which she replies to with a soft twittering note, a soft version of the food offering call. The first hole in the egg appears in the evening and this is followed by the chick hatching out the next morning. The hole is made by the egg-tooth which appears on the front of the ivory-coloured bill. This tooth is not lost until the emergence of the second down, after around 14 days. During the first few days of an owlet's life it is quite helpless and on the first day of its life it does not appear to take any food. However, by the second day the owlet is noticeably larger and stronger and begins to utter begging snores and gives chittering notes, which in turn are answered by the next owlet that is due to hatch. This may help the first owlet to maintain close contact with the clutch, as any owlets that strayed away from it are ignored by the female and subsequently starve.

Derek Bunn et al found one example of a strayed chick that was 3 days old and on the brink of starvation even though it was only 23cm away from the incubating hen. They believed that in nidicolous hatching, where most of the chicks in a nest hatch out more or less simultaneously, the young are bonded to each other naturally by

At the point of fledging the owlets resemble their parents. Up until then they go through various stages of development.
a) Owlet at approximately 7 days old. b) right at 14 days old. c) 28 days old. d) 35 days e) 50 days and f) at the fledging stage

the need to keep warm, and, because they are all together, each one can gain from their parent's attention which is directed at the nest contents. In asynchronous hatching, where the young are mobile from very early on then the first, and perhaps second, chick is in the greatest danger unless it can maintain some contact with the rest of the brood. This is because all of the female's attention is focused on to the nest contents, and any owlets that stray out side of the nest centre will be ignored and will not be fed. Chicks of owls that nest in buildings may also wander from the nest and fall to the floor. They also will be ignored. It may be that in some of the tree-nests that I have seen with small nesting chambers, this might not be such a problem and this might be worthy of consideration when constructing nest-boxes. The smaller the better perhaps? Bunn et al also described an incident at one nest where two chicks, one of one and the other of three days, were displaced accidentally by the hen. Despite being fairly helpless and blind, by listening to the calls of the un-hatched chicks in the other 3 eggs, they managed to eventually make their way back to the nest. They believed that they were able to do this because they were capable of differentiating between the distress calls of their sibling and the more contented calls of the unhatched young.

In areas where it is not easy to see the nest contents, then recorded sightings of barn owls are likely to give an indication of when incubation is taking place (in that if they are incubating they are least likely to be seen). Apart from August, when birds may be moulting, I found in my Suffolk study that April and May were the months when barn owls were most unlikely to be seen on the wing (Fig. 3) and this is also a time when the males may become very secretive. Whether this is a deliberate ploy to ensure that unwanted attention from predators is not drawn to the nest, or an attempt to prevent rival males from finding the nest and copulating with the female when he is away hunting, is difficult to say. At this stage the males do spend a great deal of time with the females, presumably to prevent this. June and July were the months when more barn owls were recorded, and that was undoubtedly due to both parent birds being out hunting for the young.

A remarkable occurrence of incestuous breeding was reported by Petty et al who discovered that on July 11th, 1984, a pair of barn owls was caught in a little used farm building on the edge of the Kielder Forest, Northumberland. Both birds were ringed and both had histories with the authors. The female had been ringed as a breeding female 13 miles away at Wark Forest on May 9th, 1982. The male had also been ringed in the same place on July 11th, 1983, but as one of this female's earlier broods. Barn owls can breed at a very young age (breeding has been recorded at six months, and even four months) but incestuous breeding does not appear to have been recorded before or since.

Although some pairs appear to stay together throughout the year, others spend much of the time, outside the breeding season, in different parts of the breeding territory occupying different roosts, and this aspect of their biology should be taken into consideration when applying a nest-box scheme.

THE OWLETS

Young barn owls have been described as 'proverbially ugly' and it is difficult, therefore, to believe that this 'large-headed, pot-bellied, weak-legged' creature, measuring only 50mm, and weighing around 20g, grows into the lovely and attractive creature that we see winging its way gracefully over our farmlands.

Amongst the family of owls the barn owls are unique in that the owlets have two distinct phases of plumage. When they are born they are blind and naked, but after a few days they develop a soft, thickish grey-white down or plumage which is known as the protoptyle plumage. The bodyweight then develops very rapidly and between the 6th and 15th days it increases by 12g. By then, patches of skin are beginning to emerge through the protoptyle plumage until the original down filaments scarcely cover the body. In the meantime, at around 13 days, tiny quills appear, which quickly open to form the long second (mesoptyle) plumage which, contrary to the protoptyle plumage, is pure white and is far more dense. As the hen stops brooding the young when the oldest is around three to four weeks old, it is important that the majority of the owlets have an adequate down to keep them warm. Those owlets that have not yet acquired the second plumage will be able to obtain sufficient warmth by huddling up close to their older siblings that have attained a warm down. It is at this stage that the hen starts to leave the chicks to go off hunting. Before then the male works mostly alone to feed the young, the hen and himself and it is because of this workload that barn owl sightings begin to increase from around late May, with the frequency increasing in June (Fig. 4) when both birds commence hunting.

Derek Bunn et al found the female barn owl to be a most assiduous parent, constantly tending the young and ensuring that the nest is kept clean. She feeds the very young owlets by tearing strips of meat from the prey and offers it to any snoring owlet, which she feeds until it falls quiet. They were of the opinion that feeding sessions are lengthy due to the care that the female barn owl takes over feeding the young, and in one instance they found it took seventy minutes for a single common shrew to be disposed of. In these early days the female continues to feed the small chicks throughout the hours of daylight and because there is no roughage in the food they eat, there are no deposits of pellets. The chicks defecate at the edge of the nest so keeping the interior clean, which is comparatively easy when the owls are nesting in a barn, but tree-holes present a different problem.

As the chicks grow, then the amount of snoring increases, which in turn results in a greater amount of food being brought into the nest. Should food be slow in arriving then the older owlets become restless and start nibbling at the nest debris and also at their siblings, as if searching for food. Brooding by the hen gradually decreases as the owlets get older and by the time the oldest chick is around 4 weeks old, she only visits the nest to feed the chicks. If a female of a nesting pair succumbs during the course of travelling backwards and forwards for food, then it is unlikely that the male will rear the brood, unless they are able to swallow their prey whole. The male will not feed them in the manner of the female by tearing of small pieces of meat.

The chicks steadily put on weight until they exceed that of their parents, and while in the nest the relationship between the owlets is very good, mild bickering does break out when they are hungry. Bunn remarked that at one nest a 56-day-old chick was observed to ferociously attack two of its nest-mates because it had missed out on a feed and pecked at one violently amidst much screaming, before knocking it to the floor below. It was on the verge of attacking another owlet when the male returned with food, which it grabbed from him and gulped down greedily.

In the past many barn owl accounts have explained the staggered hatching as an opportunity for the oldest owlet to eat its younger nest-mates in times of food shortage, but Bunn et al believed that from the evidence, barn owls were more prone to cannibalism than most other species. It has long been known that the nestlings of many diurnal birds of prey will kill and eat their smaller siblings, but why they do this is not known, although the general consensus of opinion would appear to be that this is due to a shortage of food.

For many years observers have recorded the mysterious disappearances of young barn owls from the nest and a number of theories have been suggested as to why this happened. One claimed that in large broods of eight or nine, the eldest owlet might eat the later ones as they emerged from the egg, while some others pointed out that it was not always the youngest that got eaten. It has even been suggested that the parents carried the young away from the nest after disturbance. The answer is more simple than that and is a survival strategy that involves either a sibling, or a parent eating other young in the nest to allow others to survive in times of food shortage. Occasionally dead chicks are found in a partly consumed state and Taylor discovered that sometimes the remains of chicks were found in the pellets of the other chicks.

This unsavoury action may cast such an attractive species, voted Britain's best loved bird, in an unattractive light. The truth was brought home rather vividly on the BBC Springwatch programme in 2007 when, in one nest-box that was being monitored through a miniature television camera, the seemingly eldest of a brood of barn owls calmly waddled up to the smallest owlet, which was alive and just a few days old, picked it up by the head and promptly swallowed it!

Bunn further believed that some youngsters disappear through moving around the nest and accidentally falling to the floor where they are ignored. Young barn owls also disappear from tree nests, but it is unlikely that they fall to the ground below, so again that might not be the full reason. Derek Bunn's conclusions were that cannibalism does take place in many barn owl nests but not as often as some commentators believe. During the course of my survey I knew of few barn owl broods of more than 3 young, and so I am apt to believe that in Suffolk cannibalism takes place fairly frequently but I cannot be sure. Unless a nest was of the most fragile nature, then few barn owls in Suffolk would have fallen to the ground below. I found that most nests were either well down inside the trunk or inside nooks or crannies that are often to be found inside big pollard oaks.

The theory that disturbance causes cannibalism could be assessed through the many nest-box schemes that are now in operation. If, say, six boxes in one project are left relatively undisturbed, while a further six of the same project are monitored in the usual way, then by counting the eggs and young it may well be possible to assess the impact that disturbance has on barn owl nests. The undisturbed boxes could be monitored once the hen is incubating a full clutch and is away from the nest for exercise and then again just prior to the young fledging.

FLEDGING

When the owlets are seven to eight weeks old, they begin to make short flights. In the course of their study Bunn et al did not think that there was a conscious attempt by parents to lure young from the nest by tempting them with food. They considered that owlets make their first flights in attempts to secure prey from the parent birds because the parents were unwilling to approach too close to the young because of the rough treatment they receive from hungry owlets at each feed. I was observing a tree nest near Southwold in Suffolk one summer evening in 1990, when the male arrived at a nearby fence-post with prey, which he then passed to the female. She then flew to a branch close to the nest entrance in full view of the young who were looking out from the nest hole. The hen then flew off with the prey in her bill, followed by two of the owlets that had emerged from the entrance. This gave the impression that the hen lured the young from their nest, because I believe she could quite easily have passed the prey to one of the chicks.

Owlets are usually between five and eight weeks old when they first venture out to explore their surroundings, the first to leave the nest usually being the eldest. Excursions from the nest are brief at first and they maintain a strong bond with the nest-site in the first few weeks of fledging. This seems to be the case for nest-sites in barns. Elsewhere in my study, where virtually all of the barn owls nested in trees, it is possible that barn owls leave the nest when they are a little older, although I have no evidence to support this. In barns the owlets have the space in which they are able to explore their surroundings, run around and gain confidence. In my experience this could not happen in tree nests. Perhaps more information on the ages at which young birds leave the nests in lowland Britain could be gleaned from some of the nest-box conservation projects which are now in place and which are the nearest replication, in terms of space, to a natural tree nest?

On leaving the nest permanently the owlets do not disperse immediately but remain in its proximity for some while. Bunn et al were of the view that the length of time that it takes for a barn owl to hatch and rear its young to full independence was fourteen weeks, and they considered this to be an extraordinary length of time. In his Scottish study Taylor often found youngsters roosting in buildings that were adjacent to the nest two to three weeks after fledging and he reported that in the first one or two weeks after leaving the nest the parents continued to feed them sporadically, after that the feeding stopped and then the young birds usually disappeared. He highlighted a study in Anglesey, north Wales, where an intensive analysis, using back-pack radio transmitters attached to the backs of young owlets, revealed that of eight birds that were tracked, two moved away from the nest area 2 to 3 weeks after fledging, then a further two at 3 to 4 weeks, two at 4 to 5 weeks and then finally the remaining two between 6 and 8 weeks. There appears to be no indication as to whether it was the eldest owlets that moved away first or whether the movements were regardless of age. The distances that some young barn owls may travel in the first few weeks of their lives are described in chapter 6.

SECOND BROODS

In 1889 Aplin was quite clear in his view that 'The Barn Owl rears two, and sometimes three, broods in the season; the second lot of eggs being laid before the first brood are flown'. Bunn et al found that second broods were rare and they considered that the recent changes in agriculture and possibly a change in climate were having an effect. They reported that their first genuine Cumbrian record of a second brood in the wild was during the long, hot summer of 1976, although Derek Bunn has recently pointed out to me that he has an earlier record, from 1971, of a second brood in his forest study area. Out of 4 pairs, 2 bred for a second time, although sadly he found the young of one nest on the floor of the barn, having presumably fallen out of the nest-box. It is likely that the British weather precludes most clutches being started before April and the opportunity to have a second brood is rare except in unusually good years, However, Iain Taylor found that in good vole years up to 15% of his pairs reared second broods and he pointed out that second broods are more frequent in central Europe where the average brood size may be doubled in peak vole years.

AN ALL-YEAR ROUND NESTER?

Although barn owls may once have nested during the winter months, Bunn et al could find no evidence, either in their own extensive fieldwork or in the literature, of a clutch being started in January, September, October, November or December and they felt that the records that relate to those claims referred only to the presence of eggs or young and will, in most cases, mean that the observer has found owlets in the later stages of development. For those barn owls nesting close to the equator, the breeding season tends to be less well defined, but further north, as in Scotland, then the breeding season is more distinct, with periods of non-breeding from August through to February. It remains to be seen whether this will change if the planet continues to warm.

A nest in Cornwall on December 4th, 1948, was discovered, with young barn owls still dependant upon their parents for food, while

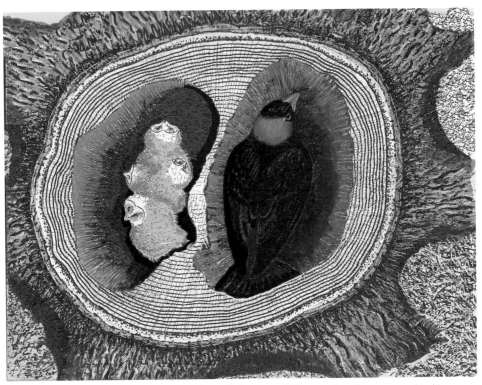

Sometimes barn owls and jackdaws will nest in close proximity.

near Helston two young that were found in a haystack on February 4th, 1954, were considered to be from a clutch that was started 'about late December'. The young flew 'about the end of March'. These are the only records that I have been able to find that suggest winter breeding, and it suggests that in warm winters a few barn owls might breed throughout the winter. Many years ago, in 1932, an instance in Suffolk was recorded where young had left the nest in early June, suggesting that the first egg had been laid around mid to late February, an early date for Suffolk's barn owls. In neighbouring Essex, a late, or perhaps early, nesting of barn owls at Chelmsford in 1912 had young in the nest on December 29th. In Suffolk there is a record of a pair feeding young on June 4th, 1953, and later feeding another brood one week before Christmas, but we do not know if it was the same pair.

NEST-SITE FIDELITY

Barn owls will often stay together throughout their lives but if one of a pair should disappear then another bird will often move in and take its place. This may happen in successive years so that at the end of a period of just a few years, the occupants of a site might have changed several times. Males seem to have stronger ties to nest-sites than females.

Provided that they are not disturbed, barn owls may use a nest-site for many years and there are a number of records that support this. At Minsmere, Suffolk, Axell and Hosking reported an ' ancestral tree was laid low. Inside the fallen, hollow giant, the compressed mass of pellets, the remains of many thousands of rats and mice disgorged by generations of these most useful birds, was more than two feet deep'. George Courthope wrote, 'There is an old tree near my home where Barn Owls have bred all my life. Some 50 years ago my grandfather told me that his grandfather told him that they had bred in the same tree all his life – he was born in 1737'. I received some examples of nest-site fidelity during the course of my survey, one of which was from a site near Lowestoft in Suffolk where barn owls had been using a nest-box within the same barn for well over 100 years. One of the best proven examples of site fidelity has recently come from Suffolk, when on March 14th, 1995, a barn owl was found dead at the nest-site Hollesley after being ringed there at an unknown age on October 23rd, 1982, a period of at least 12 years and 142 days.

Sometimes the attachment to the nest can be very strong and Parry in 1948 reported on a pair that bred in their regular nest-hole even though the tree was in the heart of the substantial flooding that took place following the very snowy winter of 1947. In 1989 the late Eric Hosking showed me a nest in a dead elm at Butley, Suffolk. The birds entered and left through a very small hole some 5 metres high in the trunk. Typical of many sites in diseased elms, the nest was some way down in the hollow trunk. On the other side of the tree, opposite the hole, a large portion of the dead trunk had fallen away, thus leaving the nest below exposed to the elements, but the birds had remained in their nesting place. It was an amazing demonstration of fidelity to a nest-hole that the owls had apparently been using for some time. Even more amazing was the fact that kestrels were nesting in the same tree using the larger hole to enter and exit!

Recently, the barn owl has returned as a breeding species to

Skomer Island, Pembrokeshire, in south-west Wales after an absence of 107 years. To colonise the island the owls travelled a distance of 1 km across open water. This is not too remarkable a journey, but it transpired through pellet analysis that the birds were feeding on prey that is not available on the island: field vole and water shrew. In other words, the birds were returning to the mainland on a regular basis to hunt and were presumably bringing the prey back for two young they were rearing in a nest-box. This interesting account demonstrates the early attachment that barn owls may form to their nesting places.

NEST-SHARING

There are several accounts in the literature of barn owls sharing their nests with other species, and Haines highlighted an instance in 1895 when the eggs of a tawny owl were found together with those of a barn owl (although the eggs of all owls are white and round, those of the barn owl are slightly more elliptical in shape and so it is reasonably easy to separate the eggs of the barn owl from those of other species).

Jackdaws are occasionally recorded with barn owls and Colin Shawyer mentioned that jackdaws often took over and occupied the nest-boxes for barn owls in his study area. In 1988 at a site in Wiltshire Crease found barn owls nesting in the central cavity of a rotting elm that they were sharing with three pairs of jackdaws, each of which was nesting in the entrance hole to the barn owls' nesting chamber. He conjectured that, because the jackdaws were blocking the entrances with their nests, if they did not move out when the owls brought food for the young, the owls would have had to walk over the jackdaws because there was no other way in or out. Out of a total of 13 jackdaw eggs, 6 hatched but only 3 fledged.

In Scotland Iain Taylor reports that barn owls often use chimneys in deserted or little used farm buildings, where they frequently evict jackdaws; or they may share these buildings with jackdaws, occasionally nesting only 2 or 3m apart, each incubating female being able to watch the other and both sharing the same entrances. He pointed out that during the course of his 14-year study, not one of the owls lost a single egg and he presumed, therefore, that the relationships were harmonious.

SOURCES USED IN THIS CHAPTER

Axell, H., and Hosking, E., 1977: *Minsmere: Portrait of a Bird Reserve*. Hutchinson, London.

Borrer, W., 1891: *The Birds of Sussex*. Porter, London.

Bunn, D.S., Warburton, A.W., and Wilson, A.A.B., 1982: *The Barn Owl*. Poyser, Calton.

Cayford, J., 1992: *Barn Owl ecology on East Anglian farmland*. RSPB Conservation Review, 6: 45-48.

Coward, T.A., & Oldham, C., 1900: *The Birds of Cheshire*. Sherratt & Hughes, Manchester.

Cramp, S., (ed.) 1985: *The Birds of the Western Palearctic* (Vol 4). Oxford University Press.

Crease, A.J., 1992: Barn Owls and Jackdaws sharing nest-site. *British Birds*, 85: 378-379.

Cullen, J.P., & Jennings, P.P., 1986: *Birds of the Isle of Man*. Bridgeen Publications, Douglas.

Fletcher, A.B., 1913: Early breeding and large clutch of eggs of barn owl. *British Birds*, 7: 18.

Gladstone, H. S., 1910: *The Birds of Dumfriesshire*. Witherby, London.

Glegg, W.E., 1929: *A History of the Birds of Essex*. Witherby, London.

Haines, R.C., 1907: *Notes on the Birds of Rutland*. Porter, London.

Harvie-Brown, J.A., 1906: *A Fauna of the Tay Basin and Strathmore*. David Douglas, Edinburgh.

Kelsall, J.E., & Munn, P.W., 1905: *The Birds of Hampshire and the Isle of Wight*. Witherby, London.

Leech, D., Barimore, C., & Crick, H., 2006: *NRS Concern List – five new species added*. BTO News, 267: 4-5.

Loughran, M.F.E., & Brown, J.G., 2006: The prey of breeding Barn Owls on Skomer, and evidence for mainland foraging. British Birds, 99: 577-578.

Martin, G.R. ,1990: *Birds by Night*. Poyser, London.

Mead, C.J., 2000: *The State of the Nations' Birds*. Whittet Books, Stowmarket.

Mikkola, H., 1983: *Owls of Europe*. Poyser, Calton.

Moore, D.R., 1983: Winter hunting territories of short-eared owls (*Asio flammeus*). *The Essex Bird Report*, 1983. Essex Birdwatching and Preservation Society.

Nazar, W., Nazar, M., & Keymer, I.F., 1988: Barn owls nesting in wells in Portugal. *British Birds*, 81: 237-238.

Parry, P.E., 1948: *Report of the Cambridge Bird Club*, 1947: 19.

Penhallurick, R. 1978: *The Birds of Cornwall and the Isles of Scilly*. Headland Publications, Penzance.

Petty, S.J., Little, B., & Anderson, D., 1986: Incestuous breeding and abnormal movement by a female Barn Owl *Tyto alba*. *Ringing & Migration*, 7: 23-24.

Ramsden, D., 1998: Effect of barn conversions on local populations of Barn Owl *Tyto alba*. *Bird Study,* 45: 68-76.

Shawyer, C. 1987: *The Barn Owl in the British Isles – its Past, Present and Future*. The Hawk Trust, London.

Shawyer, C. 1998: *The Barn Owl*. Arlequin Press, Chelmsford.

Taylor, I.R. 1994: *Barn owls; predator prey relationships*. Cambridge University Press.

Thompson, G.W. 1925: Large clutch of barn owls' eggs. *British Birds*, 19: 100-101.

Temperley, G.W. 1951: A History of the Birds of Durham. Trans. *Nat. Hist. Society of Northumberland, Durham and Newcastle-upon-Tyne*,10: 1-296.

Ussher, R.J. & Warren, R. 1900: *The Birds of Ireland*. Gurney & Jackson, London.

Walpole-Bond, J. 1938: *A History of Sussex Birds*, Vol. 2. Witherby, London.

Wardhaugh, A.A. 1984: Wintering strategies of British owls. *Bird Study*, 31: 76-77.

5 LIFESPAN

'Too many of these most useful and interesting birds pass every year through the hands of our local bird-stuffers. They cling tenaciously to their old nesting places. A pair has for many years haunted a hollow elm near the town [Harleston, Norfolk] though frequently robbed of their eggs, stoned and shot at. If this bird received the protection it deserves there would be scarcely an old homestead in the district without its pair of Barn Owls.'

Charles Chandler, 1888. *An Account of the Flowering Plants, Ferns and Allies of Harleston with a sketch of the Geology, Climate and Natural Characteristics of the Neighbourhood* (Bartlett, Liondon)

LIFE EXPECTANCY

Although barn owls can live for much longer, BTO ringing recoveries suggest that the majority die within a year of fledging. The oldest known barn owl lived in Switzerland for 21 years and 4 months, while here in Britain the oldest was just over 13 years when it died although that record was nearly eclipsed by the barn owl found at Hollesley in Suffolk (see p. 111). In 2007 I was informed of a female that was captured by a ringer at her nest-box breeding site in west Oxfordshire. Upon checking his records, he discovered that he had ringed this female, as a nestling, in another nest box 3 miles away nine years earlier.

Some aspects of barn owl mortality, particularly from poisoning and bad weather, are described later. In this section I include those aspects of mortality that are ongoing problems and not occasional events. During the period 1983-90 I kept the records of dead and injured barn owls found in Suffolk, and during that period 169 were reported (Table 12) of which 153 were reliably dated and plotted (Fig. 4). Of these 115 (67.4%) were found in the six months from October to March. This pattern is consistent with other studies.

David Glue found there are two peaks of mortality, the first of which occurs around October and which mainly features young birds, while the second takes place around February. He suggested that the autumn peak might be brought about by a shortage of food when young and inexperienced birds without territories of their own are forced to hunt in areas where food is not so plentiful, causing starvation. He then suggested that the February peak may be more complicated and that it probably occurs through a combination of prey shortage, severe weather or more dominant birds pushing weaker birds out of their territory in preparation for the coming breeding season. The displaced birds may be young or old birds. In my analysis the peak of mortality occurred in February (Fig. 4), which is consistent with the number of snap sightings that were observed (Fig. 3). This is also a period of great activity between courting barn owls and while many were no doubt found in an emaciated condition, males that are actively courting a female for the forthcoming breeding season, which involves food presentation, will leave themselves more vulnerable to such things as road traffic.

In my Suffolk survey I found that the majority of dead barn owls were found on roads (Table 12), although I think it unlikely that in Suffolk this number of road casualties would be reached again over a similar period. Barn owls have been the focus of attention in the county for a number of years and records of barn owls, especially dead ones, are diligently recorded and then published in the county's bird reports. Following my study period, I extracted the records of roadside casualties from the county's bird reports covering the years 1991 to 2005. In 1991 there were 11, 1992:10, 1993:11 and 1994:17. After this the number of recorded road casualties then fell dramatically so that in 1995 there was just one, 1996 none, 1997: 2, 1998: 2, 1999: 1, 2000: 2, 2001: 2, 2002:none, 2003: 1, 2004: 2 and 2005: none. Whilst these figures are only a guide, they do provide an indication as to the frequency at which dead barn owls have been recorded annually on Suffolk's roads in recent years, all of which were recorded against a backdrop of rising traffic levels. It is of considerable interest to note that in 1992 the barn owl was placed on Schedule 9 of the Wildlife and Countryside Act, which banned the unauthorised release of captive bred birds in to the wild. It might be that factor that has influenced these later findings and indeed my own survey, although it is impossible to be sure.

The low numbers that are now killed by road traffic in Suffolk is also likely to reflect the low number of barn owls that are now residing in close proximity to the county's main roads. Historically, very few dead barn owls have ever been found on the county's minor roads. As we know, barn owls retain a tenacious grip upon

Table 12 Circumstances in Suffolk, under which barn owls were found dead or dying in the period from January 1st, 1983 to December 31st, 1990.

	No	%
Presumed drowned	3	1.78
Found dead on road or railway	95	56.21
Found dead (in barns etc)	47	27.81
Shot/trapped by man	6	3.55
Accidentally killed by man (not on roads)	6	3.55
Found dying/ seriously injured	11	6.51
Probable poisoning	1	0.59
	169	

their nest-site, so that even under arduous conditions they retain a strong affiliation with it until they die. Colin Shawyer was of the opinion that when barn owls that live beside busy roads are killed, they are not replaced by other barn owls moving into the area, and I have considerable agreement with this view. The likely effect that modern disturbance is having on the distribution of Britain's barn owls is discussed in chapter 10.

Apart from this, any road casualties in Iain Taylor's study were in a thin and emaciated condition and it may well be that these were in the final and desperate stages of starvation. Although the majority of dead barn owls are found on roads, care should be exercised when interpreting this because owls that die in the vicinity of human activity are much more likely to be found than those that die in remote places such as tree holes whose bodies are rarely recovered.

Fig.4 Monthly recoveries of dead or injured barn owls in Suffolk 1983-1988.

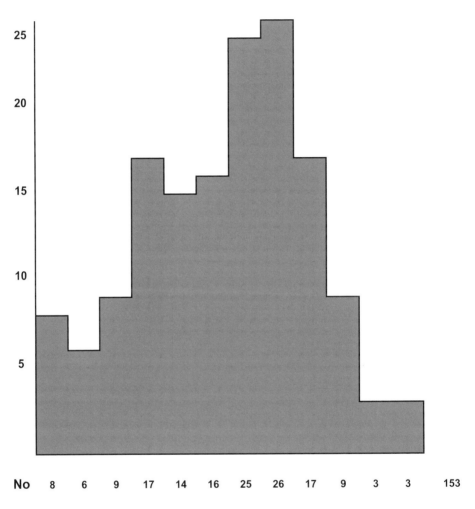

No	8	6	9	17	14	16	25	26	17	9	3	3	153
	July	Aug	Sept	Oct	Nov	Dec	Jan	Feb	Mar	April	May	June	

This analysis only shows those records where a reliable date was provided.

The analysis provided (Fig. 4) shows only those records where a date was provided and so consequently the total of 153 contrasts with the figure in Table 12.

During my Suffolk survey seven post-mortems on barn owls were carried out and the major cause of death was starvation. In addition to these post-mortems, there was evidence that one bird from Suffolk had been poisoned during the survey period and another bird had died from poisoning several years before the survey started.

Only three barn owls were reported drowned during the course of my survey although Shawyer in his study found that drowning was the second highest cause of mortality. Death from drowning will feature more highly in the pastoral areas of Britain because on the predominantly arable farmlands of East Anglia, where cattle drinking troughs are largely features of the past, there are likely to be fewer deaths from this hazard.

Power lines can often be a hazard for nocturnal species and out of a total of 171 barn owl corpses that were found at Dungeness in Kent between the years 1910-1969, 11 (6.4%) were found beneath overhead power lines. In Staffordshire, barn owls are sometimes killed or injured by overhead wires and some of these are victims of the wires running beside the railway. In 1962 a barn owl was found in Derbyshire hanging from telephone wires, while during the course of my Suffolk survey one barn owl was found dead beneath power lines.

PERSECUTION

Although the barn owl is a specially protected bird under the Wildlife and Countryside Act 1981, it is regrettable that from time to time egg-collecting, nest-robbing and illegal killing still goes on. Several cases have come to light recently in East Anglia, including my study county of Suffolk, but persecution of the barn owl occurs throughout the British Isles. It is not surprising that East Anglia is highlighted, for eastern England retains the highest number of gamekeepers in Britain and the late Francis Simpson mentioned the continuing threat of pole-traps that 'still exist'. In April 1986, for example, it was reported in the *East Anglian Daily Times* that a barn owl had been caught in a pole-trap near Wickham Market and in 1984 it was reported to me that some children had found a barn owl 'hanging upside down' from a fence post in the vicinity of Debach airfield. More recently, concern was expressed that some owls and other birds of prey may have been killed by two Suffolk gamekeepers in order to supply a taxidermist. This is an appalling state of affairs and gamekeepers who continue to persecute this harmless bird cast a shadow over the vast majority who now discriminate in favour of this owl, indeed some now actively promote its conservation.

Egg-collecting is sometimes considered to be a relic hobby of the Victorian era but there still exists a number of people dedicated to this activity. This is a worrying state of affairs because egg-collectors can negate the breeding efforts of an uncommon or rare species. According to the RSPB, there are at least 300 active egg-collectors in the United Kingdom who very often target rare species or species with attractively marked eggs. As barn owls have plain white eggs, perhaps it is the 'rare' aspect that is the attraction. Although the provision of nesting boxes has generally had a beneficial effect upon barn owl numbers, there are drawbacks. In Surrey, a long-used nest-box was raided and eggs or possibly newly hatched young were stolen. The nest-box had been taken or knocked down to the ground and a 'stunned but fortunately uninjured brooding parent was found inside'.

Although egg-collecting has been a common activity for many years, the activity was first banned under the Protection of Birds Act as long ago as 1954 and then in 1981 under the Wildlife and Countryside Act, but in recent years there have been several high profile cases in East Anglia that clearly demonstrate that this activity is still going on in a vigorous and alarming manner. For example, in September 2001 an 'obsessive' collector of rare eggs was jailed for four months after being fined £1,000 the previous May for collecting rare birds' eggs. Amongst the haul of eggs were those of the barn owl. In the same year another collector was found to have a large number of eggs in his possession amongst which there were ten barn owl eggs. In February 2005, a Norwich man was found guilty of collecting wild birds' eggs and was subsequently jailed for ten weeks. Amongst the vast collection of eggs he had amassed were those of the barn owl and on one occasion he had apparently climbed a tree to remove five barn owl eggs. The harm that can be done to isolated bird communities was highlighted during the course of the trial when it was said that the man's actions had wiped out a nightjar colony at Alderford Common in Norfolk. Similar actions could well wipe out isolated barn owl populations.

OTHER CAUSES OF MORTALITY

People have always been interested in raptors, and in recent years especially, this interest has heightened. Peregrine falcons, for instance, have staged a welcome recovery after their decline in the middle of the 20th century, but they are a threat to barn owls and there are several reported instances of barn owls being killed by peregrines. Goshawks are also predators of barn owls although there do not appear to be any records of them taking barn owls in Britain. There are other diurnal raptors that will take barn owls and recently two instances of buzzards preying upon barn owls in Britain have come to light: On March 21st, 2006, at Malvern, Worcestershire, Bullock witnessed a remarkable incident when a buzzard knocked a barn owl out of the sky, only 'a matter of metres away' from where he stood. The buzzard was then joined by a second buzzard that then proceeded to 'finish it off', despite the observer shouting and running towards it. The birds then carried off the body to a point some 150m away where they proceeded to tear it to pieces. An even more amazing story was reported by Grant who described a similar incident, which also took place in March 2006. On the 5th he and some colleagues found a common buzzard with a live barn owl in its talons on the side of a road. With great difficulty they tried to rescue the owl but to no avail and so eventually they forced the buzzard's talons open and freed the barn owl which they carried back to their car. But the buzzard did not give up and tried unsuccessfully to grab the owl out of the rescuer's hands. Even as they were driving off the buzzard flew at the car, still attempting to get the owl, which was subsequently released back in to the wild at a later date. In their study Bunn et al recounted an episode by Ronald Lockley when a buzzard flew out of a tree and grabbed a barn owl that was perched on a post. The buzzard then flew off low with the owl but dropped it, whereupon the owl flew off into a nearby wood. Later he found the feet of a barn owl in the same wood although he had no proof that the buzzard had killed it. After a long period of absence buzzards are making a return to many parts of Britain so similar instances are possible in the future.

However, by far the biggest avian threat to barn owls comes from the eagle owl; in his study Mikkola found 46 instances of eagle owls killing barn owls. After the finding of an eagle owl at Felixstowe in Suffolk on November 22nd, 1990, I speculated that eagle owls may be in the process of colonising Britain from mainland Europe. Since that time, however, there can be no doubts that enthusiasts have released some of these magnificent but aggressive owls into the wild, and the continued successful breeding of a pair of eagle owls in northern England, with just one failure, every year since 1996 has been reported. Clearly, one way or another, these owls will continue their colonisation of the British Isles and unfortunately, with so much emphasis now being placed on the conservation of birds of prey, we must expect more barn owls to be killed by other predatory birds in the future.

SOURCES USED IN THIS CHAPTER

Bircham, P.M.M. 1989: *The Birds of Cambridgeshire*. Cambridge University Press.

Bullock, J. 2006: Barn Owl killed and eaten by Common Buzzards. *British Birds,* 99: 578.

Cramp, S. (ed.) 1985: *The Birds of the Western Palearctic* (Vol 4). Oxford University Press.

Dumican, S. 1991: Bird's Eye View. *The Harrier,* 91: 6-8. Suffolk Ornith. Group, Ipswich.

Glue, D. 1973: Seasonal mortality in four small birds of prey. *Ornis. Scand.,* 4: 97-102.

Grant, K. 2007: Common Buzzard attacking Barn Owl. *British Birds,* 100: 245.

Hickling, R. (ed.) 1983: *Enjoying Ornithology*. Poyser, Calton.

Hulme, D.C. (ed.) 1963: *The Derbyshire Bird Report,* 1962: 26.

Martin, J.R. 1993: A brief summary of the Eagle Owl's status in Europe and its possible implications for Suffolk and Britain. *Suffolk Birds 1992,* 41: 11-14. Suffolk Nat. Soc., Ipswich.

Mikkola, H. 1983: *Owls of Europe*. Poyser, Calton.

Newton, I., Wyllie, I. & Freestone, P. 1990: Rodenticides in British Barn Owls. *Environ. Pollut.,* 68: 101-117.

Parsons, E. 1990: Profile of Francis Simpson. *White Admiral,* 15: 12-15. Suffolk Naturalists' Society, Ipswich.

Ratcliffe, D. 1980: *The Peregrine Falcon*. Poyser, Calton.

Shawyer, C. 1987: *The Barn Owl in the British Isles – Its Past, Present and Future*. The Hawk Trust, London.

Smith, T. 1938: *The Birds of Staffordshire*. North Staffordshire Field Club.

Stride, R. 2000: *Birds of the Isles of Surrey*. Dayfive Publications, Cranleigh.

Taylor, I.R. 1994: *Barn owls; predator prey relationships*. Cambridge University Press.

6 WHERE DO THEY GO?

I am not aware that this dark variety has received any specific distinction, but it is quite possible, as Mr Newton is inclined to believe, that the bird in question may have come across from the Danish locality, where Professor Reinhardt's example was procured. Supposing this to be really the case, the question naturally arises, whether barn owls from more eastern localities may not, occasionally at least, visit our coast in autumn?

Stevenson, H, 1866-90.
The Birds of Norfolk (Van Voorst, London)

Throughout Europe owls are essentially non-migratory creatures. Scops owl is, perhaps, the main exception. Other owls, such as the long and short-eared owls, may also travel long distances but their movements are irregular and are generally linked with food demands. In some places barn owls make long journeys but these, it would appear, are spasmodic and are not of a migratory nature.

ON THE MOVE

In general British barn owls tend to live out their lives within a short distance from the area in which they were hatched and in the previous chapter I highlighted the strong association that British barn owls have for their nest-sites. On mainland Europe things are a little different and in certain years barn owls may disperse over a wide area. These events are often referred to as *wanderjahren*, or years of wandering, and when they occur some individual barn owls may travel considerable distances in search of food, although the reason for these events may not be quite so straightforward. Both Taylor and Bunn et al urged caution in reaching definite conclusions on barn owl migration and Taylor considered that further and more extensive work needs to be carried out on this subject. In a *wanderjahr* hundreds of barn owls can sometimes disperse over a wide area and can turn up in unlikely places, such as those that were seen on ice-floes in the former Zuiderzee, Netherlands, in 1929. According to *The Migration Atlas*, the most recent *wanderjahr* occurred in 1990, when Denmark witnessed a mass arrival of young barn owls. In the following winter single birds from Germany and the Netherlands were recovered in the British Isles and so these may have been related to that event.

Without ringing recoveries it is impossible to determine the origins of individual white-breasted barn owls and until recently there was little information regarding their movements in Britain except for what was produced by Bunn et al and by Glue. However, during the course of the last twenty years or so, a great deal of effort has been put into ringing barn owls and consequently a significant amount of information has been added to the knowledge that we previously had. *The Atlas* reported that by 1997, the number of BTO ringed barn owls had reached 24, 264 and that of those 3,146 (12.96%) had been recovered. By the year 2000, 32,962 had been ringed with a recovery rate of 4,202 (12.74%) and by 2004 the number had increased to 49,102, with a recovery figure of 5,767 (11.74%). The ringing totals not only indicate a rise in the interest being shown in this species but an indication perhaps of a rising barn owl population.

In addition to these statistics concerning British ringed barn owls, *The Atlas* reported that eight foreign ringed birds had also been recovered in Britain, which illustrates the fact that with one confirmed exception, all of the British barn owls were recovered within the United Kingdom and confirms the strong likelihood of the sedentary nature of our birds, although that situation might change in the future. The exception was a bird that was ringed on July 10th, 1983, at Thorness on the Isle of Wight and which was subsequently recovered at Querqueville near Cherbourg in France on January 30th, 1987. However, with the tremendous amount of interest being shown in barn owls it is not surprising that this situation should change, and on February 1st, 2000, a barn owl that had been ringed as a nestling at Eridge in Sussex on July 2nd, 1999, was recovered at Kassel in Germany, a distance of 647 km. This was followed by the first recorded occurrence of a barn owl in Ireland that had been ringed on the British mainland. It had been ringed at Dumfries & Galloway in Scotland and was found as a road casualty in Newtown Forbes, Langford, on May 14th, 2003, while in the same year a bird that had been ringed on July 11th, 2002, near Misterton, Nottinghamshire, was later found at Oostende, Belgium, on April 22nd, 2003, although there is some doubt as to how this bird made the journey.

ALL AT SEA

Some commentators have stated that barn owls do not like crossing large expanses of water but there are a number of records in the literature that mention barn owls traversing the sea and because of this it must throw doubt on some of those assertions. Riviere in 1930 reported a 'considerable immigration of Barn Owls' that took place in Norfolk during 1891 and that a Norwich taxidermist had received forty during August and early September, although the race to which they belonged was not stated. However, the dates suggest that most, if not all, were examples of *alba*. Another report from Norfolk mentioned that 'On January 24th 1912 a great grey shrike alighted to rest on Gorleston Pier. A short-eared owl and a barn owl had alighted on the Leman and Ower light-vessel miles out at sea, as had six kestrels'. In 1909 Norman Ticehurst firmly stated that Kent was undoubtedly visited by 'wanderers from overseas'. He reported that a barn owl passed the Tongue Lightship at 8am on October 20th, 1885, flying in an east to west direction, and that on October 3rd, 1887, another passed the East Goodwin Lightship, going from south-east to north-west.

On Fair Isle in Scotland Stenhouse in 1926 reported a barn owl of the white-breasted race that had been captured on the south lighthouse in February 1924, and there are other examples. It is intriguing to wonder what compels these terrestrial birds to journey out over the sea, a few of which have turned up on the Scilly Isles. Robinson reported ten occurrences of barn owls on the Scillies, with one in 1858 and further singles in 1962, 1966, 1975, 1976, 1977 (a freshly dead specimen of the race *guttata*), 1979, 1981, 1988 (another of the race *guttata*) and 1991. In addition to these records, two barn owls thought to be *guttata* were seen from a gas platform 30 miles north-east of Yarmouth in November 1994. During my Suffolk survey Robin Biddle submitted a very interesting record when he observed a barn owl fly in off the sea at Shingle Street on October 15th, 1984, after first observing it some two miles out.

However, clearly some don't make land and this is demonstrated by a barn owl that was washed up on the beach between Lowestoft and Gorleston during a spell of cold weather in February 1956. On the Channel Island of Sark, Rountree could find only one instance of barn owls immigrating on to the island when the remains of a barn owl that had been ringed as a nestling at Isigny-Sur-Mer, Calvados, Normandy, France on August 11th, 1972, were found on December 9th,1972. It had travelled 95 km (59 miles). Earlier a 'beautiful specimen of this bird' had been found washed up on the seashore near Castletown on the Isle of Man.

During my survey I received other sightings that might have involved barn owls making long journeys over land and a most interesting record was received from J. Goddard of Leiston, Suffolk, who noted a barn owl flying very high in a north-westerly direction on April 29th,1983. He commented, 'I've seen barn owls flying very high at times when returning to a nest-site carrying prey, but never this high', and I received another record from Mr & Mrs Lyons of Middleton, Suffolk, who recorded a barn owl on July 12th, 1989, 'Flying at considerable height and being harassed by a herring gull. Flew well beyond normal area'. In northern Britain Bunn et al noted that they had occasionally observed barn owls flying at a height of 60-90m when they were crossing a valley, but in Suffolk there are no significant valleys in Leiston or Middleton, and so these records are most interesting.

SOME EAST ANGLIAN RECOVERIES

Young barn owls stay close to the nesting place for up to eight weeks after finally leaving the nest, but then where do they go and what is their survival rate? There is a considerable amount of information regarding the movements of young birds and I will highlight some of the recoveries not only from my study county of Suffolk, but also from neighbouring Norfolk and Essex. From Norfolk: of the 83 ringed barn owl fledglings that were recovered during the period 1978 to 1995, the average distance travelled from their natal sites was 23 km and their survival period was an average of more than 381 days. This is a good survival rate and perhaps indicates why Norfolk is one of the best counties in Britain for barn owls. This compares with Suffolk, where 14 ringed fledglings were recovered on average 18 km away from their nesting place, over an average period of 640 days. This suggests a higher survival rate, but the Suffolk data is based on the number of recoveries being a sixth of those from Norfolk, so we cannot compare the two counties at this time. There is no ready comparison available for Essex, although figures indicate that 60% of barn owls ringed in the county were recovered within 10 km of their place of ringing, with a further 36% having moved between 10 km and 99 km, suggesting a similar trend.

There is some interesting data from Suffolk that suggests what happens to some of the young after leaving the nest. In 1989, for

Barn owls have been observed from oil and gas platforms in the North Sea and occasionally they alight upon them.

example, three birds from one brood were later found dead, two of which were found in 1989 and one in 1991. One bird had moved 21 km away from the nest-site and lived for only 62 days but one of its siblings lived for 633 days and was found only 6km away. Three birds from a brood in 1990 were found in 1990, 1991 and 1994. One of the birds was found 16km away from the nest-site and it lived for 52 days, another was found 5km away and lived for 1,449 days while the third was found 6km away and lived for 151 days. Two other birds from a brood that was ringed in 1989 were found in 1990 and 1992. Each bird was found 7 km away from the place of ringing, one of which lived for 294 days and the other for 1,300 days. These few data are not conclusive but they do suggest that those birds that travel the furthest distance from their natal may have short lives, and in fact the two Suffolk birds that travelled further than 10km lived on average 29 days. Those birds that travelled less than 10km lived on average 765.4 days. Those birds that need to travel the least distance have a much greater chance of breeding before they succumb, and in the case of the Suffolk owls then on average those birds would have had at least two breeding seasons. This could be important in conservation terms if this is a true example of what happens to our barn owls after leaving the nest and if it was reflected throughout the British Isles.

One recovery of special interest to Suffolk concerns a bird that was ringed as a nestling at Cransford on July 17th, 1989, and which was later found dead in a cattle-drinking trough at Kimberley in Norfolk in the same year on November 15th. It is the first Suffolk-bred barn owl that we know of that has been recovered from outside of the county.

There have been some nationally important long-distance ring recoveries in Britain, seven of which have occurred in my study county of Suffolk. The first involved a bird that had been ringed as a nestling at Charlecote Park, Warwickshire, on August 5th, 1976, and which was found dead on the A45 road at Stowmarket, Suffolk, on July 13th, 1978. This represented an easterly movement of 177km and at that time represented one of the longest ever made by a barn owl in Britain. On January 28th, 1972, a barn owl that had also been ringed as a nestling in Charlecote Park (on August 2nd, 1971) was found dead at Great Wilbraham in Cambridgeshire. Remarkably, the recovery was on the same line from Charlecote Park as the one at Stowmarket some six years later. The second recovery for Suffolk involved a bird that was ringed as a nestling at Capel in Surrey on June 22nd, 1977, and was found dead in a barn at Thorington Street on September 2nd of the same year. This represented a north-easterly movement of 134km. The third recovery involved a bird that was ringed as a nestling at Padbury in Buckinghamshire on June 10th, 1988, and was found dead on the A11 road at Barton Mills on January 29th, 1989. This was a north-easterly movement of 106 km.

More recently there have been two other long-distance recoveries in Suffolk and both of those involved barn owls that had been ringed in Wiltshire. The first was ringed as a nestling on July 1st, 2003, near Oxenwood and was found dead near Cockfield, to the south-west of Bury St Edmunds, around November 20th of the same year. It had travelled 187 km in an east, north-easterly direction. The second recovery, and perhaps the most interesting, is of a male that had been ringed on November 30th, 2002, and which was found 'long dead' at Bury St Edmunds on March 11th, 2004. This bird was born earlier than the year of ringing but the exact age was unknown.

Ringing recoveries from the mainland continent are not common and so it was interesting to note that on October 24th, 1999, a barn owl that had been ringed as a nestling at Ijsselmeerpolders in the Netherlands on the September 4th, 1999, was later found dead on October 24th, 1999, near Levington just to the east of Ipswich. Although this bird had only travelled 290 km it was the first recovery of a barn owl ringed outside the British Isles and recovered in Suffolk.

The Suffolk recoveries were eclipsed by a barn owl that had been ringed as a nestling on June 14th at Tarlscough in Lancashire and was recovered at the Hythe in Colchester on November 1st, 1989. This constituted a south-easterly movement of 321 km and is one of a number of recent and interesting ring recoveries for Essex. On June 30th, 1996, a barn owl that had been ringed as a nestling at Fingringhoe was later found dead on January 23rd, 1997, beside a road in South Wootton in Norfolk, a distance of 108 km in a north-westerly direction. This was virtually repeated in the following year when a barn owl ringed as a nestling at Fingringhoe on August 4th, 1997, was recovered on April 4th, 1998, at Burnham Overy Staithe in Norfolk; this amounted to a northerly movement of 125 km. These records were followed up by another remarkable long-distance recovery from Essex when a bird that was ringed as a nestling on June 24th, 2000, was killed by a car at South Witham in Lincolnshire on September 12th in the same year (a north-westerly movement of 158km). These are some of the ringing recovery highlights for eastern England.

LONG-DISTANCE BARN OWLS ELSEWHERE
Elsewhere, a dead barn owl was found on December 12th, 1994, at Tullor, Aberdeen, after being ringed as a young bird at Coveney in Cambridgeshire on 28th June of the same year. This retrieval concerned a passage of 542 km NNW and was one of three long-distance barn owl recoveries in that year. Of the other two, one was ringed as a nestling at Detmold, in northern Germany on June 3rd, 1993, and was found dead at Ford in Strathclyde, Scotland, on July 18th, 1994, an extremely long distance of 1,028 km in a WNW direction. The final recovery was of a barn owl that was found 'long dead' on a North Sea oil-rig, some 425 km NNE of its original place of ringing in Humberside on 27th June of 1994.

In Norfolk, a bird considered to be *guttata* was found dead on or around October 29th, 1998, after being ringed as a juvenile in the Netherlands during the summer; while earlier, in 1996, a bird that had been ringed as a nestling in the Netherlands on July 4th, 1996, was found dead at Thirsk, North Yorkshire, on December 13th of the same year. This involved a north-westerly passage of 231 km.

A white-breasted barn owl (considered 'possibly very rare' in Holland) was ringed on January 22nd, 1976, at Ommen, Overijssel, in Holland and was later found as a road casualty on April 22nd, 1976, at Varades, Loire-Atlantique, France, a distance of around 800 km (490 miles).

Vehicular help?

All of these recoveries are important, interesting and exciting but Taylor has expressed caution about long-distance movements of barn owls by presenting evidence to show that dead barn owls are sometimes trapped and then transported by vehicles. He recounted a most remarkable event when the coach that he was travelling in struck a barn owl that became attached to a wing mirror. The body was conveyed for around 200 km before finally becoming dislodged and falling to the roadside. Recently Clark reported a British bred barn owl that was ringed in Nottinghamshire and which was subsequently found dead at Oostende, Belgium. She questioned whether the owl might have been transported there on a lorry, re-enforcing the opinion that barn owls, and no doubt other bird species, after being hit by moving vehicles are then transported elsewhere before either being removed or falling off.

On September 28th, 1986, Landguard Bird Observatory (LBO) at Felixstowe, in Suffolk, ringed its first barn owl; later it was found dead only 14 km to the south, at Little Tendring in Essex on February 9th , 1987. It is not known where it had originated from or how it arrived, and there is the possibility that it was transported on board a ship that had docked at the Felixstowe Dock Terminal. This certainly happened to a snowy owl that was discovered in the area on October 24th, 2001, and there are other examples of birds being transported by ship to these docks and elsewhere. More amazingly, a buff coloured barn owl, claimed as a bird of the race *guttata*, was ringed at LBO on June 11th, 1997. The origin of this bird is unknown but it is most unlikely to have been true guttata. In Buckinghamshire, two young barn owls were reared in captivity and subsequently released on August 10th, 1981; one was found dead on a lorry in a depot at Letchworth in Hertfordshire in November of that year. This was a perceptive report from Amersham in identifying the possibility of barn owls being transported after being struck by vehicles, thus obscuring the true nature of the owl's movements.

THE DARK SIDE OF THE BARN OWL

The distribution of the barn owl in Europe was described in the first chapter but here it is worth re-establishing the broad distributions of the two main races. The nominate race, or sub-species, *Tyto alba alba*, the white-breasted barn owl, lives in the western parts of Europe including western France, western Belgium, Spain, Italy and the British Isles. The dark-breasted race, *T.a.guttata*, lives in eastern Belgium, Holland, eastern France, Germany, Poland and most of the former 'Eastern Block' countries down to northern Turkey and east to the Ukraine and up to Latvia.

From time to time numbers of 'dark' barn owls are seen in the British Isles, especially during the autumn and winter months. The first claim for a British record of a 'dark-breasted' barn owl came from Epping, in Essex in March 1843, although Riviere in 1930 thought that the earliest known example was one killed near Norwich on December 13th, 1864. This specimen is now in the Norwich Museum. The Essex record states that the bird had 'the whole of the under-parts, legs, &c., of a deep ochre-yellow, with a few black spots. The face alone was white'. Undoubtedly this was not a specimen of the race *guttata*. Interestingly, Miller Christy recorded another dark specimen in December 1864 that was killed near Epping 'having the whole under-parts tawny yellow, spotted with black. The upper-parts were more mottled with grey than usual. It was a large bird and a female'. This was also another doubtful record, so it seems the Norfolk record stands. A dark female adult barn owl, considered to be of the Continental race *T. a. guttata*, was found on December 8th, 1937, in Kent. This was declared to be the first British record of this race although there can be no doubt that many of these birds had arrived on our shores prior to that event.

The idea that dark-breasted owls visited Britain in the summer and mated with the native white-breasted owls was suggested by Walpole-Bond in 1938, although he confirmed there was no indication that *guttata* was breeding in Britain, he pondered whether visiting individuals of this race over-summer. Bolam believed that the samples of barn owl skins from earlier times in Durham were much whiter than the preserved skins that were being taken at the time of his writing. He hypothesised that this was a result of interbreeding between *guttata* and *alba* and wrote 'Pure white-breasted birds used to be the common form, but are now in a decided minority, most of the nesters having the under parts somewhat yellowish in hue; while in some of them the flanks are more or less marked with small black spots, a feature which I never remember seeing amongst the breeding birds in olden days'. This could be true although Bolam was probably comparing museum skins and because of this we but we must not discount the possibility that the early skins had faded over the years. Somewhat later than Bolam's report, Wallis in 1916 mentioned a dark barn owl that was brought to the Reading Museum in Berkshire. Although he considered it slightly lighter than the 'typical German bird', he felt that it was much darker than the usual British species and gave a comprehensive description of the specimen which he had taken to a local taxidermist who stated that he had never handled such a dark specimen of the barn owl before. Despite this Wallis reported 'yet the five locally-killed Barn-Owls which happened (sad to say) to be in hands at the moment, presented an almost perfect graduation from the "White Owl," through an equally white form "with spotted breast," and others with still more spots upon faintly, or more heavily-buffed undersides to the bird I am recording'. Although spotting on the under-sides may be indicative of age rather than of race, it seems clear that Wallis was dealing with barn owls of different colour phases; though Derek Bunn has informed me that in his wide and long experience, barn owls are very variable birds in their colouring.

Of all the eastern counties in Britain that receive visits from dark-breasted birds, Kent appears to fare better than the rest, and from 1945 until 2004 23 had been seen in that county whilst Norfolk has recorded 17, Suffolk 4 and Essex 5 (Table 13). With three exceptions, all of the sightings have taken place in the period September to April. Elsewhere, Catley reported on the occurrence of 7 dark-breasted barn owls in Lincolnshire up to 2005 (1 in September 1976, 1 in October 1962, 1 in January 1974, 3 in March 1969, 1975 and 1979 and,the most recent, 1 in April 1979). He was of the view that the spring birds may well have been dark-breasted barn owls returning to the Continent in the way short-eared owls do: sightings of short-eared owls in Lincolnshire often peak in spring.

Table 13 The occurrence and numbers of recorded dark-breasted barn owls in Kent, Essex, Suffolk and Norfolk 1945- 2004.

	Jan	Feb	Mar	Apr	May	June	July	Aug	Sept	Oct	Nov	Dec	Total
Suffolk		1		1		1			1				4
Essex	1	2						1	1	1	1	2	9
Norfolk	2	1		2	1					4	1	2	13
Kent	8	2	1	2					1	5	3	1	23
Totals	11	6	1	5	1	1		1	3	10	5	5	49

(I am grateful to Tim Hodge, Archivist to the Kent Ornithological Society, for providing me with the records of dark-breasted barn owls in Kent and in Essex to Simon Woods for allowing me access to his manuscript 'The Birds of Essex' prior to publication.)

FUTURE RECORDING

Although a number of individuals showing the characteristics of the 'dark-breasted barn owl' have been recorded in Britain, we should be careful when assigning them to the race *guttata*. Caution should be exercised when describing barn owls with buff suffusions on their chest as continental birds of the *guttata* race.

The dark-breasted race of the barn owl, *T.a.guttata,* is a much darker bird than the nominate race *T.a.alba*. The under-parts are dark buffish-brown and these are covered in dark heavy spots. The upper-parts are orange and dark grey. The grey is heavily speckled and it is a more dominant colour than that found on *alba*. The flight feathers and tail are orange but again they are also very dark. The under-wings are the same as the under-body but they too are heavily spotted. The facial disc is whitish but it has a distinct purplish-brown patch spreading out from the centre and under the eyes. The ruff is brownish-chestnut with black tips. Heimo Mikkola pointed out that where the ranges of the two races meet in Europe, such as the Alps, Rhine valley, Netherlands, Belgium, Luxembourg and northern and central France, interbreeding takes place on a regular basis. This has resulted in a wide variety of individual colouring from which there is an '*independent inheritance of all variable characteristics*'. It was also pointed out that the genes that encourage the brown colouration have spread at the expense of the white colouring.

Although Mikkola gave some guidance in using plumage to separate 'dark-breasted' and 'white-breasted' barn owls, he also pointed out that there were some physical differences between the two races but he cautioned that little work has been carried out on this subject. The average wing length for fresh specimens of *guttata* was given as 297mm, and that for alba as 291mm. The average weight of the dark-breasted barn was given as 346g and that for the white-breasted race as 337g, although his conclusions were based on the findings of Baudvin, and those did not take into consideration the known sexual differences in weight.

Until recently there were no demands put upon observers to precisely identify dark-breasted barn owls in the field, and clearly many of the records that have been published in the past are ambiguous, unconvincing and should, perhaps, be discarded. To publish a record along the lines of 'A barn owl thought to be of the race *guttata*' or 'showing the traces of the race *guttata*' is not satisfactory, although from Essex Pearson provided the best description that I have seen.

Following a decision by the British Birds Rarities Committee in 2006, it was decided that more stringent rules were needed before records of *guttata* would be accepted. Detailed notes and, where possible, photographs would be required to support any future claims. It was also announced that 'simply looking like *guttata* is not definite proof of origin' and that in future all records that appear to be genuine *guttata* would be published 'with the caveat that some might be unusually dark *alba*'. This issue will continue to be a problem, and I am sure that it will, in the fullness of time, become an even more interesting subject.

SOURCES USED IN THIS CHAPTER

Bolam, G., 1912: *The Birds of Northumberland and the Eastern Borders*. Henry Hunter Blair, Alnwick.

Bunn, D.S., Warburton, A.W., and Wilson, A.A.B., 1982: *The Barn Owl*. Poyser, Calton.

Catley, G. Dark-breasted Barn Owls in Lincolnshire. www. lincsbirdclub.co.uk

Clark, J., 2004: Latest findings from ringing. *BTO News,* 255: 6-7.

Cobb, F.K. (ed.), 1956: Suffolk Bird Report 1956. *Trans. Suffolk Nat. Soc.,* 10: 136.

Glue, D.E., 1971: Ringing recovery circumstances of small birds of prey. *Bird Study,* 18: 137-146.

Kehoe, C., 2006: Racial identification and assessment in Britain: a report from the RIACT (Race Identification Amongst Changing

Taxonomy) sub-committee. *British Birds*, 99: 619 – 645.

Merne, O.J. (ed.), 2005: Irish Ringing Report, 2003 and 2004. *Irish Birds,* 7: 575-596.

Palmer, P., 2000: *First for Britain and Ireland.* Arlequin Press, Chelmsford.

Patterson, A.H., 1930: *A Norfolk Naturalist.* Methen & Co. Ltd., London.

Pearson, M., 2002: Dark-breasted Barn Owl. *The Essex Bird Report 2002.* Essex Birdwatching Society.

Ralfe, P.G., 1905: *The birds of the Isle of Man.* David Douglas, Edinburgh.

Riviere, B.B., 1930: *A History of the Birds of Norfolk.* Witherby, London.

Robinson, P. ,2003: *The birds of the Isles of Scilly.* Helm, London.

Robinson, C. (ed.), 1980-1: *Report 4*: Systematic list. Amersham & District Ornithological Society.

Rountree, F.R.G., 1974: *The Birds of Sark.* Sark Ornithological Club.

Stenhouse, J.H., 1926: Rare birds in Fair Isle. *British Birds,* 20: 28.

Taylor, M., Seago, M., Allard, P., and Dorling, D., 2000: *The Birds of Norfolk* (2nd. ed.). Pica Press, Sussex.

Ticehurst, N.F. 1909: *A History of the Birds of Kent.* Witherby, London.

Van den Berg, A.B., & Bosman, C.A.W., 1999: *Rare Birds in the Netherlands.* Pica Press, Robertsbridge.

Voous, K.H., 1988: *Owls of the Northern Hemisphere.* Collins, London.

Wallis, H.M., 1916: Dark-Breasted Barn Owl in Berkshire. *British Birds,* 9: 210-211.

Walpole-Bond, J., 1938: *A History of Sussex Birds,* Vol. 2. Witherby, London.

Wernham, C.V., Toms, M.P., Clark, J.H., Siriwardena, G.M. & Bailie, S.R. (eds.). 2002: *The Migration Atlas: movements of the birds of Britain and Ireland.* Poyser, London.

The annual bird reports from Suffolk and Essex

7 The first barn owls in the British Isles

'The artificial environment created by man in the British countryside during the last two thousand years or so would appear to suit the Barn Owl very well indeed. It can never have been a woodland bird, since its method of hunting requires the existence of open spaces with a thick ground layer of vegetation to provide a suitable habitat for its small-mammal prey.'

D.S.Bunn, A.Warburton & R.Wilson *The Barn Owl*, Poyser, Calton, 1982

I now will attempt to throw some light upon the barn owl's early life in the British Isles, from the end of the last ice age to the Tudor period, around the year 1500 and to the dawn of the great changes that were to take place in the countryside.

The Ice Age

The Pleistocene began some 2 million years ago and lasted until the end of the last ice age (about 15,000 years ago). We know that barn owls were present in Britain during the Pleistocene because the evidence to support this comes from their remains, along with the remains of their prey, that were laid down during that time in various parts of the country such as Derbyshire and Devon, as well in the Wookey Hole cave system in Somerset. Previous to these finds the Norfolk and Suffolk fossil beds, which are around 500,000 to 600,000 years old, have also yielded the remains of a bird not unlike a barn owl.

The last glacial coverage of the British Isles reached its maximum extent around 20,000 years ago and although the ice-cap did not reach southern Britain, the climate was sufficiently severe to ensure that very few species of wildlife survived; practically all of Britain's present fauna and flora arrived after that event.

The last ice age stuttered to a close, in a series of warming-up periods,with subsequent colder spells. Although the underlying trend was for a gradual warming of the climate, southern England still remained a very barren landscape in which there was very little biological activity. Then, at around 18,000 years ago, the climate began to warm and the ice started to melt, so that by around 15,000 years ago it had warmed to such a degree a tundra-type vegetation appeared; this was later replaced by birch scrub as the climate warmed even further. It is important to remember that at that time there were land-bridges connecting the present day Ireland to the present day British mainland, which in turn was connected to the present day Europe. This meant that as the climate warmed even further, and the land became hospitable to wildlife, those bridges allowed many species from southern Europe to colonise the British Isles, including Ireland.

However, there was a brief cold interlude during this time and from around 11,000 to 10,200 BP (before present) the birch scrub disappeared and the tundra returned. This period of intense cold is known as the Younger Dryas Period and it was during this phase that collared and Norway lemmings also returned and when they did, their colonisation was tracked by snowy owls, which were relatively widespread throughout much of the British Isles at that time.

Eventually the Younger Dryas Period came to an abrupt end, and then the climate warmed quickly and sufficiently to once again encourage the growth of scrub and this rapidly colonised the countryside. Birch was again the first tree to arrive, followed by pine, hazel, oak, alder, lime and elm.

As the ice melted it diminished in size as well as weight, and the relief of the pressure upon the land was extraordinary, for as the weight lifted, the land in northern Britain commenced to rise and as it did so, southern England reciprocated by slowly starting to sink. Even today the western Highlands of Scotland continue to rise at the present rate of 3mm per year, whilst southern England continues to sink at the rate of around 2mm per year, and this action has implications for our present-day barn owls. But the repercussions of the ice-melt do not stop there, for the melting ice not only relieved the pressure on the land, it also caused the sea-level to rise. At around 18,500 BP, the world-wide sea-level was 120m lower than it is now, but with the continued melting of the ice, it started to rise even further until at the start of the post-glacial period it was 55m lower than at present and by around 5,000 BP, the sea was probably at its present level.

During the post ice-age period barn owls colonised the British Isles from southern Europe although, apart from a few cave remains, it is difficult to track their progress. Their movements would have been dominated by the expansion in the ranges of their prey, notably small mammals, so it might be better to follow their fortunes, which are easier to track. Before that, however, there are some major events to deal with, for it was during the course of sea-level rise that a significant event occurred in western Europe: the land-bridge between Britain and what is now Ireland was broken.

This occurred some 9,500 years ago and, although it did not happen overnight, it did take place over a relatively short period. It is not clear whether a semi-permanent bridge remained for a while, but whatever happened it was enough to ensure that creatures such as snakes, water voles, field voles, bank voles, weasels, moles, common shrews, tawny owls and probably the woodpeckers, along with some other hole-nesting bird species, did not get the opportunity to colonise the area of land that was eventually to become Ireland. A land-bridge might have existed between Ireland and Britain at around 11,000-10,000 BP but, if it did, then it was not substantial enough to allow burrowing animals, such as water and field voles, to cross. It would, however, have allowed wood mice, which are capable of making extensive movements on sand-dunes, to traverse a sandy low-lying causeway.

No satisfactory explanation has been given as to why barn owls are present in Ireland and tawny owls are not but it is likely that their absence is due to a problem that also arose for barn owls in Great Britain during the latter part of the 20th century: the absence of nest-sites. It would appear that at the time when the land-bridge between Ireland and Britain was broken, some 6,000 years ago, there were four main tree species present on the island. These were birch, pine, oak and hazel, but of those four, only the oak matures in a manner that readily creates holes suitable for hole-nesting birds such as the tawny owl.

The fact that barn owls are present and tawny owls are not suggests the oaks that were present in Ireland, when the land-bridge was finally severed, had only a tentative toe-hold and so they probably would not have matured sufficiently to allow cavities to develop, precluding the tree-hole nesting tawny owl from colonising. Barn owls, however, are less specific in their choice of nest-site and so, as the small mammals populated the future Ireland, barn owls would have followed, nesting in caves and on rock ledges. Nest-sites, such as mature trees and buildings perhaps, arrived much too late for tawny owls. If a land-bridge did exist between the

British mainland and Ireland, Ireland is likely to have been devoid of the substantial cover which tawny owls prefer. Barn owls on the other hand are birds of the open countryside and tend to wander, so presumably they would not have found this a problem.

Recently Rackham presented a distribution for Ireland's trees around that period (which he calls the Atlantic Period and which lasted for 2,400 years, ending in 3,800 BC): that oak was confined to south-west Ireland while the central areas were dominated by hazel and wych-elm. Whatever distribution is chosen, it is still unlikely that large trees, capable of developing suitable nesting cavities, were present before the land-bridge was broken.

Were barn owls present in Ireland when that event happened or did they colonise Ireland afterwards? It is possible that barn owls could have populated Ireland after the break but this seems unlikely because of the distance between the two land masses, which is around 30 km at the nearest points: Kintyre in Scotland and Antrim in Ireland. While barn owls do make occasional long journeys, for successful colonisation to have occurred, a considerable influx of barn owls from the mainland would need to have taken place at any one time and in a concentrated area.

Evidence that barn owls are unlikely to have colonised Ireland after the land separation comes from the fact that up until 2002, none of the 3,146 British ringed barn owls have been recovered from Ireland. Similarly, no Irish ringed barn owls have been recovered on the British mainland (although Ireland is poorly represented by barn owl ringing sites). However, in 2003 a barn owl that had been ringed on 18th July 1997 at Kildonnan in Dumfries and Galloway, Scotland, was found dead on a road at Newton Forbes, Longford, in Northern Ireland on May 14th, 2003, so there is a slim possibility that colonisation could have occurred many years ago.

There seems little doubt that barn owls continued to colonise Ireland during the course of the break, being sustained by wood mice, whose progress they would have tracked, before the land-bridge was finally broken. Barn owl remains dating from the Pleistocene period have been found in the top level of Edenvale Cave, County Clare, and at a lake village in County Meath. A genetic study, based on DNA could, perhaps, provide more detailed information.

It is interesting that barn owls were able to establish themselves in Ireland even though the spectrum of prey was small, which is a factor that has implications for our present-day barn owls. It was

Following the clearance of the 'wildwood' much of Britain, and especially central England, was a landscape of open countryside with few trees and hedgerows. With the coming of the Agricultural Revolution in the 16th and 17th centuries, new hedgerows were planted; where that was not practical, dry-stone walls were built to perform the same function.

thought that pygmy shrews might have remained present in Britain throughout the Younger Dryas Period, but now there is evidence to suggest they were introduced to Ireland from Iberia. If pygmy shrews were absent at that time of land separation then the choice of food was very much less then than it is today. In Ireland the black rat might have been present during Roman times although much later it was replaced by the brown rat, a species present in contemporary Irish barn owl diets. The house mouse might also have been available as it has been present in Britain since at least the Iron Age, but even so the spectrum of prey that was available to its barn owls after Ireland separated from mainland Britain was remarkably small, with the wood mouse likely to have been the only other small mammal available.

The severance of Ireland from Britain after the last ice age is only part of the story because at around 8,000 years ago, the climate became so warm, the ice-caps melted further. This caused another rise in sea-levels and it was during this period that Britain became separated from mainland Europe. It was a significant event, for up until then many animals and plants had begun to migrate north into Britain from southern Europe, where they had retreated during the last ice age. When Britain separated from mainland Europe then, just like Ireland, further colonisations by terrestrial wildlife ceased.

In the post-glacial period the choice of food for barn owls on mainland Britain was greater than it is today because, along with field voles, root voles were also present; the arrival of those two voles was preceded by wood mice and perhaps pygmy shrews. The field vole never made it to Ireland and neither did the root vole, a species that was to die out in Britain during the early post-glacial period, although its Bronze Age remains have been recorded on the Isles of Scilly.

By the time the land-bridge between Britain and mainland Europe was severed, much of the land in the south was covered by 'wildwood'; the terrain was blanketed in mature deciduous woodland from around 7,000 to 5,000 BP, although within it there would have been open areas, which would have been kept open by grazing animals, such as wild oxen, boar and deer. Rackham dates a fully developed wildwood from 6,200-3800 BC.

There, in those glades and on the edge of wildwood, barn owls established themselves. Other areas, such as river estuaries and marshland, were less reliable due to the possibility of flooding. Caves and rock fissures provided nesting places along with isolated and wood-edge trees although, at that time, the wildwood was a place for tawny and long-eared owls and it is likely that during that period they were more numerous in Britain than they have been at any time since.

When animals colonised the land they would have been followed by man; around 4,500 years ago he started to clear the wildwood for farming, a culture that was brought to the British Isles from Southern Europe. This was the Neolithic or New Stone Age society, which continued through into the Bronze and Iron Ages. According to Rackham the clearing of the wildwood was a substantial and significant achievement that would have have had a detrimental effect on the populations of tawny and long-eared owls, for after the clearance a large open-field farming system was adopted in many parts of central and northern England. This would change again, but not for some four thousand or more years. For the barn owl these changes would have had different effect, because the clearance opened up the landscape so that in many places a lightly wooded habitat was created, comprising small fields, hedgerows and trees (see below).

AFTER THE WILDWOOD

After the clearance large parts of Britain became grassed land and Yalden draws attention to the large proportion of water voles that have been found in some small mammal remains. In the Neolithic levels of Dowel Cave in Derbyshire, 55% of the small mammal remains were of water voles and 34% were of field voles, with a further six species of small mammal making up the remaining portion, and similar patterns have been found in small mammal relics elsewhere.

In the middle of Salisbury Plain, at Snail Down in Wiltshire, the small mammal remains contained a high proportion of water voles and this site is 7km from the nearest main river, which is the Avon. Dr Yalden says that water voles have changed their morphology in the post-glacial period and have become larger. The abundance of water voles in these finds tends to confirm the view that barn owls seek out the heaviest prey, perhaps because they provide the greatest sustenance for the least effort. They also support the hypothesis that water voles were once found well away from water.

The decline of the wildwood changed the status of some other small mammals. Wood mice would have declined as the trees were cleared and grasslands were created, although where arable farming existed they would have turned their attentions to eating grain and other crops. Common and pygmy shrews may not have been badly affected because they can live in woods and pasture, but bank voles would certainly have declined. Not only would they have suffered due to a loss of woodland, they would also have experienced competition from field voles as the amount of grassed land increased. In the absence of field voles, however, bank voles will quite readily live in more open habitats including grass.

Later, when the Romans arrived, they set about bringing order to the country and created many substantial buildings. Yalden expressed surprise at the high number of water and field vole

remains that were found in the early 1990s in a Roman granary at South Shields and because of these numerous remains he considered that they were probably the consequences of one or more barn owls depositing pellets within the building.

There can be little doubt that the owls were lured to the granary by wood mice that were feeding on grain and it is, perhaps, the first example we have of barn owls using a man-made structure in Britain.

We can, of course, only assume that barn owls were relatively widespread in the British Isles in this post ice-age era, for records are few. Even so, apart from the previously mentioned records, barn owls were present at Glastonbury in around 250BC, as well as at a Roman site in St Albans in Hertfordshire and Cranbourne Chase in Dorset.

THE DARK AGES
In AD410 the Romans withdrew to Rome and Britain started its journey into the 'Dark Ages' during which some farmlands were deserted and the re-growth of woodlands began. This abandonment of farmland might have been brought about by the onset of plague in the 6th century and is likely to have been bubonic plague, a

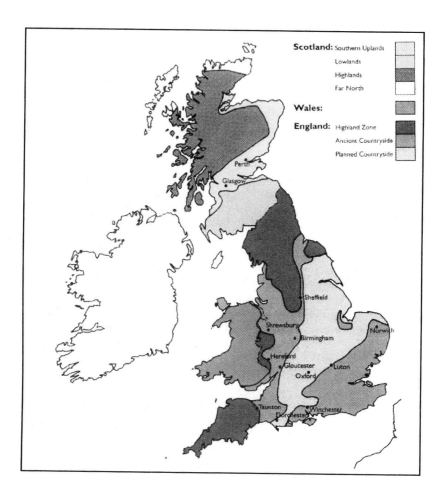

Fig. 5 Rackham (2006) presented his distribution of Ancient Countryside which spread in a narrow strip from around Middlesborough, through to Sheffield, then Shrewsbury, Birmingham, Hereford, Gloucester and south to Taunton. In the south-east of England it stretched from Winchester through to Luton, the whole of Essex and Suffolk and into east Norfolk. It is important to point out that Anglesey, the island off the north-west coast of Wales, also forms part of Ancient Countryside and a good population of barn owls has been recorded there in every national bird and barn owl survey since the first national barn owl survey in 1932.

disease that was brought to Britain by black rats.

The re-emergence of woodlands would certainly have had some benefits for barn owls in the early stages of re-growth, as small mammals, and especially voles, colonised the ground cover. Later, as the trees grew larger, they would have shaded out the vegetation, which would have then died off together with the voles. The resultant woods would then have become homes for wood mice, bank voles and perhaps tawny owls, although the woodland increase was not substantial.

Although the Dark Ages provide us with little barn owl information, a find at Repton in Derbyshire, where in AD873 the Great Viking Army over-wintered, throws some light. According to Yalden it appears that the army created a cairn over a ramshackle building to cover a mass grave of some 250 bodies. Before that event, however, it seems that one or more barn owls had been living there and had left an interesting selection of small mammal remains. Notably absent were the remains of any black rats, while water voles were few despite the site overlooking a grassy flood plain. Field voles were the principal prey species, but harvest mouse and water shrew were also present. Dr Yalden suggests that Anglo-Saxon Britain was too inhospitable for black rats to survive and that replenishment of the rat population was no longer taking place in post-Roman Britain, due to the breakdown of the trade routes between Britain and Europe.

Throughout the first millennium and into medieval times, farming continued to be important in the economy of the country and because of this barn owls would, no doubt, have found plenty to eat as a result of the grain harvests. Grassland, too, would have remained an important part of the countryside scene and Yalden has suggested that a sample of 3,283 amphibian and small mammal bone fragments which have been dated prior to AD1225, and which were found in a latrine shaft in the castle at Middleton Stoney in Oxfordshire, were probably deposited by barn owls attracted to mice that had possibly been feeding on stored grain.

This find comes from a period of growth and prosperity. The human population had been increasing at a great rate and food was plentiful, suggesting that if food, such as meat and bread, were readily available, then small mammals would also have found plenty to eat.

However, not all of England was an open landscape; Rackham has carefully described a pattern of Ancient and Planned Countryside which existed at the time of Domesday and which had been in existence to the present day since the clearance of the wildwood. The Ancient Countryside comprised small and enclosed fields that were created by clearing parts of the wildwood, with some trees and hedges left to form a wooded boundary. The creation of Ancient Countryside took place on a gradual basis from the Neolithic to the medieval period and it dominated parts of England, such as Essex, Suffolk, south and east Norfolk, Kent, Sussex, parts of Hampshire, Herefordshire, Worcestershire, Shropshire, Lancashire, Anglesey and parts of Yorkshire, east of the Pennines (Fig. 5).). The Planned Countryside was to come later but before then, much of central and northern England especially consisted of large unenclosed fields and because of these formations Dr. Yalden concluded that this pattern of countryside has had repercussions for the distribution of some of our small mammals, but I go further and suggest that this has also had repercussions for the present-day distribution of our barn owls.

The creation of medieval deer parks was also important and may have played a role in ensuring that areas were set aside for wild species. It has been estimated that by about AD1300, there were some 3,200 deer parks in England covering around 2% of the country. These parks were used for keeping deer but sometimes other animals, such as sheep and cattle, were included. Rackham tells us that they were rarely used for hunting. Some of the parks were wooded but others contained grassland with pollard trees and perhaps one of the best examples is at Staverton Park, near Butley in Suffolk, where there are over 4,000 ancient pollard oaks. Indeed the late Eric Hosking informed me that Staverton Park was home to nine pairs of barn owls just before the Second World War

The 14th century was a time of great upheaval and it is worth touching on some key events. From the year 1310 to 1330, northern Europe witnessed one of the worst periods of weather in the Middle Ages and during that time there were some severe winters, coupled with cool and rainy summers. Starting in 1315, there then followed three years of heavy rain and this precipitation heralded a long spell of unpredictable weather over the next 5 centuries. The rains were so severe and the effects were so drastic, that in 1317 the Great Famine set in and as a consequence, a large number of people throughout Europe died. What effect the weather and subsequent famine had upon the small mammals is difficult to say, but we can speculate that the countryside was stripped of any possible foods by the human population, leaving little sustenance for mice, shrews and voles.

Then, after a gap of 700 years, plague returned to Europe and from 1348 to 1350 the Black Death spread throughout the British Isles, during which time between 30-45% of the human population perished. This left a shortage of farm labour and as a result much of the countryside was once again allowed to fall into a state of neglect and some of it would have returned woodland. To exacerbate the problem, plague returned in 1361-64, 1368, 1371, 1373-75, 1390 and finally 1405, by which time the population of Britain had halved.

Apart from killing the human population, cats, dogs and other creatures also perished, although it seems horses were not affected.

Then, in the winter of 1408, Walsingham reported in his *Historica Anglicana* that the winter period, from December to March, was very severe, and that during its course almost all blackbirds and thrushes perished. This event heralded a series of bad winters which were to dominate the weather for several centuries to come. It was the start of the event that has come to be known as the 'Little Ice Age'.

SOURCES USED IN THIS CHAPTER

Andrews, P. 1990: *Owls, Caves and Fossils*. Natural History Museum Publications, London.

Cabot, D. 1999: *Ireland*. Collins, London.

Corbet, G.B. & Harris, S. 1991: *The Handbook of British Mammals* (3rd ed.). Blackwell Scientific Publications, Oxford.

Fisher, J. 1966: *The Shell Bird Book*. George Rainbird, London.

Hutchinson, C.D. 1989: *Birds in Ireland*. Poyser, Calton.

Merne, O.J. (ed.) 2005: Irish Ringing Report, 2003 and 2004. *Irish Birds,* 7: 575-596.

Rackham, O. 1986: *The History of the Countryside*. Dent, London.

Rackham, O. 1994: *The Illustrated History of the Countryside*. Weidenfeld and Nicholson, London.

Rackham, O. 2006: *Woodlands*. Collins, London.

Woodruffe, G. 2004: Wildlife Reports – Mammals. *British Wildlife,* 15: 350.

Yalden, D. 1999: *The History of British Mammals*. Poyser, London.

Yalden, D. 2003: Mammals in Britain – a historical perspective. *British Wildlife,* 14: 243-251.

8 Revolution, persecution and warfare

'So the survivors of the 30,000 British men who fought the battle of Waterloo returned to a country that was fast changing its very appearance, and whose wealth was rapidly increasing by reason of new methods of manufacture and transport. But still the factory areas were a small part of the whole, and most English towns were picturesque country towns, set in a countryside of unspoilt beauty. The villages, to which most of them came home, were still the main focus of life for most Englishmen, and had almost completed their eighteenth century transformation. The countryside was now drained, ditched, hedged, and enclosed to an extent that would have amazed their grandfathers. Nearly all the old open fields had been enclosed; and the commons and wastelands had been enclosed nearly as much as they were ever to be. This meant that agriculture had become more efficient. Improved methods of tilling, of rotation of crops, and of stock-breeding had become well known, even if they were not yet universally adopted by the farmers.'

David Thomson, *England in the Nineteenth Century*
(Penguin Books, 1978)

The dawning of the 16th century marked a new era for British farming. The country, indeed the world, was on the verge of the Industrial Revolution although before that, the Agricultural Revolution was to have a major impact upon a large portion of the countryside. It was also a time which marked a growing interest in natural history and which led to the emergence of the conservation movement.

THE AGRICULTURAL REVOLUTION

The 16th century appears to have been a period of relative tranquillity in the British countryside. Sheep farming was an important factor in the economy and with a population of around

8 million they outnumbered humans by 3 to 1. Although this large number of sheep meant there was plenty of grass, it was unsuitable for voles, due to the close-cropping of feeding sheep. Many large fields were still in existence of which a number were a thousand acres or more, and this suggests that in the absence of hedgerow trees, nesting places would have been scarce in many places. Barns had yet to make an impact upon the farmscape. However, the presence of barns was not important everywhere and in Ancient Countryside trees for nesting were much more important. In Essex, where elms were numerous, Hunter viewed them as a near monoculture, such was their profusion.

The Enclosure Acts during the Agricultural Revolution had the greatest impact upon the open field system that had prevailed for hundreds of years after the clearance of the wildwood. This was the Planned Countryside that Rackham has described (see below) and which ultimately had a positive effect upon barn owl numbers. Before we enter that period, it is important to draw attention to the first determined effort since Roman times to drain the wetlands when, in 1630, the Dutch engineer Vermuyden, who had already drained 70,000 acres of Yorkshire marshland, was appointed to drain the East Anglian Fens.

This drainage scheme heralded the start of the Agricultural Revolution and it brought a great deal of land into cultivation. Subsequently, other places, such as Romney Marsh in Kent, the fenlands of Lincolnshire and the Somerset Levels were also drained. In most cases those wetlands had been the subject of earlier, less successful drainage schemes.

It is difficult to place a precise acreage on the area that was drained in East Anglia; 95,000 acres were allotted to the 'adventurers' who had sponsored the project and by around 1655, most of the East Anglian Fens had been drained. Draining of the Fens continued into the 19th century and indeed maintenance of the water levels continues to the present day. This enterprise was the first major step, for many hundreds of years, towards changing the landscape of Britain, as this vast wetland was claimed for agriculture.

There can be no doubt that this, and similar projects, brought about an increase in the numbers of small mammals as they exploited new food sources. For barn owls this would normally have had a very positive effect but, due to a lack of nesting places, it did not. However, things were likely to have been different for the ground-nesting short-eared owl.

During the course of this draining another major change was taking place and this did enable barn owls to exploit the countryside. Before the 18th century a substantial portion of land, particularly in central England and northern Britain, consisted of large open fields. This changed when a series of governmental 'Enclosure Acts' were brought in and from around 1750 until 1850 approximately 4,500,000 acres of open fields were enclosed. This amounted to around fifty per cent of the arable land in England and Wales.

These governmental enclosures were set out in a more rigid and straight manner than those in Ancient Countryside and consisted of miles of hedgerows and millions of trees, which then formed the landscape that Rackham has described (Fig. 5) as Planned Countryside. As a consequence there were more hedgerow trees by the mid 18th century than ever before or since.

Although it took time for the hedgerow trees of the new enclosures to develop nesting cavities, the quick-growing hawthorn hedges would have provided food and shelter not only for birds, but for many small mammals that would have been able to infiltrate the countryside without having to cross large open areas thus exposing themselves to predation. Where it was impractical to construct hedgerows, then dry-stone walls were often built to form the enclosures and these too would have enabled small mammals to penetrate the countryside. In other places, such as the Somerset Levels, drains were dug, and allowed to fill with water, to form another type of enclosure which no doubt allowed water voles to become more numerous.

Then, at around 1716, brown rats arrived from Europe and their rapid colonisation of the countryside coincided with the creation of the enclosure hedgerows. Within a relatively short time they had spread throughout the British Isles and this was an important event for Britain's barn owls.

Apart from forming a stock-proof barrier, hedges could be a source of food for the human population and so they were managed in a way that ensured that fruits were allowed to form. This management was also good for birds and small mammals and in the absence of poisons, species such as shrews, would have also thrived.

As a corridor for moving from one area to another, hedges are considered to be more important to small mammals rather than birds. In those areas of Ancient Countryside the small mammal fauna is richer than that of the Planned Countryside (see Yalden

1999), thus providing a slightly greater spectrum of prey.

It is so very easy to go out into the East Anglian countryside and see Ancient Countryside today, as it is in Herefordshire, Worcestershire, Shropshire, etc. There are some splendid examples of Ancient Countryside not that far from where I am writing these notes. The distribution of yellow-necked mouse (so common in Essex and Suffolk but rare in Norfolk), is a classic example of the distribution of Ancient Countryside; but that's another story.

The enclosures had one aim, and that was to increase food production. Beef production increased in many places and more grass was needed for the cattle. It was also required as fodder for the horses that headed up the new metal ploughs. This ensured that hay meadows and other grass fields were available to provide food throughout the year for the cattle and horses; as a consequence, grassland was an integral part of most farms. This grass, together with the abundant hedgerows that now surrounded many of the fields, provided a wide variety of prey for barn owls from a variety of habitats throughout the year, while rats were everywhere. There can be no doubt that it was due to the creation of these habitats that in 1781 the naturalist and eminent ornithologist John Latham considered the barn owl was 'very common in most of the European countries and none we believe more so than in this kingdom!'. In Wiltshire, the local naturalist Maegillivray considered that barn owls were mainly to be seen in the enclosed and wooded parts of country and considered the barn owl was 'abounding in all places'.

Where elms had been encouraged to grow, then nesting places would have been abundant due to their nature of creating cavities when large boughs fall off, which they do quite regularly. Elsewhere, in the Planned Countryside, other trees were plentiful but young, and so it would have taken some time for them to provide suitable nesting places. There can be no doubt that it was the appearance of many barns that was to lead to an increase in the number of Britain's barn owls. However, it was not just the provision of barns that was important, it was the materials that were used in their construction that was significant.

During the period of enclosure, the construction of many farm buildings in Britain was inclined to fall into two contrasting segments, reflecting the broad type of farming that went on. In the north and west the farming tended to be pastoral, while to the south and east it was inclined towards arable. On arable farmland the barns tended to be large because the threshing and storing of

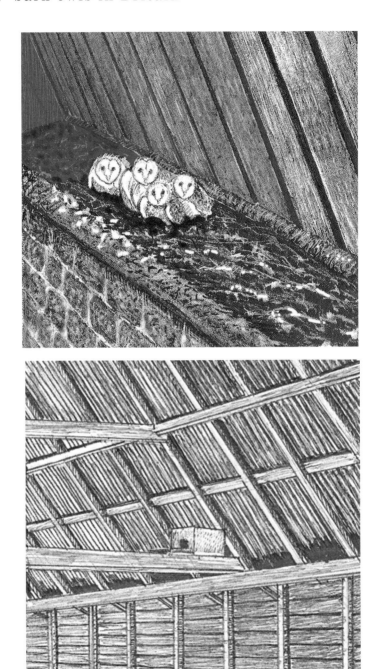

In the stone barns of western and northern Britain the tops of walls and other similar sites are often ideal places on which barn owls may nest. In the wooden barns of eastern Britain there are few ledges and in many cases well sited nest boxes may help solve the problem.

grain took place within them. Not only were they large, they tended to be made of wood, although here and there brick was sometimes used. In the pastoral areas of Britain the barns were built of stone and in general they tended to be small because they were used for keeping cattle. The building materials that were used usually reflected the types of materials that were to hand locally.

In the pastoral areas where stone was relatively cheap and easy to acquire, the barns were usually built with stone and the coming of the Industrial Revolution produced tools that enabled it to be fashioned more easily into building blocks. Sometimes wooden barns were built but, unlike many of those in the arable areas, few have survived. In the arable regions of southern and eastern England stone was scarce but wood was readily available and so most of the barns there were built of wood.

Of course there were exceptions and Norfolk and Sussex spring to mind. In those counties flint-stone was often more readily available than wood; while many of those in Norfolk were built of flint and brick.

Although barns have always been an important feature of agricultural Britain (the word 'barn' comes from the Old English 'bern' which means 'barley-house', barley being the main crop of the Anglo-Saxon farmers), it appears they became more abundant during the 17th century and into the latter part of the 19th century, when their decline was largely brought about by the introduction of the threshing machine. This meant that it was no longer necessary to thresh cereal crops indoors.

It seems then that due to an increase in the number of farm buildings that occurred during the course of the Agricultural Revolution, an abundance of secure nesting places became available for barn owls in parts of the British countryside where perhaps they had either never been before or where they had been few in number. This factor, together with a likely abundance of prey that was to be found not only in the boundaries of the new enclosures, but especially in the grasslands of the pastoral areas, suggests that barn owls were possibly more common in the British Isles than they had ever been, and the comments of the naturalists of the day suggest this was the case. However, there was a downside to this, for, as Rackham tells us, at the same time that barn owls appear to have been numerous, the number of hedgerow trees started to decline while at the same time a decline in hedges also began. It seems likely, therefore, that as a consequence of the rising importance of barns for nesting, in 1883 the white owl was given the official name 'barn owl'.

The reasons why barn owls adopted barns so freely are various. Many barns that were constructed of stone often have ledges, tops of walls and other nooks and crannies on which the birds can safely nest. Contrary to this, timber-framed barns have fewer suitable places to nest in and this provides a clue as to why more barn owls in the pastoral areas of Britain tend to nest in buildings, while those in the arable areas tend to nest in trees, although that is only part of the reason.

THE IMPACT OF THE INDUSTRIAL REVOLUTION

In 1803, Britain and her allies had been at war with France for some time, but when the allies withdrew their support Britain decided to go it alone. As a consequence, the government struggled to feed the people and it had to resort to purchasing grain from elsewhere in the world. This was expensive, unreliable and caused eventual food shortage. Clearly Britain was agriculturally unprepared to feed its people in times of war, but with the end of the conflict in 1815 Britain entered a period of relative peace.

There can be no doubt that by the end of the Napoleonic Wars barn owls were common throughout most parts of the British Isles. Indeed in 1819 the naturalist Edward Donovan stated 'it need scarcely be said that the white owl is common in every part of England', although that was a slight exaggeration. Fenland, heathland, moorland and mountainous areas would have held very few pairs, as is still the case. P.J. Selby, writing in his *Illustrations of Ornithology* in 1833, stated that the barn owl 'is the most common of the British species and is found in every part of the Kingdom', again a slight exaggeration, but a further indication of the barn owl's status at that time.

Shortly after Selby's comments, however, the first indications of a decline in Britain's barn owls were observed, and this decline has continued to the present day. As usual with the barn owl, there is more than one factor to blame although there can be no doubts that the prime reason in the first instance was the persecution from gamekeepers, of which I have more to say later. The persecution started from around the 1850s and continued, unabated, until the First World War, after which it began to taper off. Britain experienced a series of bitter winters during the 19th century (especially those of 1838 and 1855, as well as those of 1860, 1878-79 and 1880-81)

and this series of winters has come to be regarded as the ending of the 'Little Ice Age'. We know that barn owls sometimes suffer in times of severe weather and so presumably some of the decline that was noted in the latter part of this century can be attributed to that. In addition to these problems there was an agricultural depression, for which some of the blame for the decline has also been attributed, but this does not stand up to investigation.

The agricultural depression that took place in Great Britain from around 1870 until the 1930s came about largely through the importation of cheap grain from North America. This resulted in many farms either going out of food production altogether, or reducing their output. The effects of taking this land out of production would then, presumably, have been good for wildlife in much the same way as it was in the late 20th and early 21st centuries. It is very likely, therefore, that because of this the numbers of voles, mice and rats would have increased in a number of places and that the effects of the wholesale slaughter of barn owls that undoubtedly occurred during the Victorian era was compensated for to some degree by a plentiful supply of food. In other words, yes, there were a lot of barn owls killed by gamekeepers and probably as a result of bad weather, but in a number of places they were able to replace those losses because there was plenty of food available and although trees were declining there were still enough, along with the prodigious number of barns that had been built following enclosure, to provide nesting places. As an example let us look at my study county of Suffolk, which is within the region of East Anglia.

In many parts of East Anglia land was actually brought into arable production during the 1800s. This was because shortly after the Napoleonic Wars there was a marked shift in agricultural policy and from the 18th but especially the 19th centuries much grassland was ploughed up for cereals and other crops. In wartime the price of grain usually increases and the effects of the earlier Napoleonic Wars, followed by the Crimean War in 1854, ensured this happened. As in the First and Second World Wars, Britain suffered food shortages due to a lack of home-grown food and so measures were taken to ensure that this did not happen again.

Farmers, now armed with the new mass-produced clay tile drains for field drainage, set about pipe-draining the heavy clay lands. This, along with the ability to employ the use of new farm machinery and fertilisers, brought many areas into cultivation that had previously been unused or under-used and there can be little doubt that during this period my study county of Suffolk was, as it is now, perhaps the most important agricultural county in the British Isles; reliable accounts (for example Babington, 1884-86), record the barn owl as a common bird in the county during the 1800s.

Today, the destruction of large areas of grassland would be a disaster for many barn owls but during the 1800s the loss of grassland in favour of arable crops might not have affected barn owls quite so much. As the field voles lost their habitat and their numbers decreased, the increase in grain production that resulted in these changes would have attracted numerous rats and mice due to the manner in which grain was harvested and stored in those days, so it is likely that any loss of food through vole shortages would have been compensated by an increase in the numbers of rodents. Of course, we cannot be sure of this but there is a copious amount of information in the past literature that tells us rats and mice were once plentiful on our farmlands. It is very likely that the agricultural depression had a negative effect upon some of our birds, but perhaps for many barn owls that was not the case and indeed it might well have sustained their numbers in the face of the slaughter from gamekeepers.

SHOOTING ESTATES

If the Agricultural and Industrial revolutions brought benefits for some barn owls, there was also a downside: in the mid-1800s breech-loading fire-arms were introduced. This meant that with the advent of the cartridge, guns could be loaded easily and fired quicker than the old-fashioned muzzle loading guns. As a result of this invention, the shooting estate emerged as a major factor in the countryside economy.

There was concern amongst those who owned the shooting estates that the game on their land would be predated and so consequently, keepers were employed to ensure that predatory creatures were eliminated. Any bird with sharp talons and a hooked beak was looked upon as vermin; through trapping and shooting, many thousands of hawks, buzzards, kites, falcons and owls, along with other creatures, were slaughtered. In some instances, such as with the red kite and polecat, the persecution was so effective it almost exterminated them. According to the census of 1871 there were about 17,000 gamekeepers in Britain but this figure rose to around 23,000 by the year 1911.

Guns were not the gamekeeper's only killing instruments. Many predatory bird species are habitual 'post-hoppers' and the pole-trap was another ingenious invention of the Industrial Revolution that was responsible for the deaths of many owls. This small metal trap, with two sprung-loaded toothed jaws, was placed on top of a post so that when an owl landed, the jaws snapped together, usually breaking the legs of the victim. The trap was attached to the post by a chain so that as the hapless creature tried to fly off it would be restrained, thus ending its days hanging upside down. If the birds were fortunate, then a diligent gamekeeper, doing his rounds, would put them out of their misery rather than suffering a lingering death.

The wages of the estate worker were low at that time and most relied upon the owner for their housing. Gamekeepers, therefore, were under pressure from their employers to ensure they were seen to be removing the predators. The gibbet, or 'keeper's tree', evolved as a method by which a gamekeeper could display his catches, so demonstrating his effectiveness to his employer.

Despite the fact that barn owls feed upon small mammals, they were also destroyed in thousands due to the belief that their hooked beaks and talons threatened game birds. Very often their destruction was also used to satisfy the Victorian desire for barn owl feathers which were used to decorate clothing as well as to adorn such items as fire-screens and to provide stuffed specimens for display on the side-board. Many gamekeepers supplemented their incomes by providing the taxidermist with plentiful supplies; the carcasses of many dead barn and other owls were sent to places such as Leadenhall Market in London to supply the taxidermy trade. Yet, despite the slaughter of barn owls, they continued to thrive in many places because rats, mice, voles and nesting sites were readily available; if they had been totally wiped out, a valuable source of income to the gamekeepers would have been lost!

From time to time, there were influxes of birds considered to be from abroad: the autumns of 1887 and 1888 were particularly plentiful. Their arrival was always reflected 'in the bird-stuffer's windows'. In Oxfordshire Aplin in 1889 stated that he had seen 'as many as fifteen in a bird-stuffer's shop in May, all of which had recently been received'.

Although there is a great deal of evidence supporting the view that due to persecution, a decline of barn owls took place in Britain during the late 19th century, the evidence is surprisingly not so great across East Anglia. In Norfolk, Stevenson in 1886-90 considered that the barn owl was no longer common due to its persecution, but just to the south, in Suffolk, the Pagets in 1834 regarded it as 'common' in the Yarmouth area and when Churchill Babington (1884-86) produced his review of Suffolk's avifauna he stated that it was 'Reported from many localities as common and not mentioned as rare in any'. There was no mention of gamekeepers, although without doubt they were at work.

Even so, Hele in 1890 mentioned a pair that were once brought to him at his home at Aldeburgh, in Suffolk, 'by a rustic who, having enquired whether "I bought birds", produced these from his pockets tied by their legs. He had taken them from their hollow tree at

Aldringham.' Hele then recounted how he had released them into a hay barn from where they eventually escaped, only for one to be killed in a garden at Thorpe the next day.

In neighbouring Essex there was a hint of a decline when Miller Christy (1890) stated that is was a 'Fairly common resident, breeding in old hollow trees, church towers, dove-cotes, & c' although he stated that 'Fifty years ago, before scientific farming came in, and before a cheap, abundant supply of coal was obtainable in Essex, numerous large old pollarded trees stood in the hedge-rows [almost certainly elms] in all parts of the county, and afforded logs for the winter fires.' These trees were, according to Dr Laver in the same volume, 'invaluable to the farmers, as they formed the retiring and nesting places of numerous Owls'. Most of these pollards are now gone, and with them have disappeared the Owls to a great extent'.

In Kent, Ticehurst in 1909 reported that it was 'resident and fairly common', being distributed throughout the county' and stated that it was 'more numerous in the well-wooded districts, more especially those occupied by large parks containing old timber than in the neighbourhood of the towns and marshes'. He further remarked that 'No locality is, however, without a pair or two of these useful birds … Many of the marshes contain elm trees, either singly or in rows in the hedges, and these also here and there afford suitable quarters for these birds'. In neighbouring Sussex, the barn owl was not quite so common: although the bird was 'generally dispersed', it was 'nowhere numerous'. Later, it was reported that it was the 'commonest owl of its kind in the county'.

Then, in 1880, events started to turn in the barn owl's favour as the first Wild Birds Protection Act was passed. Initially this gave protection to all wild birds between March 1st and August 1st each year, when it was unlawful to kill or catch them, and there were subsequent amendments to this Act in 1881, 1894, and 1896.

The introduction of this act was followed in 1889 by the formation of a 'society to protect birds', which then became the official Society for the Protection of Birds in 1891 and which subsequently received its Royal Charter in 1904. This was the same year that the pole-trap was banned.

Across Britain a growing number of reports were being received that suggested more was being done to protect barn owls. In Cornwall, Hearle Rodd in 1880 stated that 'people by using their common sense and powers of observation are at length beginning to admit its utility and spare its life', while in Shropshire, 'farmers and others recognise its usefulness in destroying mice, and do not shoot it, it is gradually increasing its numbers'.

On the Isle of Wight Morey in 1909 was proud to report that 'I am glad to say I never saw one here hung among other victims on a Keeper's tree; indeed, I think our gamekeepers on the Island are on the whole a very enlightened body of men, who do not go in for that indiscriminate slaughter of owls and hawks'.

In Gloucestershire it is thought that from the evidence available, barn owls were more plentiful at the end of the 19th century than in 1982, while in Nottinghamshire Whitaker reported in 1907 'keepers are much more inclined to protect them than in days past, and we seldom see them now on the tree of death'. He proceeded to say that while shooting in a friend's wood, he pointed out that there were lots of owls in it. His friend then stated 'I like them and know what good they do, and always tell a new keeper that the first owl he kills he may take a month's notice from that day'.

Further north, in Yorkshire, Nelson in the same year remarked that in Wensleydale, and some other localities, the decrease of the barn owl was to be deplored but then pointed out that 'numerous correspondents allude to its receiving protection from the farmers: and now that this class of the community has learned to appreciate the services rendered by this bird, it is to be hoped that before many years the game preserver may be as fully alive to the equally valuable services of the woodland species'. From Northamptonshire Lord Lilford wrote in 1895 that in most parts of England gamekeepers were beginning to understand that by killing barn owls they were removing a predator of rats and mice from the countryside.

URBANISATION

As one problem subsided, however, another, of a more persistent nature, reared its head. Towns and cities were growing and in the early part of the 20th century the 'extension of towns, in absorbing suitable habitats for bird life, and turning what was previously agricultural land into areas now covered with bricks and mortar, has driven the former denizens further afield'. The growing number of people that were drawn to work in the towns and cities were often farm workers who had to leave their work place as the effects of the Industrial Revolution began to take effect. It is likely that some of those workers then made the agricultural machines that had made them redundant!

Earlier, in 1844, Thomas Allis boldly stated 'Barn Owl –

Becoming scarce in the neighbourhood of Halifax, Huddersfield, and Hebden Bridge, where factories and tall chimnies have driven them from their former haunts. It is plentifully met with in other parts of the county'.

Indeed, during the Victorian era the expansion of such towns and cities as London was quite remarkable; in 1782 a German visitor, called Carl Moritz, wrote a description of London from the top of St Paul's Cathedral. In that account he stated 'beneath me lay a packed mass of towers, houses and palaces, with the London squares – their green lawns and their midst – adding pleasant splashes of colour in between. At one end of the Thames stood the Tower of London, like a city with a forest of masts behind it; at the other lay Westminster Abbey lifting up to its towers. The green hills skirting the Paddington and Islington districts smiled at me from afar while nearer lay Southwark on the opposite bank of the Thames. At this stage St James's Park was 'nothing more than a semi-circular avenue of trees enclosing a large area of greensward in the midst of which is a swampy pond. Cows feed on the turf and you may buy their milk quite freshly drawn from the animal'. This account, whilst taken just over two hundred years ago, is very important for our modern-day story for it clearly demonstrates the loss of habitat that the expansion of the towns and cities brought about.

Census returns of 1801 and 1811 indicated that the population of England and Wales had increased by 1¼ million, to 10,488,000 in just ten years and that the greatest increase was in the northern and middle parts of England where the towns and cities had grown substantially. The largest city in the western world was London, with a population just over a million, followed by Manchester, with 137,201 then Glasgow and Edinburgh, both with populations over 100,000.

The swallowing up of London's surrounding countryside took some time, however, until its vast and rapid expansion during the 1920s. In the Home Counties barn owls were still quite common in a number of places, although during the latter part of the 19th century the influence of London, as it encroached further into the countryside, began to be felt. In Surrey it was noted that 'The Barn Owl is a common resident in the rural districts of the county, and is occasionally noticed in the immediate vicinity of London'. Barn owls had been observed earlier at Tooting, and they still frequented the elms at Belair and Dulwich. Other places mentioned as having barn owls were Putney Hill, Croydon and those parts of the Thames Valley that were close to London. There is an account of an aged farm labourer remembering owls in the barns at Stoke d'Abernon that were so tame they would pounce on to mice while the men were threshing in the same barn.

In 1877 barn owls were reputedly common in almost all districts of Hertfordshire and in Middlesex they sometimes bred in Canon's Park, Edgware. Later, in 1911, barn owls had frequently been heard in Regent's Park and had also bred there. They were also recorded as nesting occasionally in Hampstead (1902), Enfield (1909) and more regularly at Clapton but despite these demonstrations of their continuing presence in and around the capital, the pressure on Britain's barn owls continued in the countryside, for we should not forget that in 1911, there were 23,000 gamekeepers who, despite the growing opposition, continued to ply their trade.

However, it was the government that was to come to the aid of predatory creatures in the early part of the 20th century, when in August 1914 Britain engaged itself in the Great War and over the course of the next four years millions of men enlisted into the armed forces. Many gamekeepers were included in that recruitment and as a consequence of their absence the numbers of many predators, including barn owls, were measurably allowed to recover.

Even so, problems still arose when, at the end of November 1916, a sharp cold spell set in, which continued through into 1917. January was cold with a great deal of snow in many places and this wintry weather carried through into February which, although very dry, was very cold with some unusually severe frosts, and many birds died on both the British and Irish mainlands. As the cold continued into March, the eastern half of England bore the brunt, although other places, notably Scotland, Northumberland and Ireland, also suffered. Jourdain and Witherby considered these last two months were critical as many birds, already weakened through the winter, eventually succumbed.

Not surprisingly no decrease in barn or tawny owl numbers was reported because many owls and other tree hole-nesting species would have died in some remote and unobserved place. A report from Ireland, however, stated that in March and early April 'some disease' had attacked Ireland's barn owls and that 160 had been found dead, all in a greatly emaciated state.

Initially it was thought that the owls had picked up poisoned vermin but then, as no long-eared owls had been found in a similar condition, this could not have been the cause. It was also noted that several correspondents throughout Ireland had found dead barn owls about their buildings. Clearly, no connection was established between the severe weather of the time and barn owl mortality and this issue would be over-looked again in the future.

However, it appears that the effects of this winter were not widespread, for the 1917 Lancashire Bird Report stated that 'In spite of senseless persecution the Barn Owl is apparently increasing and extending its range in Southern Lancashire ... Mr I. Whitaker informs me that the bird has returned to a disused room in a mill in a busy part of the town, where some years ago a pair nested. Mr Greening records it in the immediate neighbourhood of Warrington and Mr F. Taylor tells me that between Manchester and Oldham it is certainly extending its range' but this optimism was not to last.

SOURCES USED IN THIS CHAPTER

Aplin, O.V. 1889: *The Birds of Oxfordshire*. The Clarendon Press, London.

Babington, C. 1884 (Part 1): *Catalogue of the Birds of Suffolk*. The Proceedings of the Suffolk Institute of Archaeology and Natural History, Bury St. Edmunds.

Brown, R.J. 2004: *English Village Architecture*. Robert Hale Ltd., London.

Bucknill, J.A.S. *The Birds of Surrey*. R.H.Porter, London.

Dymond, D. and Martin, E. 1989: *An Historical Atlas of Suffolk (2nd ed.)*. Suffolk County Council & Suffolk Archaeological Institute, Ipswich.

Forrest, H.E., 1899: *The Fauna of Shropshire*. L.Wilding, Shrewsbury.

Gladstone, H. S. 1910: *The Birds of Dumfriesshire*. Witherby, London.

Hearle-Rodd, E. 1880: *The Birds of Cornwall and the Scilly Islands*. Trübner, & Co., London.

Hoskins, W.G. 1988: *The Making of the English landscape*. Hodder & Stoughton, London.

Hague, W. 2005: *William Pitt the Younger*. Harper Perennial, London.

Hancock, J. 1874: *A Catalogue of the Birds of Northumberland and Durham*. Williams and Norgate, London.

Hele, N.F. 1890: *Notes or jottings about Aldeburgh, Suffolk*. S & W.J.King, Ipswich.

Holloway, S. 1996: *The Historical Atlas of Breeding Birds in Britain and Ireland: 1865-1900*. Poyser, London.

Hunter, J. 1999: *The Essex Landscape*. Essex Record Office, Chelmsford.

Jourdain, F.C.R. and Witherby, H.F. 1918: The effect of the winter of 1916-1917 on our resident birds, Part 1. *British Birds,* XI: 266-271.

Jourdain, F.C.R. and Witherby, H.F. 1918: The effect of the winter of 1916-1917 on our resident birds, Part 2. *British Birds,* XII: 26-35.

Lack, P. 1992: *Birds on lowland farms*. HMSO, London.

Lilford, Lord. 1895: *Notes on the Birds of Northamptonshire and Neighbourhood*. Porter, London.

Miller Christy, R.1890: *The Birds of Essex*. Essex Field Club.

Nelson, A.T.H. 1907: *The Birds of Yorkshire*. A.Brown & Sons Ltd., Hull and York.

Paget, C.J. & Paget, J. 1834: *Sketch of the Natural History of Yarmouth and its neighbourhood*. Longman, Rees & Co., London.

Perrow, M, Peet, N. and Jowitt, A. 1992. The small mammals of drainage ditches - the influence of structure. *Trans. Suffolk Nat. Soc.,* 28: 3-9.

Plumb, J.H. 1963: *England in the Eighteenth Century*. Penguin Books, London.

Rackham, O. 1986: *The History of the Countryside*. Dent, London.

Sanford, M.S. 1991 *The Orchids of Suffolk*. Suffolk Naturalists' Society, Ipswich.

Shawyer, C. 1998: *The Barn Owl*. Arlequin Press, Chelmsford.

Sidney, W.G. 1980: Redundant on the farm. *Essex Countryside.*, 28:12.

Smith, C. 1864: *The Birds of Somersetshire*. Van Voorst, London.
Temperley, G.W. 1951: A History of the Birds of Durham. *Trans. Nat. Hist. Society of Northumberland, Durham and Newcastle-upon-Tyne,* 10: 1-296.

Stevenson, H.1886-90: *The Birds of Norfolk*. Van Voorst, London.

Ticehurst, N.F. 1909: *A History of the Birds of Kent*. Witherby, London.

Whitaker, J. 1907: *Notes on the Birds of Nottinghamshire*. Black & Co., Nottingham.

Williams, W.J. 1918: Mortality among barn owls in Ireland. *British*

Birds X1: 21-22.

Williamson, T. 2006: *England's Landscape: East Anglia.* Collins, London.

Yalden, D. 1999: *The History of British Mammals.* Poyser, London.

9 THE ORIGINS OF THE PRESENT-DAY DECLINE

'In relation to agriculture, horticulture and food production generally, the wild bird life of this country has an importance which it would be folly to underestimate, especially in these days when every ounce of food we can grow at home is urgently needed'.

Bulletin No 140: Wild Birds and the Land
Ministry of Agriculture and Fisheries, 1951.

THE MEN RETURN

In November 1918, the survivors of the First World War returned to a Britain that was never going to be the same as it was before the conflict began. During the years 1914-20, 32 peerages and 35 baronetcies became extinct, while a further 300 peers, or their eldest sons, also perished; it was because of this that death duties on their estates had to be paid. In a few instances, where a father and his heir died, then double death duties had to be paid and Holmes (2005) points out that as a result of all of these deaths, 25% of the land in England and Wales changed hands as a number of estates were either sold off or fell into disrepair due to a lack of maintenance. Apart from the financial impact of the war, a large number of estate workers did not return from the war or if they did, they did not return to the land. It was these factors, coupled with a decline in the number of gamekeepers that meant that predatory creatures creatures were never persecuted as they had been before 1914. The ending of the war raised other issues that were ultimately to affect Britain's barn owls. The men had fought a war to end all wars and in return for their efforts they wanted a better quality of life.

THE EFFECTS OF THE AGRICULTURAL SLUMP

An agricultural slump existed in Britain from around 1870 to 1930: a policy of free trade, coupled with cheap imported wheat from North America, started a long-term decline in UK farming and in turn this led to a great deal of land coming out of food production. This led to an agricultural slump in the 1920s – but did this slump have an adverse effect on the barn owl in the British Isles?

Despite a somewhat reduced resurgence of gamekeeping after the First World War, it appears that barn owls fared quite well in the immediate post-war decade. In Somerset, for example, they had a patchy distribution during the 1920s: although every one of the 16 farms on the North Perrott estate had a resident pair, it appears that they were scarcest in the pastoral areas. In Hampshire and the Isle of Wight there was little evidence of a decline while in Scotland Gladstone reported that the barn owl had now made a welcome resurgence although their distribution still tended to be local.

In East Anglia, they were very common in north Norfolk although Riviere in 1930 considered they were 'nowhere abundant'. To the south, in Suffolk, Ticehurst in 1932 reported that the barn owl was 'the most generally distributed and commonest of owls', but this comment was made before the severe winter of 1929.

The MAFF returns for the period 1875-1932 indicate that arable farming in Britain declined by some 2.3 million hectares, while the amount in grass rose by 2.79 million (Table 14). It was around this time, however, that farming began to emerge from the depression and this brought problems for the barn owl. In a number of places the destruction of hedges and the felling of trees began as a result of farmland being brought back into production as arable farming became more intensified, and these losses were further exacerbated by another outbreak of elm disease in 1927.

Elms have been affected by disease for thousands of years, but in 1918 a new strain was found at Picardy, in France. It was identified a year later by scientists in Holland and for that reason was subsequently named Dutch Elm Disease (DED). The outbreak was widespread throughout Britain, and in 1928 was the subject of several local surveys from which it was deduced that it was a non-aggressive virus that was rarely fatal! Then, in 1937, the disease began to decline, having killed off some 10%-20% of all English elms.

BUILDING FOR THE FUTURE
Apart from these important changes to farming that were taking place during the early 1930s, other changes had already begun to take place on some of England's farmlands in the mid-1920s. Dagenham was was the first of Britain's 'new towns' and is one of

Table 14 Area of grass and arable land in Britain from 1875-1932 (million hectares).

	1875 Area	% of total land	1932 Area	% of total land	+/- Area	% +/- Area
Pasture						
England	4.15	32.1	5.49	42.6	+ 1.34	32.29
Wales	0.71	34.4	0.85	41.2	+ 0.14	19.72
Scotland	0.44	5.5	0.63	8.1	+ 0.19	13.19
Total	5.30		6.97		+ 1.67	+ 31.51
Rough grass						
England	1.16	n/a	1.82	14.1	+ 0.66	56.89
Wales	0.57	n/a	0.87	42.2	+ 0.30	52.63
Scotland	4.31	n/a	4.47	50.2	+ 0.16	3.71
Total	6.04		7.16		+ 1.12	+18.54
Arable						
England	5.47	42.3	3.54	28.1	- 1.93	35.28
Wales	0.45	21.8	0.25	12.1	- 0.20	44.44
Scotland	1.40	17.7	1.23	15.9	- 0.17	12.14
Total	7.32		5.02		- 2.30	- 31.42

Re-calculated from O'Connor & Shrubb (1986) and based on figures from the Ministry of Agriculture, Fisheries and Food

the largest housing estates in the world. It was constructed during the years 1921-1932 and initially comprised 27,000 homes. With an initial estimated population of 100,000, it covered thousands of acres of farmland. The former Ministry of Agriculture stated that each year, between 1925 and 1939, urban development took some 65,000 acres of agricultural land out of production and because of this some 1,000 miles of hedgerows were lost annually.

Yet, despite all of this upheaval, barn owls could still be found on the urban fringes. In 1923 a pair raised two broods in the roof of a house at Clapton Common, north-east London, while to the south-east, at Stratford, there existed in the 1920s some open areas of land that linked Hackney and Stratford marshes to the Thames marshes further south. The area around Carpenter's Road was one of them and at a meeting of the Essex Field Club, at Stratford Museum on Saturday November 30th, 1929, the curator 'showed the skin of a barn owl recently shot at Carpenter's Road, Stratford, where, judging from the contents of its stomach, the bird found plenty of mice to feed upon'. Elsewhere, Col. H.W.Madoc was watching starlings assembling around Trafalgar Square in London on October 30th, 1936, when he saw a barn owl 'plainly illuminated by the street lamps' as it flew over the Strand. It was, perhaps, one of the few remaining barn owls in the London parks.

It was not just British barn owls that managed to retain a toe-hold in some of the larger cities of the modern world. In the United States, a pair managed to rear young each year on the Smithsonian Institution building in Washington DC. According to Jim Steed, who at the time of writing is the Associate Archivist of the Smithsonian, the ornithologist Alexander Wetmore recalled in 1971 that over the years barn owls were present in the institution's towers at different intervals until around 1953. After that the towers were closed up due to the mess the owls were making and so breeding ceased.

THE FIRST NATIONAL BARN OWL SURVEY (BLAKER, 1934)

By 1932 many reports had been received suggesting a declining barn owl population and because of this a young man called George Blaker considered it desirable to 'find out the real state of affairs'. The purpose of the survey was to establish the barn owl's status with a view to recommending conservation measures. Blaker was concerned to minimise disturbance early in the breeding season and so the survey did not commence until May and went through to December. He acknowledged the difficulty in establishing whether there had been a decline because there were no previous statistics to use as a comparison.

A Recorder's Pack was issued, which comprised a census form, a map on which to mark the nests and a leaflet describing the barn owl 'in order that there should be as little confusion as possible with the Tawny', a problem that Blaker rightly anticipated and one that continues to the present day.

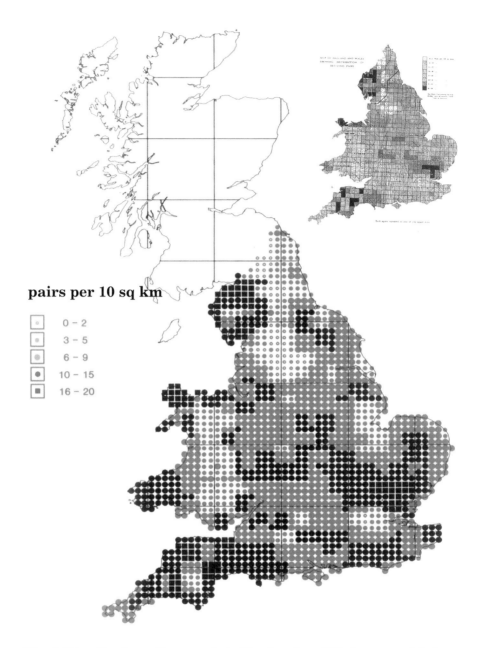

pairs per 10 sq km

- 0 – 2
- 3 – 5
- 6 – 9
- 10 – 15
- 16 – 20

Fig. 6 Distribution of barn owls in England and Wales, 1932 (Blaker, 1934) inset, then re-drawn on a 10km square basis by Shawyer (1987).

At that time, the survey was one of the most ambitious wildlife enquiries ever undertaken in Britain and during its course 915 nests were reported, of which 214 were confirmed as breeding records. In addition 5,000 other records were received and from those it was calculated that there were around 12,000 breeding pairs plus a further 1,000 non-breeding individuals, making a total of 25,000 birds.

Blaker acknowledged the possible limitations of his survey by pointing out that apart from breeding records, the conclusions resulted from collective opinion. Even so, he considered the barn owl had undergone a decline throughout England and Wales, although he thought that in some places, and here he included parts of Essex, southern and central Suffolk, Somerset, Devon, Cornwall, and notably Anglesey, the decline had not been severe and he calculated that in some places, numbers were as high as 41-50 breeding pairs per 100 square miles (Fig. 6).

Cumberland and Westmorland (now known as Cumbria), along with Northumberland, were the only counties to record an increase, which Shawyer later partly attributed to the mild snow-free winters that Britain had been experiencing since the beginning of the 20th century. He also thought that the creation of conifer plantations in some Border areas helped to increase vole numbers.

It is not possible to establish how well the country was surveyed because most of the data was destroyed during the Second World War, but it is clear that the population was underestimated and Bunn et al. thought that Blaker was 'extraordinarily over-confident about the accuracy of his results'. They presented evidence to show that the quality of reporting from farmers, with regard to assessing whether they had barn owls on their land or not, varied remarkably.

Further evidence that Blaker's results are questionable comes from my study county of Suffolk, where in the 1930s the late wildlife photographer Eric Hosking carried out much of his early pioneering work in Staverton Park, near Butley. When he was questioned about the status of barn owls in the park during the 1930s, he was of the view that at least 9 pairs were in residence during that period. However, Blaker reported that in his view the 10-mile square, within which Staverton Park lies, only held between 15 and 20 pairs, so it is highly likely that the population, at least for that area, was significantly under-estimated and probably elsewhere. Indeed according to Colin Shawyer, the British barn owl population peaked in 1933. In addition I have some views of naturalists and gamekeepers who were alive in Suffolk at that time and which suggest many more existed.

Commenting on Suffolk ornithology during the 1930s Payn thought 'there was probably no more than a score or two of people living in the county who were both interested in its birdlife, and competent to identify what they saw' and it is likely that a similar state of affairs existed in many other parts of Britain. I suggest, though, that a significant problem in obtaining records from places such as Suffolk was that many people would have failed to recognise the 'white owl' as the barn owl that Blaker was seeking.

Apart from this, advertising the survey was difficult; the study was undertaken at a time when there were fewer birdwatchers than there are today and media coverage not as great. It would have been difficult to have adequately promoted the survey without that help. An article from the *Daily Telegraph*, on October 25th, 1932, features Blaker who stated that 4,000 people in England and Wales were taking part in the census and in 'each area observers are surveying for possible nesting sites'. This is the only publicity that I have been able to find.

Clearly, Blaker believed that there was a decline and he contemplated that there were several reasons for it, chief of which was the food supply which he thought had diminished due to improved methods of threshing and a 'cleaner' farm environment. He thought the increasing occurrence of diurnal hunting by barn owls was an indication that food was scarce.

He felt the extensive use of poisons, such as arsenic, barium, strychnine and phosphorus, were having an impact and expressed concern that 'During the last year an alarming number of owls have been found dead in and about their barns, and in troughs and water-butts, and even in buckets.' He reported that two birds had been examined for the cause of death, one of which had died of phosphoric poisoning and the other had starved. The availability of nesting sites was an important factor and, interestingly, trees were placed slightly in front of buildings as the preferred sites. If we accept that tree nests are more difficult to find than those in buildings, then clearly many were not located.

Persecution was continuing to play a role in suppressing barn owl numbers and at the end of his report Blaker presented a map illustrating the counties where barn owls were protected. In those days local authorities could determine whether a bird species was protected or not. The counties where barn owls were not fully protected were Hertfordshire, Gloucestershire, Worcestershire, part of Lincolnshire, Durham, part of north Wales and Anglesey. Interestingly, apart from Lincolnshire, those places reported good numbers of barn owls.

Urbanisation was not mentioned as a contributing factor in the decline though many towns and cities were growing in size. It is interesting to note, therefore, that one of the surveyors, Eric Hardy of Liverpool, wrote upon his survey form that although there appeared to be adequate nesting places, there had been a decrease 'due to urbanisation in some areas'. Hardy, who died recently, was a well respected and knowledgeable all-round local naturalist who frequently wrote wildlife articles in the *Liverpool Echo* and elsewhere.

CONCLUSIONS OF THE 1932 SURVEY

There is no doubt that barn owls did suffer a decline in the late 1920s, possibly through a bout of elm disease, a partial restoration of gamekeeping, urban expansion and perhaps as a result of farming as land was brought back into cultivation. However, it seems likely the event that really prompted the survey was a sudden dearth of barn owls after the severe winter of 1929 and although he made no reference to it, Blaker did state that 'The decrease ... has tended to become a little more precipitate since 1928'.

Only England and Wales were surveyed, Scotland was not included. It is not clear why, although a perceived absence of barn owls or perhaps the sheer enormity of including Scotland might have been a deciding factor. In a letter that appeared in the *Field* on June 15th, 1940, a Mr Trout wrote, 'I was brought up in the west of Scotland. The only common owls there were the tawny and long-eared. I have spent long periods in East Lothian at odd intervals, and I have shot on many estates in that district. I have lived half of the year in England since 1910. Consequently I am well acquainted with the barn owl, its appearance and its habits; but I have never seen (or heard) one in Scotland, or even heard of one for that matter.' Contrary to this, John Fraser, of Oban, also in western Scotland, wrote a letter to the late Eric Hosking dated February 11th, 1943, stating 'The Barn Owl is not uncommon here although the Tawny is by far the most numerous.'

The importation of cheap wheat might have meant less grain for scavengers such as mice and rats but land taken out of production would have provided grass and weed seeds for small mammals. Rats were common and there were reports such as the 'rat-ridden hedgerows of some agricultural fields in Suffolk (being) a disgrace'; brown rats were common in the diets of many barn owls (as emphasised by the observations of Andrews, 1939).

Understandably, Blaker did under-estimate the barn owl population but I think he was generally correct in determining the prominent areas of distribution. Many of the areas that Blaker reported as having high populations align quite comfortably with Ancient Countryside (Fig.5) and nearly 80 years later some are still the best places in Britain to see barn owls,

After the survey no great conservation measures were put into place and barn owls faded from the public eye, suggesting the population had stabilised. Much later, Shawyer was to conclude that from the ringing records of the period, barn owl numbers probably peaked at an 'all time high' in 1933 which he thought might have been due to high numbers of voles.

Although towns and cities were expanding during the inter-war years, much of rural Britain retained a quiet atmosphere. It is difficult for the majority of people who are alive today to appreciate what the greater part of rural Britain was like just seventy years ago. Recounting his first visit to Suffolk in 1937, Nissen said, 'There was a sense of remoteness and isolation about this part of the English countryside, which betrayed few signs of life: farm workers gathering the harvest, little or no traffic on the roads, and only the odd pedestrian in the hamlets through which we drove.'

In this remote countryside the seeds were sown which were to cause so much future controversy when the Wheat Act, 1932, was introduced. This not only guaranteed wheat prices to the farmer, it was designed to produce cheap food and so offset the decline in arable farming. Consequently, a great deal of unproductive farmland was brought back into cultivation. In some places, notably southern and eastern England, there was a shortage of agricultural workers. To solve this problem, farmers from Scotland and northern England were encouraged to move south, and indeed it was a Scot who had moved to the English Midlands, who in the late 1940s designed the first tractor-mounted hedge cutter. As farmland was brought back into production, there appears to have been a decline in barn owl numbers. Notwithstanding the previously mentioned tree losses, much former grassed land was brought into cultivation which meant that there would probably have been a decline in vole numbers, although in some of the arable areas the effects of any vole decline might have been offset by the availability of mice, shrews and rats.

By the late 1930s then, barn owls appeared to be declining, and in Surrey, Parr thought the barn owl continued its slow decline through the 20th century until the late 1940s, after which the decrease accelerated; while in Lancashire Oakes and Battersby considered that not more than three pairs of barn owls were known to be nesting in east Lancashire during the late 1930s. In Staffordshire, Smith stated that 'Barn Owls are rarer than formerly everywhere and in many parts of Staffordshire are almost, if not quite extinct'. In Durham it was considered to be 'much scarcer than the Tawny Owl, and apparently diminishing in numbers', while at Bishop Auckland it was 'quite a rare bird in Mid-Weardale'. In Wales barn owls were considered to have declined throughout the 1920s and 30s and so it is clear that by the time Britain entered the Second World War barn owl numbers were falling virtually everywhere.

THE SECOND WORLD WAR, 1939-45

Shortly after the outbreak of war, there was another bad winter, but, though it was severe and average temperatures dropped to -6°, it does not appear to have affected barn owls.

Gamekeeping declined during the early part of the war and consequently the number of sparrowhawk chicks that were ringed during the first two years of the conflict increased considerably, before dropping down to a lower level around 1942 as gamekeeping picked up again. Shawyer has shown a similar pattern for barn owls during the same period, although perhaps not all of the barn owl decline was due to gamekeeping. There were other factors that must be taken into consideration, and most of these revolved around the war effort

The Second World War was the critical event that sparked off the process that was to lead Britain into a new era of farming as the country strove to become self-sufficient in food. Land that perhaps had never been ploughed was brought into cultivation. Soil fertility was improved by the use of chemicals such as phosphorus and potassium and greater use of silage was promoted along with a more intensive use of pasture. In many places two cuts of grass per year, instead of the usual one, were taken, while the use of rodenticides was stepped up and these measures would have

The destruction of habitats that was witnessed in the latter part of the 20th century had its roots in the 1930s.

affected small mammal numbers.

Huge areas of land were turned over to the military and establishments, such as airfields, not only required huge amounts of land, they created considerable disturbance during their construction and operation.The effects of these and other airfields that were already in use was particularly noticeable after the United States entered the war in December 1941, and altogether 444 new airfields were constructed, some of which were enormous. The United States Army Air Force base at Stansted in Essex, for example, covered 3,000 acres and was the largest USAAF base in East Anglia.

Due to its relatively flat landscape and its close proximity to mainland Europe, eastern England was a prime area in which to site those airfields, although no part of the kingdom was left unaffected. During the Second World War Britain's barn owls continued their decline which, for understandable reasons, went largely unnoticed. In Hertfordshire by 1944 barn owls had virtually 'become extinct' in the Elstree area and had also decreased around Baldock and

Bishops Stortford.

A report in the London Evening Standard on January 15th, 1945, read 'Barn owls are among the finest rat-catchers and their gradual disappearance is throwing an additional strain on the official pest officers in areas where vermin are particularly prevalent'. Continuing concern was expressed for the barn owl in a report in the *Dundee Evening Telegraph and Post* on November 7th, 1946: 'Farmers are concerned over the gradual disappearance of the barn owl. It is a great rat catcher.'

There were naturalists who thought that the number of barn owls suddenly declined at the end of the war, but numbers had been falling for several years and it is likely that those assumptions were based upon what was noticed when normality returned.

DRAMATIC WEATHER

A sudden drop in numbers occurred some twenty months after the end of the war, when the very severe weather of January 1947 took place and large numbers of birds were wiped out.

From January 22nd until March 17th, snow fell every day somewhere in the UK and according to the Meteorological Office it was the snowiest winter since 1814. Most of Britain was covered by deep snow but it was the south-west of England that was particularly affected. During this episode the temperature rarely rose a degree or two above freezing.

In the aftermath of that winter, Ticehurst and Hartley carried out an enquiry to assess its effects upon birdlife, and they received 121 reports from around the British Isles. They found that January and February were very cold months and they were particular to point out that on the morning of January 30th, a reading of -5° F (37° of frost) was recorded at Writtle in Essex and that on that same day a temperature of -6° F was recorded at Elmstone in Kent. Elsewhere on the same day, seven inches of snow fell in the Scilly Isles, and in Teesdale it lay to a depth of 44 inches. Falls of a foot in other places were frequently reported though on the lee side of the Pennines and in Wales the snowfall was lighter.

Great numbers of birds were found dead and amongst the fatalities were around two dozen each of tawny, little and barn owls which must have been a fraction of the true number; many would not have been found because they would have died in their nest or roosting hole.It appears that barn owls became extinct in one area and declined significantly in a further four. In other places they declined very little or no change in their status was recorded. One of the reports mentioned a barn owl that was in such a distressed state, it took dead house sparrows from the hand.

In 1947 an interesting record came from Suffolk when Copinger-Hill reported that 'During the recent snowy weather, persisting from 28th Jan. to well into March, a Barn-door Owl was picked up in a very emaciated condition in the garden, and a Little Owl flew to my window, at Buxhall Rectory'.

Then the problem compounded, for on March 10th mild air from the Atlantic moved into the south-west of England and this brought about a swift thaw. The ground, which had been frozen for several weeks, was unable to absorb the water from the melting snow and by the evening of the following day there was a vast amount of flooding in southern England. The warm air continued northwards and as it did, the melting snow caused more and more rivers to burst their banks so that large areas of the countryside became flooded.

To add further trouble to the already mounting problems, a deepening depression from the Atlantic brought rain and severe gales. The wind conditions in eastern England then caused great waves on the fenland drains, which pounded and broke the dykes, flooding the area. As the rivers broke their banks, a great deal of farmland became inundated and there can be no doubt that the flooding caused the deaths of many small mammals as it did elsewhere.

NEW TOWNS

Prior to these problems, a governmental decision had been taken in 1946 to provide new homes in the south-east of England. In 1945 the New Towns Committee was formed and upon their recommendation it was decided that a chain of new towns was to be built. In 1946 the New Towns Act was passed which led to 11 new towns being designated between 1946 and 1955 of which 8 were London 'overspill' towns. In those days there was no requirement to carry out environmental impact assessments and the creation of these towns caused a great deal of disturbance and destroyed large amounts of farmland, with their associated trees, fields and miles of hedges.

As well as the destruction of trees and fields, miles of hedges were destroyed.

Taking Hertfordshire as an example of what happened, where

Table 15 Agricultural trends in England 1900-1960 (acres).

	1900	1920	1930	1940	1950	1960
Cereals [1]	5,296,103	3,580,720	4,061, 631	4,894,382	6,312,183	6,148,884
Crops	2,845,500	3,418,446	2,989,970	2,779,493	2,928,216	2,836,913
Clover [2]	2,768,038	2,161,759	2,124,434	1,745,668	3,054,206	3,812,517
Permanent grass [3]	13,391,877	15,399,389	13,473,798	12,542,695	9,013,621	9,038,525
Rough grazing	n/a	n/a	3,575,469	3,722,613	3,632,127	3,307,095
Horses						
Agricultural	834,063	706,848	604,294	469,361	n/a	n/a
Other	318,258	497,892	232,249	228,654	n/a	n/a
sub-total	1,152,321	1,204,740	836,543	698,015		

[1] wheat, barley, oats and rye
[2] clover and rotation crops for hay and grazing
[3] excluding rough grazing but including mountain and heath land
Data from MAFF June census statistics

Table 16 Loss of hedges between 1947 and 1969 in randomly chosen areas in Rutland, as shown by aerial photographs.

	Length of hedge present yards per acre		% loss	yards/acre/ annum
	1947	1969		
Arable areas				
Total	32.9	25.3	23.2	0.36
Grassland areas				
Total	43.3	39.7	8.4	0.17

Re-calculated from Pollard,E., Hooper, M.D. & Moore, N.W. 1974

Table 17 Rates of hedgerow removal in eastern England, 1946-70 as shown by aerial photograph studies (miles per annum).

Date	Rate
1946-1954	800 m/a
1954- 1962	2,400 m/a
1962-1966	3,500 m/a
1966-1970	2,000 m/a

From Pollard, E., Hooper, M.D. & Moore, N.W. 1974

the long-term decline of barn owls started at the beginning of the 20th century: the county has undergone a considerable amount of urbanisation and the development of 16,691 acres of land must be taken into account when assessing the decline of its barn owls. Gladwin and Sage thought the decline was due to pesticides, loss of grassland, road deaths, the felling of old trees and the loss of farm buildings. However, Sage had earlier, perhaps, put his finger on the cause of the problem when he stated, ' It is only to be expected that the Barn Owl will become scarce in places such as Stevenage and Hemel Hempstead, for it is hardly likely that it will find a congenial habitat in the vicinity of the satellite towns, new towns, or whatever other name you care to give these hideous blots on the face of the county', but the creation of these towns was only part of the continuing expansion of London and other towns and cities into the countryside. This post-war loss of farmland to development was less than in the 1920s and 30s, however, and during the 1950s only 36,000 acres were taken per annum but by the mid-1960s this had increased to 43,000.

THE PAST AND FUTURE THREAT TO THE EAST COAST

After the winter of 1947 a parliamentary decision was made to introduce the 1947 Agricultural Act. The essence of this act was to produce cheap food for the consumer and this was achieved at the expense of paying farmers guaranteed prices to a predetermined level. It was also designed to encourage farm improvement and renovation. It took time for the bill to make an impression on the countryside and the interlude was, perhaps, long enough for the barn owl to stage a modest recovery. The passing of this Act

Until the onset of modern-day farming, farmyards were good places for barn owls to find plenty of food in the form of abundant small mammals.

was important for the welfare of Britain, for it eventually enabled the nation to become self-sufficient in grain. It was also largely responsible for bringing about the present plight of Britain's barn owls, although along the way there were some spectacular events that were to temporarily dominate and cloud the underlying problem.

During the early 1950s, bird reports were in their infancy and those that were being produced were primitive compared to the present day. Norfolk was publishing a report but the barn owl's fortunes raised no comment except when something drastic happened, such as when Seago commented that there were no nests from the Breydon area and that this was probably due to the floods along the east coast in January of that year. That important incident has received scant ornithological attention over the years but for us it requires some detailing.

On January 31st, 1953, a great storm that had been raging in the northern parts of the North Sea moved south and with it came huge waves. A combination of factors then drove the tides to a higher than expected level and as this happened so the storm moved down into the bottleneck of the southern North Sea. Consequently, many of the existing coastal defences were breached and the countryside flooded. Virtually all of the coastal areas from Lincolnshire to Kent, as well as many coastal parts of the southern Netherlands, were badly affected as the surge continued southwards. During that storm a considerable amount of land was submerged and many people lost their lives. In a number of places the sea penetrated the coastal areas up to three miles inland and many creatures, including small mammals, died. The flooding affected much of the coastal grazing marshes along eastern England, including such places as the Dengie Peninsula and Foulness Island in Essex, and further north to Aldeburgh in Suffolk, but these examples were far from isolated.

On the morning after the storm a Suffolk naturalist decided to take a walk near to the River Orwell where it was noted that 'The river wall at Long Reach [near Chelmondiston] was apparently broken in at least six places, and the enclosed meadows were completely flooded. All that could really be seen of the wall was the top most two feet, with the water level equal on both sides'.

At Havergate Island, in Suffolk, 'The island was entirely covered by water in the flood of the 31st January, 1953. Only the tops of some of the highest bushes and the two living huts protruded above the flood. It probably had, therefore, a disastrous effect on the resident mammals'. The report continued, 'Two drowned hares and two drowned stoats were found after it, and the small number of Short-eared Owls seen this year indicates that the stock of small mammals has, at any rate, been seriously reduced.' The account then indicated the signs of a menace that was to linger on, long after the floodwaters of that terrible storm had subsided. It read 'At least one rat made an unwelcome visit [after the floodwaters had dropped] and was successfully destroyed by poison'. The report concluded by pointing out that in July a dead field mouse had been found along with a dead juvenile field vole that had 'probably been killed by a Kestrel, and may have been carried onto the island from the mainland'.

In the year following the east coast floods, a significant but unconnected milestone was reached in the conservation of barn owls and other birds of prey when the Protection of Birds Act 1954 was introduced.

A NEW AGRICULTURAL REVOLUTION

Following the introduction of the Agricultural Act in 1947, there began the process of shifting the emphasis of grazing to the western and northern parts of the British Isles, while in eastern and southern parts, farming began to concentrate on intensive cereal production. The time of change on Britain's farmlands was defined by Pollard et al: '1950 may be taken as the time when hedge landscape, largely intact after centuries of evolution and reflecting in all its variations the social and geographic factors which found it, was on the brink of the period of change...' but it was not just the destruction of hedges that was to create problems in the countryside.

The ability to produce large quantities of grain in the eastern parts of Britain came about through mechanisation, for, although petrol-driven farm machinery was in use before and during the Second World War, in the immediate post-war years we see the effects that it had upon farming and consequently upon our barn owls.

The decline of the farm-horse went hand-in-hand with the acceleration in the number of tractors – from 10,000 in 1920 to 500,000 by 1980. There were still around 10,000 farm-horses in 1965, but since then they have become history, as they will eventually become throughout Europe. The invention of the mechanised hedge cutter was previously mentioned and by 1971 there were around 38,000.

The replacement of horse-drawn machinery by motor vehicles had a huge impact. For example, in 1948 there were around 5,000 combine harvesters in Britain but this number had increased to around 52,000 by 1960. Correspondingly, the number of agricultural horses declined from 834,063 in 1900 to 469,361 by 1940 (Table 15); by 1950 the future for the farm-horse was indicated by its absence from that year's agricultural returns. Much of the machinery, and particularly the combine harvesters, needed space to manoeuvre and so the process of large-scale hedge removal began. However, it was not just the need for space that brought about the removal of hedges.

As many parts of Britain, and especially eastern England, moved away from mixed farming, the need for hedges was no longer there. With no cattle to keep in, they became superfluous. Pollard et al considered that the removal of hedges in the eastern region was due to the decline in cattle farming, diminishing the need to confine animals, compared to the pastoral areas of west and northern Britain. To demonstrate this, they chose the old county of Rutland and surveyed 10 different areas within it over a period of 22 years (Table 16). They chose Rutland because they thought it was a county that was representative of where the pastoral areas of Britain met the arable areas.

The results showed that between 1947 and 1970 the average rate of hedge removal in Britain was 0.22 yards per acre of farmland per year, which totalled just over 3,000 miles per annum (Table 17). They further deduced that whilst hedge removal was widespread, eastern England was the most affected region and that the removal of hedges provided a considerable amount of extra land upon which to grow crops.

In recent decades eastern England has rightly come in for a great deal of scrutiny regarding the decline of barn owls during the post-war era, and so here my study county of Suffolk should form part of the story. South-west Suffolk is just one area within a larger region, sometimes known as the 'East Anglian Heights', a region that comprises north-west Essex, west Norfolk, north-east Hertfordshire and south-east Cambridge. This locality has a comparatively dry climate and a slightly undulating landscape, which means that the soil is well drained, thus making it an ideal place to grow cereals. It is also a region where Blaker recorded a high number of barn owls in 1932.

Much of the eastern region has been affected but the changes are particularly noticeable in areas such as south-west Suffolk which the former Suffolk bird recorder, W.H.Payn, considered was 'the most intensively cultivated portion of a county rightly renowned for high farming'. He observed the agricultural changes that took place during the post-war decades and noted 'In south-west Suffolk the trend has been particularly manifest, many farmers being obsessed with the alleged merits of "prairie farming". Hedges and trees have been swept away wholesale, to the detriment of the amenities of all wildlife'. He recorded that in 1941 his house in Hartest was 'entirely surrounded by small arable fields and meadows with high hedges and hedgerow trees, all providing the varied habitat so typical of the Suffolk scene in those days'. He then described the same scene some forty years later where 'Gone are the five old pastures with their high hedges, gone the five or six small fields of the 1930s, their place taken by three vast arable fields, a wasteland of stark plough or unrelieved corn crops throughout most of the year, with little to support or attract birds'. In another account of south-west

Suffolk, Steggall commented upon a farm at Stradishall that was formerly divided into forty fields. By removing the interior hedging and filling in and piping all of the ditches, a 'new' farm consisting of one field of 600 acres was created.

An example of the farmland transformation that occurred in eastern England was recounted to me on one farm of 350 acres at Rendham, Suffolk. In the early 1950s it had 7-8 working horses, with 2 mares normally in foal and around 2-3 other foals in attendance but by the end of the 1950s machinery had replaced them. With their loss there was no call for the extensive pastures that were needed for grazing and no need for the hay meadows to feed the horses and cattle during the winter. Today, like so many others, the farm is devoted to cereal production. We should also note that as well as losing grassland, threshing machines were redundant and grain began to be stored in rodent-proof silos. The farmyard was no longer a place for hunting barn owls and so, with the loss of the threshing machine and the sanitisation of grain storage, the final incentive for farmers to maintain the traditional type of barn disappeared which in some parts of Britain was very important.

THE PESTICIDE PROBLEM

In the early 1960s, serious declines were noticed in several predatory bird species. The declines were particularly observed in the southern and eastern counties of England and consequently an enquiry was launched. A questionnaire was circulated to various bodies and individuals around the British Isles although it is fair to point out that not all of the country was covered (Fig 7). The survey publicity stated that there was a pressing need to obtain information.

It was found that the barn owl had undergone a general decrease although the reasons for this presented 'a rather complicated picture'. Only eight counties reported little or no decline; where there was a decline, then four principal factors were considered responsible. These were toxic chemicals, which affected the bird's breeding success, loss of habitat due to agricultural changes, disturbance and the hard winters of 1946/47 and 1962/63. The report found that some regions had been affected by several or all of these factors and that it was difficult to isolate the effect of any particular one. It was further stated that all the respondents from the eastern counties, with the interesting exception of Norfolk, reported a very evident decrease in the late 1950s and early 1960s 'which was thought to be

*English (*right*) and smooth-leaved elm.*

attributable to toxic chemicals'. Prestt astutely noted that a similar and sudden decline had occurred in the mainly pastoral areas of Britain, namely parts of Cumberland, Westmorland, Lancashire, Yorkshire, Hampshire, Dorset, Somerset and the Isle of Man where toxic chemicals were unlikely to be responsible due to livestock.

The returns from the survey conducted by Prestt revealed that 76% of the recorders felt the number of barn owls had fallen during the period 1953-63 and that their decline was only overshadowed by a decline in the number of sparrowhawks. Barn owls and sparrowhawks are dissimilar in their habits. Barn owls are mainly nocturnal while sparrowhawks are diurnal. Barn owls feed largely on small mammals while sparrowhawks feed on birds. The common denominator that links the two is that barn owls may feed on seed-eating mammals, and sparrowhawks may feed on small seed-eating birds. Subsequent investigations into the decline of these, and other species during the late 1950s and early 1960s, have shown that organo-chlorine pesticides were most definitely involved in the decline of the sparrowhawk, and that they had some impact upon barn owl numbers and particularly those living in eastern England.

One of the chief compounds involved was dichlor-diphenyl-trichlor-ethane, better known as DDT. This chemical was not widely used until 1946 but when it was, it was considered to be the ideal insecticide. With predatory birds this compound is responsible for poor breeding performance, its main effect being upon the eggs, causing shell-thinning and its subsequent liability to breakage. It also causes embryo mortality in unbroken eggs, but perhaps the most significant event occurred after 1955, when the more toxic organo-chlorines, notably dieldrin, aldrin, heptachlor

*Fig. 7 Map indicating those parts of Britain that returned completed
questionnaires (after Prestt, 1965).*

and endrin, were introduced. In the main these were used as seed dressings and were applied as a thin coating that protected the seeds against insect attack. Unfortunately it is also poisoned seed-eating creatures such as rats, mice and birds; as the residues built up inside raptors and owls as a result of them eating contaminated prey, it either caused their direct mortality or affected breeding performance.

The analyses of barn owl tissues for the presence of organo-chlorines indicated that between 1963 and 1989 of 627 analysed specimens 56 (9%) were thought to have probably died as a result of organo-chlorine poisoning and that of those 22 (40%) were from the eastern counties of England. By 1971 it appeared that barn owls were no longer showing significant contamination by these chemicals and more recent studies indicate that although many barn owls contain some background residues of pesticides, the amounts concerned were far from lethal and that by the late 1980s, post-mortem analyses on barn owls confirmed that deaths from pesticide contamination had fallen to nil. Later, Percival was to confirm that residue levels and post-mortem analyses on barn owls indicated that organo-chlorine pesticides 'almost certainly' contributed to the decline in eastern England during the 1950s and 1960s. When it was recognised that these poisons had a drastic affect upon wildlife their usage declined so that by the mid-1970s only small amounts were being used until eventually they were withdrawn from use. Since that time we have witnessed a remarkable recovery of the sparrowhawk. However, this has not been mirrored by the barn owl and therefore throws doubt upon the perception held by many that poisons were responsible for the overall decline of the barn owl during this period. It was a contributing factor but it was not the main one. It was the loss of habitat.

THE WINTER OF 1962/63

Many commentators fail to recognise the impact of this winter on barn owls and all too often we find their thoughts concentrated on pesticides. Prestt's survey was compiled in the wake of the 1962/63 winter, which remains the most severe on record. It was heralded by the first snow falling in November 1962 and ensuing snowfalls meant that much of England eventually lay under continuous snow cover from December 26th to early March. It was the most severe winter on record, but it was not as snowy as the winter of 1947, so when the thaw came there was much less flooding.

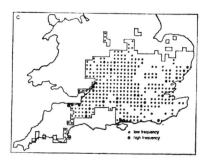 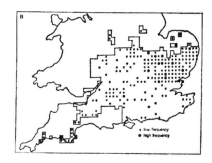

*Fig. 8 Distribution of elms in southern Britain; English elm distribution (*left*) and East Anglian, or smooth-leafed elm (*right*) (after Pollard et al, 1974).*

Dobinson and Richards canvassed opinion from 261 areas around the British Isles that involved between 750 and 1,000 observers. They found that once again barn owls were severely hit because in the subsequent breeding season, 8 contributors considered that barn owls had gone from their area, 1 thought there had been a 95% reduction and 7 others thought there had been a large decrease. The results from the survey suggested that there had been a large fall in the barn owl population.

There are some interesting records from Essex that indicate what the conditions were like during that period. For example, at Mundon a farmer was surprised to find a barn owl flying in front of him 'obviously weak from hunger'. He managed to capture it and gave it food, which was eaten ravenously. The farmer noticed that the bird had a tick in the corner of one of its eyes and thought that this had hampered its ability to hunt. Although the tick was removed and the bird was then released, it seems more likely that the bird was suffering from its inability to catch prey beneath the snow rather than because of the tick. Elsewhere, an adult that was found dying at Kirby-le-Soken was considered to be 'showing all the symptoms of poisoning', although the evidence for that is thin and it is more likely that it too was starving and had passed the point of recovery.

The decline of the barn owl in the early 1960s arouses great emotions and numerous accounts have blamed pesticides for this without fully recognising the ravages of habitat destruction that were being thrust upon the countryside at that time. Not only pesticides and the severe winter of 1962/63 caused the population crash during the early 1960s. Behind the scenes there were dramatic

*Table 18 Tree species used by nesting barn owls in Suffolk, 1983
- 1988.*

Species	No	%
Elm	22	35.50
Oak	11	17.70
Beech	3	4.80
Unspecified	26	42.00
total	62	

changes going on as large areas of farmland were transformed in the
quest to grow more food. This issue was to have a more persistent
effect upon barn owls than poisons or snow and would shortly be
aggravated by elm disease.

THE RETURN OF ELM DISEASE

Dutch Elm Disease (DED) is a fungus, *Ceratocystis ulmi*, which
blocks the water-conducting vessels and affects an elm's growth-
controlling substances, causing the tree to wilt as if killed by
drought. The disease is usually transmitted from infected trees to
healthy trees by elm bark beetles, particularly *Scolytus scolytus*
and *Scolytus multistriatus*.

In 1965 another outbreak of DED was discovered; in marked
contrast to previous outbreaks, this one was particularly virulent.
It was first found in Tewksbury followed by additional findings
in Bristol, Southampton, London, Plymouth and Ipswich. The
first inland outbreaks were recorded from north-east Hampshire,
Breckland and Buckinghamshire and radiated out throughout
southern Britain at a speed of around 12 km per year, finally
reaching most of Scotland by 1977.

The English elm caught the full blast of the disease; the East
Anglian or 'smooth-leaved elm', of which Suffolk and indeed Essex
still retains a number, was not affected so drastically, although
even many of these have now succumbed. A similar pattern appears
in Cornwall where the Cornish elm has also shown a greater
resistance to the disease (see Fig 8). Wych elm is not included as it
is not a species that is important for barn owls.

Fig 9 Distribution of breeding barn owls in Britain 1968-72.
(after Sharrock, 1976).

The impact of the loss of elms on bird species was worst for barn owls, and in southern England elms had provided much of their nesting opportunities.

From 1983-8 I monitored the tree species that were being used by Suffolk's barn owls. I found that where the tree species was specifically identified, elms (Table 18) were the most common trees used. A number of records I collected concerned dead or dying trees and it is likely that most, if not all, were elms.

The reason why elms are favoured by barn owls is straightforward. These trees unexpectedly tend to shed large boughs and in time the wounds develop into cavities. The barn owl, along with some other bird species such as stock dove and kestrel, has exploited this type of site site to great advantage. The following are good examples of their suitability: at Romford in Essex, Parker in 1968 described a site where barn owls were nesting in an old elm stump. The nest entrance hole was 6 metres (20 feet) above the ground and was created by a broken off lateral bough that led into a chamber in the centre of the tree. Previously, Phillips in 1939 recorded a site from Hampshire where 'The nest was about seven feet from the ground in the hollow trunk of the old elm tree, no branches of which were lower than about fifteen feet. There were two holes – the result of the breaking off of branches – one at each end of a cavity some five feet long and three feet wide'. The impact of DED (and the general loss of farmland trees) has been dismissed as a significant factor in the barn owl's decline and while that might be true for parts of Britain, it would be wrong to deny that the loss of over 20 million elms, many of which were found in the lowlands of England, would not have impacted upon the barn owl population.

The most recent elm census was undertaken by the Forestry Commission. It found that 70 per cent of the 23 million elms over 6m tall had been killed and they estimated that by 1981 it was probable that some 20 million trees had died. The only surviving elms were populations of the East Anglian 'smooth-leafed' elm and the Cornish elm. It reported that the disease had had a devastating effect on the landscape of southern Britain but in the north, where there were an estimated 7 million elms, the rate of disease, in general, had been much slower.

FIRST ATLAS OF BREEDING BIRDS 1968-72 (SHARROCK)
In 1968 a survey to map the distribution of all breeding birds in the British Isles was launched and the subsequent records were

mapped on a 10-km square basis. Once a species was confirmed as breeding in a particular square, no attempt was made to establish the density of breeding within it. Due to the difficulties of surveying barn owls, special efforts were made in the final stages of the survey to locate breeding pairs through radio appeals.

The results for the barn owl indicate large gaps in the distribution (Fig 9)compared with Blaker's results just forty years earlier, and this is especially relevant for the eastern counties of England, and specifically on the 'East Anglian Heights', where the loss of habitats for small mammals, i.e. grass and hedges, was taking its toll. The distribution appears to be more concentrated in some northern and western areas of Britain, suggesting perhaps that in the largely pastoral areas barn owls were doing better. It is also possible to identify the larger towns and cities and to trace the path of the new M1 motorway. Meanwhile, although there was a little national optimism, it was clear that by the late 1970s Britain's barn owl population had been severely ravaged and it had not recovered from the traumas of the 1950s and 60s.

In 1979 a new wildlife protection bill, the Wildlife and Countryside Act, was introduced to the House of Commons. This bill incorporated into it the Protection of Birds Act of 1954, and whilst retaining and enhancing all of that law's original ingredients, it also gave certain species much greater protection than they had formerly enjoyed and as a consequence of its scarcity in many places the barn owl was placed in Part One, Schedule One of the Wildlife and Countryside Act 1981.

And then, in the winter of 1979, something interesting happened – it snowed, and it was not long afterwards that the second national barn owl survey was launched.

SOURCES USED IN THIS CHAPTER

Anon., 1923: *Metro-land*. The Metropolitan Railway, London

Anon., 1953: *The Battle of the Floods: Holland in February 1953*. Netherlands Booksellers and Publishers Associates, Autesden.

Ballance, D.K. 2006: *A History of the Birds of Somerset*. Isabelline Books, Falmouth.

Blaker, G.B. 1934: *The Barn Owl in England and Wales*. Royal Society for the Protection of Birds, London.

Brownlow, H.G. 1953: Mammals on Havergate Island after the Flood. *Trans. Suffolk Nat. Soc.,* 8: 110-111.

Bunn, D.S. Warburton, A.W. and Wilson, A.A.B. 1982: *The Barn*

Owl. Poyser, Calton.

Copinger-Hill, H. 1947: Observations. *Trans. Suffolk Nat. Soc.,* 6: 158.

Delve, K. 2005: *The Military Airfields of Britain: East Anglia, Norfolk and Suffolk*. The Crowood Press, Ramsbury.

Dobinson, H.M. & Richards, A.J. 1964: The effects of the severe winter of 1962/63 on birds in Britain. *British Birds,* 57: 373-434.

Fenton, J.T. 1953: The Morning after- on the Orwell, Feb 1st. *Trans. Suffolk Nat. Soc.,* 8: 229-231.

Gladstone, H. S. 1910: *The Birds of Dumfriesshire*. Witherby, London.

Gladwin, T. and Sage, B. 1986: *The Birds of Hertfordshire.* Castlemead, Ware.

Holmes, R. 2005: *In the Footsteps of Churchill*. BBC Books, London.

Morley, C., 1929: Editorial. *Trans. Suffolk Nat. Soc.,* 1: 75.

Newton, I. 1979: *Population Ecology of Raptors*. Poyser, Berkhamsted.

Newton, I. 1986: *The Sparrowhawk*. Poyser, Calton.

Newton, I., Wyllie, I. & Freestone, P. 1990: Rodenticides in British Barn Owls. *Environ. Pollut.,* 68: 101-117.

Newton, I., Wyllie, I. & Asher, A. 1991: Mortality causes in British Barn Owls *Tyto alba,* with a discussion on aldrin-dieldrin poisoning. *Ibis,* 133: 162-169.

Nissen, J. 1989: *Winning the Radar War*. Robert Hale, London.

Osborne, P. 1982: Some effects of Dutch Elm Disease on nesting farmland birds. *Bird Study,* 29: 2–16.

Parker, A. 1968: Some observations on the Little Owl (*Athene noctua*) and Barn Owl (*Tyto alba*) at their Nests Near Romford, Essex 1968. *London Bird Report,* 33: 81-87.

Parr, D. 1972: *Birds in Surrey*. Batsford , London.

Pashley, H.N. 1925: *Notes on the Birds of Cley, Norfolk*. Witherby, London.

Payn, W.H. 1952-3: The birds of south-west Suffolk. *Trans. Suffolk Nat. Soc.,* 8: 92-100.

Payn, W.H. 1978: *The Birds of Suffolk (2nd ed.)* Ancient House Publishing, Ipswich.

Payn, W.H. 1981: The Breeding Birds of a Suffolk garden 1941-1981. *Suffolk Birds, 1981*, 55-56. Suffolk Naturalists' Society,

Ipswich.

Percival, S.M. 1991: Population Trends in British Barn Owls – a review of some possible causes. *British Wildlife,* 2: 131-140.

Phillips, F. G. 1939: *The Barn Owl.* (Appendix A).

Pollard, E., Hooper, M.D. & Moore, N.W. 1974: *Hedges.* Collins, London.

Prestt, I. 1965: An enquiry into the recent breeding status of some smaller birds of prey and crows in Britain. *Bird Study,* 12: 196-221.

Rackham, O. 1986: *The History of the Countryside.* Dent, London.

Riviere, B.B. 1930: *A History of the Birds of Norfolk.* Witherby, London.

Robinson, A.H.W. 1952: The Changing Coastline of Essex. *The Essex Naturalist*, 29: 79-93.

Sage, B.L. 1959: *A History of the Birds of Hertfordshire.* Barrie & Rockcliff, London.

Seago, M.J. 1953: *The Norfolk Bird Report, No1.* The Norfolk Nat. Trust and the Norfolk and Norwich Nat. Soc., Norwich.

Sharrock, J.T.R. (ed.) 1976: *The Atlas of Breeding Birds in Britain and Ireland.* Poyser, Calton.

Shawyer, C. 1987: *The Barn Owl in the British Isles – Its Past, Present and Future.* The Hawk Trust, London.

Shoard, M. 1980: *The Theft of the Countryside.* Temple Smith, London.

Smith,G. 1997: *Cambridgeshire Airfields in the Second World War.* Countryside Books, Newbury.

Smith,G. 2003: *Essex Airfields in the Second World War (4th. Ed.).* Countryside Books, Newbury.

Smith, T. 1938: *The Birds of Staffordshire.* North Staffordshire Field Club.

Steggall, P. 1979: *East Anglia.* Robert Hale, London.

Summers, D. 1978: *The East Coast Floods.* David and Charles, Newton Abbot.

Temperley, G.W. 1951: A History of the Birds of Durham. *Trans. Nat. Hist. Society of Northumberland, Durham and Newcastle-upon-Tyne,* 10: 1-296.

Ticehurst, C.B. 1932: *A History of the Birds of Suffolk.* Gurney and Jackson, Edinburgh.

Ticehurst, N.F. & Hartley, P.H.T. 1948: Report on the effect of the severe winter of 1946–1947 on bird-life. *British Birds,* 41: 322-

334.

Ticehurst, N.F & Witherby, H.F. 1940: Report on the effect of the severe winter of 1939-40 on bird life in the British Isles. *British Birds,* 34: 143-155.

Wilkinson, G. 1979: *Epitaph for the Elm.* Arrow Books, London.

Witherby. H.F. (ed.) 1936: Barn Owl in inner London. *British Birds,* 30: 232.

Witherby, H.F. & Jourdain, F.C.R. 1929: Report on the Effect of Severe Weather in 1929 on Bird-life. *British Birds,* 23: 154-156.

10 A RECENT HISTORY

'Some people might consider an apology necessary for the appearance of a book about birds at a time when Britain is fighting for its own and many other lives. I make no such apology. Birds are part of the heritage we are fighting for. After this war ordinary people are going to have a better time than they have had; they are going to get about more; they will have time to rest from their tremendous tasks; many will get the opportunity, hitherto sought in vain, of watching wild creatures and making discoveries about them. It is for these men and women, and not for the privileged few to whom ornithology has been an indulgence, that I have written this little book'.

James Fisher, *Watching Birds* (Penguin Books, 1940)

This is the final chapter of my history and covers the period 1980-2006, during which time several barn owl surveys took place and a real attempt to assess their population was undertaken; as well as environmental projects to aid them.

A VISIONARY STUDY

There seems little doubt that since the early 1980s Britain's barn owls have come in for more scrutiny than any other wild bird species in the British Isles. However, barn owls were being intensively studied long before then, for in 1982 a classic work entitled *The Barn Owl* was published. It was the culmination of some forty years of combined study by three amateur naturalists from northern England: Derek Bunn, Tony Warburton and Robert Wilson. Although now out of print, it should remain a standard work for barn owl students.

The study had its origins early one evening around 1950 when Derek Bunn spotted a barn owl 'floating about a field' and from then on his interest was kindled, although it was to be another fifteen years before he was able to study them properly farther afield in Gisburn Forest, Lancashire. Having a fascination for 'bizarre looking species with out of the ordinary habits' he spent some time observing a family of owls and so consequently, in 1965, he decided he would like to attempt a monograph on the species. At that time barn owl students were rare and so it was difficult for him to find a like-minded naturalist with whom he could converse and share experiences, but he eventually made contact with Tony Warburton who was watching and studying barn owls in a remote part of the Lake District. Tony Warburton had a traumatic introduction to barn owls when the adults of a family of owls that he was watching were shot by a gamekeeper. It was then down to him to raise the orphans, which further inspired him to study the species. Together, these amateur naturalists pooled their knowledge and commenced writing their highly acclaimed monograph in which they were ably assisted by Robert Wilson, who carried out much of the essential literature research.

In the Scottish Borders Iain Taylor undertook intensive research from the late 1970s until the early 1990s: his work concentrated on the relationship between small mammals and barn owl populations and it is a useful model for future barn owl workers, although its application might be restricted in southern and eastern England. It is important to point out that both of these studies were carried out in the pastoral areas of Britain, where the barn owls that featured in them nested in buildings and hunted predominantly over grassland.

Setting the scene
The 1980s was the decade that saw a renewed concern for Britain's barn owls and no one could have predicted the impact that the second national barn owl survey was to have either politically or in the wildlife conservation movement. This was also a period of great change in the British countryside, and the passing of the Wildlife and Countryside Act 1981was a portent for the future.

Considerable changes to many parts of Britain were underway as the programme of motorway and other road construction continued; as a result of this, vast swathes of the countryside were destroyed. Those barn owls that were not directly affected by the destruction of their nest-sites and hunting grounds were gradually displaced by disturbance, although being creatures of habit they would have tenaciously hung on to their territories until they were killed by traffic or starved to death.

During the 1980s, especially, the various county bird reports and avifaunas from around the country were littered with comments stating the impact of road traffic. In Shropshire, for example, within two years of the Oswestry by-pass being opened in 1986, 18 barn owls had been reported to the RSPCA either dead or injured, and between the years 1980-90, 33 more were reported from other localities. In Cambridgeshire a significant number of barn owls were found dead, while in Somerset Ballance reported that since 1975 a number of barn owl casualties had been noted on the M5, especially on the section from Puriton to Huntworth. He considered that sometimes non-motorway traffic was responsible for local extinctions and I think it likely that in areas with pristine barn owl habitats then, sadly, road casualties should be expected to continue unless the population is wiped out completely.

Although no new towns were started in Britain after 1970, the 1980s became a period when home ownership was strongly promoted and when piecemeal urban expansion, with its subsequent commuting, took on a new aspect. Many towns and villages that had, perhaps, previously undergone little or no change for many years, began to see new housing and estates being built within and around them. With new and better roads, faster cars and an improving transport system, more and more people sought to move out of the cities and into rural areas. It is against this backdrop of urban development and road-building, coupled with the continuing problems of intensive farming, that concern was raised for our wildlife, and in 1983 this concern was expressed in a new barn owl survey.

It was shortly after the publication of *The Barn Owl* that another national barn owl survey was launched and this time it was organised by the Hawk and Owl Trust. It came, as did the previous national survey fifty years earlier, in the aftermath of a severe winter (1978/79, which was considered to be the coldest since 1962/63). In many parts of Britain deep snow persisted for some weeks.

There are some contrasting views that once again tend to cloud the reason why barn owls were in decline at that time. In Buckinghamshire, Lack and Ferguson pointed out that in 1978 there was an extensive programme of elm felling, and this was followed by the 'hard winter' of 1979. Lack and Ferguson stated that after 1979 there was a sharp downturn in the status of the barn owl and that birds had disappeared from their previous strongholds. Paradoxically, in 1979, Moore reported breeding behaviour from 52 localities in Suffolk, 'showing a continued increase in numbers'.

THE SECOND NATIONAL BARN OWL SURVEY (SHAWYER, 1987)

The main objectives of the Hawk and Owl Trust's survey were to establish the number of barn owls in each of the 3,862 ten-kilometre squares in Britain and Ireland, to ascertain the extent of the decline that had occurred since the time of Blaker's survey, and to determine the factors that were causing it. The survey also sought to establish a baseline for future monitoring and to provide a way forward for barn owl conservation.

The survey methodology is explained in Shawyer's report; suffice it to say that it was publicised using a variety of methods, including radio and television along with articles in journals and magazines. Through these media it was estimated that notification of the enquiry reached over 40 million people, although it was recognised that this included those who would have been alerted to the survey more than once. Even so, some 11,500 records were received in the four years of its existence.

During the enquiry a table was drawn up to indicate how many pairs were thought to be present in each county and from this it was estimated there were 4,418 pairs in England, Wales and Scotland. Within that figure the estimated number of pairs for England and Wales was 3,750 compared to the 12,000 that were reported from the 1932 survey, with a further 650 pairs in Scotland for which there was no comparison. These figures suggested that in England and Wales there had been a 69% decline since 1932 and indicated (Fig. 10) that the distribution was very similar to that which Sharrock reported (see Fig. 9)following the first national breeding bird survey as organised by the BTO, although in some places, such as the south-east corner of England, there had been a slight contraction in range. The Home Counties were most affected but barn owls also appeared to be absent from central and northern parts of England. Colin Shawyer thought the chief reasons for the decline were a worsening climate, reduced food supplies and loss of habitat, while urbanisation, road building, loss of nest-sites, poisoning and competition from the tawny owl were lesser problems.

In dealing with climate he felt that it was deteriorating and that the increased amount of annual snow cover was having a detrimental effect upon barn owls; he later reiterated his concern. Certainly there was a severe bout of weather in 1979, just before the start of the survey, but whether this was relevant as claimed is questionable. Weather is not the same as climate. A bout of severe

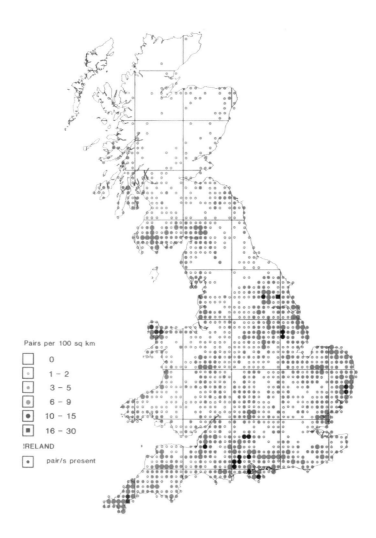

Fig. 10 Distribution of barn owls in Britain 1982-1985 (after Shawyer, 1987).

weather, whether it is cold, hot, wet or dry, may not be indicative of the climate of a particular region or country and any change in climate needs to be ascertained over a long period of time, including the period of warm weather that has existed for several years and which is thought to be contributing to the melting of the polar ice-caps. Dennis was interested to note that Shawyer considered that a worsening climate was responsible for the decline of the barn owl in Essex and he challenged this by stating that 'despite the run of unseasonably mild winters there has been a further rapid decline [in the county] in many areas', suggesting that there are other factors at work bringing about the decline, rather than weather or indeed climate.

Today, barn owls are absent from much of the land in Britain 2-300m above sea-level, and in eastern England they are largely, but not totally, absent from the area that I previously described as the 'East Anglian Heights'. In Suffolk, the land rises at its highest point above sea-level, 'a mere 420ft' (128m) in the vicinity of Elms Farm, Depden, while not far away, near Saffron Walden, the land rises to its highest in Essex at just over 120m. These high points are well below the 300m height that is so often quoted as the reason for a lack of barn owls, but the fact that they are uncommon in that region has nothing to do with weather or climate, it is due to a lack of nesting and feeding habitats. Elsewhere in the British Isles, apart from the severe winters of 1978/79 and 1987, the climate has generally remained clement for the last 20 or so years at least, yet barn owls have not returned to many of their former haunts on the higher ground.

There is no doubt that in former times, when barn owls were more abundant than at present, they did once range over higher land in many parts of Britain, and in 1933 Coombes found three nests all above 1,000 feet on the hills of Westmorland, one of which was at nearly 1,500 feet. In Scotland in 1936 a barn owl was reported hunting in daylight nearly 2,000 feet up amongst the hills in Scotland, although the nest was below in the glen.

I am sure that Colin Shawyer was correct in drawing attention to the losses of grassland and other feeding habitats that were taking place in Britain as being an important factor. From 1960 to 1980 the amount of land devoted to cereal crops in England rose by 57,221 acres, while grass fell by 59,055 acres (Table 19), and, although the amount of grassland continued to decline after his survey finished, the decline was substantially less than previously.

It was in 1987 that the first of the 'modern day' farming initiatives was launched with the introduction of the Environmentally Sensitive Area (ESA), a project that was largely designed to encourage farmers to retain grassland. In my study county of Suffolk there had been an overall 71% loss of grass during the period 1939–89 (Table 20) and so it was appropriate that in 1988 Suffolk was host to one of the five schemes in the second phase of this project.

The hay-rick was mentioned by Shawyer as an important winter refuge for small mammals and thus a source of food for barn owls, although perhaps they were important throughout the year. Today the 'traditional' hay-stack, or rick, is no longer and is just one of the reasons why so few barn owls are now encountered in and around our farmsteads. There are many straw-stacks to be found in their place, and, though they are constructed of bales rather than put together by pitchfork, they still offer warmth and shelter during the winter months – but where are the barn owls?

The problems of urbanisation and road building were considered to be less threatening to barn owls than the loss of habitat and climate but now, some twenty years on, the threat is real. At the time of writing, this issue is high on the political agenda and in the future urbanisation will play an increasingly important role in determining the distribution of barn owls in the British Isles.

Attention was drawn by Shawyer to the poisoning of barn owls through eating prey that had been contaminated with rodenticides, for although the threat from pesticides has gone away, the danger from poisoning is still present. The rodenticide warfarin is an anti-coagulant of relatively low toxicity that has been used for many years to control rodents and it appears to have been used without any harm being done to barn owls. However, over the years rodents have become immune to its effects and so because of this, new and more highly toxic anti-coagulant poisons, namely brodifacoum and difenacoum, have been introduced. These poisons, commonly known as 'second generation' rodenticides, have been introduced with dramatic effect. For example, on an oil palm plantation on the Malay Peninsula, a sudden decline in the number of barn owls had coincided with the introduction of brodifacoum and difenacoum. When these were withdrawn and warfarin reinstated, barn owl numbers recovered. There are two other second-generation rodenticides in commercial use, bromadiolone and flucomafen, but these two poisons are restricted in their commercial use because of their high toxicity.

Table 19 Agricultural trends in England 1960 -1980.				
	1960	1970	1980	+/- since 1960	%
Arable (acres)				
Cereals [1]	384245	431835	441466	+57221	14.89
Other crops	226803	204465	185760 [2]	-41043	18.09
Grass (acres)				
Permanent	123472	86503	73346	-50126	40.59
Rough grazing	20612	18884	11683	-8929	43.32
[1] Wheat, barley & oats				
[2] Not included 11,377 hectares (28113 acres) of grass less than 5 years old				
Source of data DEFRA farming returns				

The effects of these poisons upon barn owls may cause them to become listless and unable to fend for themselves. In severe cases bleeding may occur from the orifices as well as the eyes, feet and chest. The thighs may also show signs of severe bruising. Care should be exercised when assessing a barn owl that is found listless or dead for no apparent reason, and a number of dead barn owls found in Suffolk during the snowy winter of 1986/87 were presumed to have been poisoned. Upon investigation, however, no evidence of poisoning was found and it was considered that they died of starvation.

Even so, Newton et al analysed 145 wild barn owls for traces of rodenticides and found that 15 of these had either difenacoum or brodifacoum present in their bodies. They tested two batches of 6 captive bred barn owls that had been fed on a 1-, 3- and 6-day feeding programme. One batch that had been fed on difenacoum-dosed mice showed no traces of external haemorrhaging and the conclusion was that difenacoum might not have fatal consequences. However, in the second batch, which was fed on brodifacoum-dosed mice, four of the owls died. From this they concluded that brodifacoum is more lethal than difenacoum.

At the time of writing these poisons do not appear to be having an effect on Britain's barn owls. Newton considered that, although all barn owls in the British Isles are widely exposed to second-generation rodenticides, not all are likely to receive a lethal dose. With voles now playing a more important role in the diet of Britain's barn owls, the effects of these poisons is likely to be less. Johnson confirmed this, stating that of 37 suspected cases of second-generation anticoagulant poisoning cases investigated during the years 1990-94, only one was thought to have died because of it. He concluded that if the application of these poisons is carried out properly then the risk to barn owls would be minimal.

Colin Shawyer dismissed the loss of nesting sites in Britain as a primary reason for the barn owl's decline although more recently he has recognised that a shortage of nesting places is an important issue. In the north of England Derek Bunn found that his former study area had become abandoned by barn owls due to a loss of nesting places and disturbance. Along with his fellow authors he was concerned for the loss of nesting sites through barn conversions and the dereliction of buildings, and they also expressed concern at the loss of elms which they believed was a problem that was largely confined to southern and eastern England, to which I have more to say shortly.

In conclusion, Colin Shawyer's survey was important in drawing attention to the plight of the barn owl, for there is no doubt that in many places they have declined to a serious level or have gone completely He raised several important issues and we must be under no illusions that without his tremendous efforts, barn owls would not now be so high on the conservation agenda.

THE SUFFOLK BARN OWL SURVEY (MARTIN, 1984)

In 1983 I launched the Suffolk Barn Owl Survey to establish the distribution and abundance of this once common farmland bird. It was completely separate from the survey that was conducted by the Hawk and Owl Trust. To obtain the records, members of the main natural history and wildlife bodies were invited, via their respective journals, to submit records for the survey. But because the barn owl is such a well known creature, it was decided to try and enlist the help of those members of the public who were not necessarily involved with the wildlife movement but who might be useful. For this purpose all of the local radio stations and newspapers were contacted and from these there was considerable

Table 20 Grassland trends in Suffolk from 1939 to 1989 (Figures in hectares).

Census year	Grass under 5 years	% +/-	Grass 5 years and over	% +/-	Total	% age +/-
1939	25,533		86,224		111,757	
1960	26,802	+4.97	49,989	-42.02	76,791	-31.28
1970	15,130	-43.54	35,021	-29.94	50,151	-34.69
1980	9,375	-38.03	27,812	-20.58	37,187	-25.84
1985	6,813	-27.32	25,177	-9.47	31,990	-13.97
1986	6,374	-6.44	24,848	-1.30	31,222	-2.40
1987	6,267	-1.67	24,421	-1.71	30,688	-1.77
1988	7,141	+13.94	23,999	-1.73	31,140	+1.54
1989	7,373	+3.25	24,949	+3.95	32,322	+3.79
Loss since 1939	18,160	-71.12	61,275	-71.06	79,435	-71.07

Extract from the agricultural census as gathered by the Ministry of Fisheries and Food

Agricultural Development and Advisory Service (Cambridge)

support. Further help was received from the farming community who published details of the survey in their magazines. A number of lectures were presented which were designed to raise awareness, to aid with identification and to encourage recording. As the barn owl is a specially protected species, no requests were made to search for nests.

There was an excellent response to the survey and by the end of 1988, over 2,000 records had been submitted, of which the majority were subsequently plotted in the Suffolk Biological Records Centre. Some were rejected because the locations were vague, while others suggested confusion with the tawny owl. Surprisingly there was also some confusion with short-eared owls and I witnessed two occasions when they were misidentified as barn owls. I found this startling in view of the fact that the light was good and that on both occasions the observer was a seemingly experienced birdwatcher. Derek Bunn informs me that during the course of his study, where the terrain is much hillier than the relative flatlands of East Anglia, and where short-eared owls shared the same habitat, barn owls can sometimes look similar to short-eared owls when viewed from above.

From the early returns of the survey it soon became clear that in Suffolk trees were of paramount importance for nesting and barns were less significant. This posed a particular problem during the survey because of the belief by a great number of people that barn owls nest only in buildings. Consequently any breeding records that involved man-made structures were treated with caution and checked for authenticity. Tawny owls may choose to roost, and occasionally nest, in farm buildings; I once disturbed a tawny owl, in daylight, which was roosting in a small barn in south-west Suffolk.

A notable feature of the map that was compiled during the first year of the survey (Fig. 11) was that the distribution differed significantly from that which Blaker produced in 1932. Very few barn owls appeared to be present in west Suffolk and most were now to be found in the east of the county. There also appeared to be a slight contraction of range from that which Sharrock reported in the first national breeding birds survey.

At the end of the year it was unclear whether the records I had gathered were a true reflection of the barn owl's distribution or an indication of where most birdwatchers congregated. With this in mind, the recording effort continued for several more years and at the end of 1990 it was clear that the distribution that had been obtained in the first year was a true reflection of the distribution of Suffolk's barn owls. The distribution map that I was able to present was later confirmed by two subsequent bird surveys conducted by Wright (2001) and Piotrowski (2003). This trend continues to the present day, for more recently Steve Piotrowski (2006) has commented upon the scarcity of barn owls in west Suffolk. Together, the three surveys clearly illustrate that the barn owl's distribution has not changed for nearly twenty years and it is likely that this state of affairs has existed since at least the early 1960s. Suffolk now uniquely has three barn owl distribution maps, which have been compiled over a twenty-year period. They show that barn owls have suffered a massive decline since 1932 and that the decline has been greatest inland and away from the coast. I believe that a similar pattern and timing of events exists for many other parts of the British Isles.

Later, all the records up to 1988 were plotted on to a 1k square map (Fig. 12), which illustrates that many barn owls, particularly those populations where they are at low density, often frequent riverside grassland and grazing meadows, although in the coastal regions it is more difficult to decipher that trend due to the abundance of records. Only in the north-west fenland areas of Suffolk does the distribution appear to be more random, but this is due to the vegetation alongside the numerous drainage ditches which normally holds good numbers of small mammals

I was able to validate the importance of riverside grassland by assessing the records and then comparing them with the aerial photographic records held by Suffolk County Council. I then followed this up with fieldwork, which confirmed that where riverside grass was present, barn owls were usually present as well, but where there was little or no grass then they were usually absent.

This is further demonstrated in neighbouring Essex, where the greatest numbers of barn owls are to be found in the low-lying coastal areas with some penetration up the river valleys. Further afield, in Somerset for example, few barn owls now inhabit the higher land of Exmoor and since 1964 the main concentrations have been on the Levels between the Mendips, the Poldens and elsewhere. In the West Midlands, clusters of barn owls are apparent on most of the main river valleys although not all barn owls are recorded from those locations. In Shropshire, the distribution of barn owls follows a similar pattern, while further north, in Cumbria, there appears to be a marked preference for low-lying coastal areas and river valleys. Even so, by 1987 the barn owl population in Cumbria was the lowest since the early 1960s with barn owls being present at only 120 sites, suggesting a decline of 84% since 1932.

It is not, however, just the presence of grassland that determines the distribution of barn owls. Many of the coastal areas of Suffolk, and indeed elsewhere in Britain, are designated Areas of Outstanding Natural Beauty (AONB) and within those areas many of the landscape features, such as hedgerows and trees, are protected due to stricter planning controls which may also apply to buildings.

It is important to relate Dutch Elm Disease to the decline of the barn owl in Suffolk. In 1979 the Planning Department of Suffolk

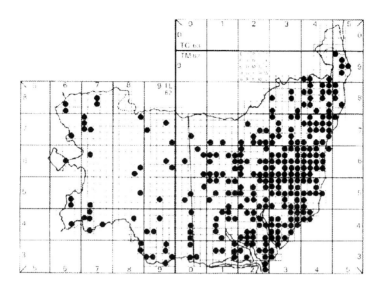

Fig 11 Distribution of barn owls in Suffolk 1983.

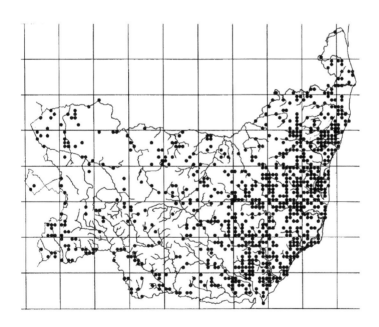

Fig 12 Distribution of barn owls in Suffolk 1983-1988 plotted on a 1km square basis.

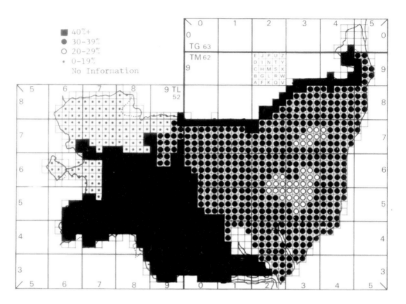

Fig. 13 Isolated hedgerow elms per landscape area shown as a percentage of all isolated trees.

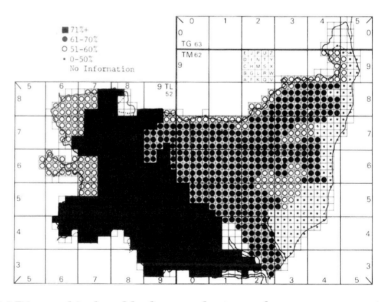

Fig. 14 Diseased isolated hedgerow elm trees shown as a percentage of all hedgerow elms per landscape area (Suffolk County Council and re-drawn on 10km basis).

County Council carried out a survey of the impact that the disease had had on the county's elms. It found that elms constituted 33.1% of all isolated hedgerow trees and that they were the dominant hedgerow species of south-west Suffolk. In the east they were less plentiful (Fig. 13). The survey also found that 65.1% of the county's elms were diseased and that the disease was more prolific in the south-west (Fig. 14). The report concluded that the disease was steadily increasing, that the rate of diseased trees had increased from 98,000 (65%) in 1978 to 108,000 (79%) in 1979 and that 29,000 (21%) healthy trees remained.

No similar exercise appears to have taken place in neighbouring Essex, although around 1975 Essex County Council produced a leaflet on DED in which it stated that by the end of 1974 the total number of dead and dying non-woodland elms had risen to 300,000 compared to 232,000 in 1973 and 158,000 in 1972. It was considered that at the time the disease was not spreading so rapidly in the northern half of the county as it did in the south because there was a higher proportion of wych and smooth-leafed elms.

The recent status of Essex elms has been described by Hanson (1990) who commented 'I don't know of any large tree [English elm] that has survived the epidemic', although he pointed out that on the Dengie peninsula there were a number of the East Anglian, or smooth-leafed, elm clones which are either more resistant to elm disease or less susceptible to attack by the beetle that transmits the disease. In 1996 Dennis reported that there were around 25 pairs of barn owls in this location. There are still small pockets of smooth-leafed elms in east Suffolk, which was the area least affected area when SCC carried out its survey, but they too are slowly becoming infected. Here I would draw the reader's attention to the elm maps produced by SCC and my own map from the first year of my study. There is a strong correlation between the density of barn owl records in the central part of east Suffolk and the areas that were least affected by DED. It was the decline of elms in Suffolk and the importance of trees for barn owls which drew me to conclude that the erection of properly sited nest-boxes may become increasingly important to ensure the barn owl's survival.

SURVEY RESULTS

The conclusions I drew from my survey were that now most barn owls are to be found in areas where there is plenty of grassland which have suitable nesting places and which are relatively free from disturbance. The survey strongly suggested that most barn owls resided in east Suffolk and my results were subsequently confirmed by two other ornithological surveys in the county. This contrasts sharply with Blaker's 1932 national barn owl survey. At the time of writing there is an indication that barn owls in Suffolk are increasing in some places largely through the provision of nest-boxes, but I believe this may well be tempered by further losses of isolated pairs or those living in fragile surroundings, such as urban fringes or busy roads. The key to their future success, as it is in many other places in the British Isles, is to restore the lost populations to inland areas through habitat improvement.

Following the Hawk and Owl Trust's Barn Owl Survey, Colin Shawyer estimated that the number of barn owls in Suffolk was 149 pairs, which reflected the estimate of 120 to 160 pairs which I believe was a realistic estimate at the time. Whether, however, we should be concerned with trying to solve the perennial question, 'How many barn owls are there?' I am not so sure. Perhaps a more rewarding undertaking would be to monitor the distribution on a regular basis, rather than trying to count numbers.

THE WINTER ATLAS (LACK, 1986)

In 1981 the BTO embarked upon a three-year survey to assess the distribution of those birds that winter in the British Isles, whether resident or winter visitors. Following a pilot survey in the winter of 1980/81, the survey started in November 1981 and ran for three winters, finishing on February 29th, 1984. Again I will not enter into the detailed methodology but the essence of the survey was for birdwatchers to count the birds seen in an allocated 10km square during the period of an hour. There were no allocated tetrads to survey. Casual, or supplementary records were also accepted. The map for barn owls that was produced from this survey suggested a distribution pattern that lay approximately between that which was shown on the map for the first breeding survey (Fig. 9), and the one produced later for the second breeding atlas (Fig. 15).

In assessing the winter distribution as shown in the atlas, David Glue astutely pointed out that the wintering distribution of barn owls in central and southern England can often be attributed to the lack of rodents on the intensively farmed arable lands and the disturbance by man in the built-up highly urbanised and industrial areas, where they may suffer from disturbance. He also pointed out that because barn owls are secretive some are likely to have been missed. He also pointed out that barn owls may be affected by bad weather and that there was a bad winter during the winter of 1981/82. In assessing this winter within the atlas, Peter Lack reported that on December 8th, 1981, most of Britain was covered by quite heavy falls of snow and that there were record low temperatures of -23°C in Shropshire and –12.5°C at Co. Westmeath, Ireland. He also stated that temperatures of -10°C were widespread across central England. The bad weather continued into January with blizzard conditions in many parts, but especially in southern Britain. It was also pointed out that the 1981/82 winter was colder than average and this was mainly due to two ten-day periods of severe weather in December and January. It should be remembered that this winter was in the wake of the bad winter of 1979.

Starting with this winter, Britain then experienced the worst decade of weather it had possibly experienced for many years, for it was shortly after the publication of the first winter atlas that in 1987 Britain experienced one of the worst winters since 1962/63. The weather conditions, together with an apparent shortage of small mammals, caused the deaths of many barn owls in Suffolk, and no doubt elsewhere in the British Isles, but few were recorded. With the exception of a barn owl that was ringed at Landguard Bird Observatory on 28th September 1986, and which was subsequently found dead at Tendring on February 9th in the following year, no dead barn owls were reported from neighbouring Essex, though it was pointed out that despite breeding records from 13 sites none were recorded from Foulness which was 'known to be one of its strongholds in the County' (EBR 1987).

ANOTHER NEW AGRICULTURAL REVOLUTION

For some years prior to 1987 widespread concern had been expressed regarding the direction that British farming had taken since the Second World War. In the arable lowlands of England especially, farmers were being paid subsidies to ensure that Britain became self-sufficient in cereal production – something they achieved, but at the expense of wildlife. Elsewhere, in the largely pastoral upland areas of Britain, farmers were not so well rewarded.

It was largely due to pressures from the wildlife conservation movement, but also a recognition that too much wheat was being produced, that there emerged a 'new outlook' to farming during the later part of the 1980s. From then until the present, a variety of different farming schemes were introduced into the British Isles that were designed to either lower food production, enhance the landscape or improve the abundance and quality of wildlife.

The destruction of grassland was one of the issues at the forefront of the argument but the appreciation of the archetypal British landscape and its conservation was also important.

Schemes promoting environmentally friendly farming were initially instigated in 1987 by the introduction of Environmentally Sensitive Areas (ESAs) of which there were five: The Norfolk Broads, Pennine Dales, the Somerset Levels, South Downs and West Penwith. In 1988 a further five were added. By entering into a management agreement, farmers received an annual payment for every hectare they put into the scheme. The more land that a farmer was prepared to dedicate for the benefit of wildlife, the greater the financial rewards. By the end of 2005 there were 22 ESAs in England and the scheme was then closed to new applicants. By that time the number of agreements had risen from 9,950 in 1998 to 12,500 and involved an area of 650,000 hectares of land, which was an increase of 148,745 during the same period.

Shortly after the launch of ESAs the 'set-aside' scheme was introduced. This entailed farmers having to take taking land out of food production on a compulsory basis; alternatively they could take more out of production if they wished to. Set-aside provided various payments for farmers, depending on how long the agreement was drawn up for. There was some criticism of set-aside from farmers and conservationists.

Grassland has its obvious benefits for barn owls and other creatures of waterside vegetation but in terms of set-aside it would seem that the benefits are not so clear. As the set-aside scheme came under review it was proposed that the numbers of small mammals had increased in recent years as a result of it and that because of this barn owls and kestrels have thrived, but this view is worthy of inspection. Concern for the future of both species has been expressed both in the UK and in Europe since at least the early 1970s, and indeed the barn owl has been on the BTO's 'concern list' for some time due to a decline in brood size that was discovered through their nest record scheme, so it is most interesting to see that the kestrel has recently been added to the list for precisely the same reason. It would appear, therefore, that although there have been some success stories for both barn owl and kestrel, this is unlikely to be the case everywhere.

Following the ESAs, a variety of schemes were introduced over the next 20 years of which the most recent at the time of writing was the Environmental Stewardship scheme. This has three elements: Entry Level Stewardship, a 'whole farm' scheme which is open to all farmers and land managers who farm their land conventionally but who meet the scheme's requirements; Organic Entry Level Stewardship, again a 'whole farm' scheme designed for farmers who manage all or part of their farm organically and who are not receiving other grants from other organic farming schemes; and Higher Level Stewardship which will combine with the previous two schemes and aims to deliver higher and more significant benefits in higher priority situations and areas.

In addition to Environmental Stewardship there is a plethora of other schemes under the England Rural Development Programme including Countryside Stewardship, Farm Woodland Premium Scheme, Organic Farming Scheme, Woodland Grant Scheme, Energy Crops Scheme. At present it is not clear for how long these environmental schemes will continue but they will not last forever, especially as some are now closed to new applicants.

In general this approach to raising the quality of our landscape and wildlife has been welcomed by farmers, allowing many to take portions of their land out of production. Some have even taken all of their land out of farming. For many farmers this new approach to husbandry will have come as something of a surprise – not since the farming depression of the late 19th and early 20th centuries has so much land been taken out of production.

It is too early to see what long-term benefits these schemes will have for barn owls. There have been some success stories, particularly those involving grassland, but until we see barn owls returning to the farmlands of inland Britain in significant numbers we cannot claim success. At present there is continuing concern for many of our seed-eating farmland birds and the lack of their presence on arable farmland despite the schemes. Much of the grassland that once covered substantial parts of inland England has been lost and so we cannot rely upon barn owls living off field voles as they do in the river valleys and coastal areas. The abundance of mice, bank voles and shrews is a key issue in returning barn owls to these places.

In 1988 the BTO launched a second survey of Britain's breeding birds. This ran for four years, the results of which were published in the *New Atlas of Breeding Birds in Britain and Ireland: 1988-1991*. This survey was more detailed than the first breeding bird survey because it was not only concerned with mapping the distribution of each species in each 10-km square, it also sought to establish the breeding density of each species within them.

The barn owl distribution map produced from the survey (Fig. 15) shows further and more significant gaps in the distribution map than that which was presented earlier. It was suggested that the absence of barn owls from large parts of central England might have been partly due to climate, although perhaps weather is a more pertinent word. Barn owls do not normally inhabit high ground, such as the Pennines for example, due to inclement weather conditions, and the effects of the winter of 1987 may well have influenced the survey's results.

It was thought that the difference in survey techniques from this survey and the first BTO breeding bird survey made the comparison of numbers between the two surveys questionable, and that the patchiness in the distribution map of the second atlas was partially due to the location of barn owl enthusiasts rather than the real distribution. Twenty years on from the first breeding bird survey there were more people interested in birds than there were when that survey was carried out. By that time the barn owl's profile had been raised to such a degree, it seems unlikely to have been overlooked by even the most inexperienced bird watcher. The distribution map for the second survey was probably a reasonable view of the barn owl's distribution in the British Isles at that time. A great deal of the 'patchiness' that was described in the atlas was due to urban expansion and the tremendous increase in the amount of road-building that had gone on since the first national survey. In conclusion, there was a plea in the second atlas for a 'thorough and integrated monitoring system' to provide further information on barn owl numbers.

The distribution map for the barn owl in the second atlas clearly suggests a coastal bias in eastern and north-western parts of England and at the time of writing this is still largely the case. Since the 1960s the majority of bird reports and county avifauna that relate to counties with coastlines have consistently remarked on the lack of inland records for the barn owl; Hampshire is, perhaps, an exception. This is because coastal areas reflect a kinder environment for wildlife and much of Britain's coastline and its hinterlands are of high conservation value, with substantial amounts designated as AONBs or SSSIs.

The results from the survey and various local studies suggested that there were good pockets of barn owls to be found in various parts of the British Isles such as Wiltshire and Hampshire, where the barn owl population has been estimated to be between 150 and 200 pairs (Clark and Eyre, 1993). The main concentrations in Hampshire were in parts of the Avon and Test river valleys and the coastal areas south of the New Forest. The lack of barn owls in the seemingly attractive area of the Forest itself is thought to be due

Fig 15 Distribution of breeding barn owls in Britain 1988-1992 (after Gibbons et al, 1993).

to the effects of grazing which leaves insufficient cover for small mammals. The situation in Hampshire at that time compared favourably with Colin Shawyer's survey when it was estimated that there were 144 pairs; perhaps the provision of over 200 nest-boxes had helped to meet the shortage of nest-sites brought about by the demolition of old buildings and lack of trees due to Dutch Elm Disease.

Elsewhere, the rural counties of Shropshire, Worcestershire and Herefordshire also contain good numbers, along with the equally quiet rural areas of Carmarthenshire and the lowland Border areas of Scotland. It seems unlikely that the distributions of barn owls in those areas occur either by accident or through observer bias. Their relative tranquillity, along with the aforementioned coastal areas, must surely play an important role as well as the designation, in a number of places, of ESAs. Recently the Council for the Protection of Rural England produced a tranquillity map for England (Fig.16) which suggests a positive correlation in a number of areas with the barn owl distribution map (Fig. 15) and the area around Norwich, in Norfolk, is a good example of this.of this. There also seems to some link with the previously discussed Ancient Countryside.

At the end of the survey the New Atlas was unable to provide an improved estimate of barn owl numbers from that which was previously given by Shawyer, because it was felt that the annual fluctuations in vole populations were tending to obscure the true picture. Whilst this is especially relevant to northern Britain, it might not be the case for southern areas where vole cycles may not be so pronounced.

THE WILDLIFE AND COUNTRYSIDE ACT: AN AMENDMENT

In 1992 there was a change to the legal status of the barn owl when it was added to Schedule 9 of the Wildlife and Countryside Act, making it illegal to deliberately release a barn owl into the wild without a government licence. This followed concerns that many barn owls were being bred in captivity and then released into the wild in an attempt to bolster the wild population, without any thought as to whether the habitat was suitable for their survival. The Hawk and Owl Trust estimated that 3,000 barn owls were released each year in England and Wales and that there were around 20-30,000 captive barn owls in Britain. It was also pointed out that since 1983 there had been a steady increase in the sales of metal close rings for barn owls by the British Bird Council, although

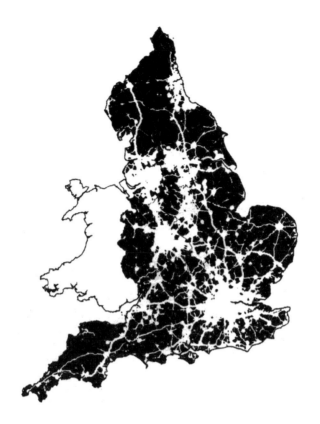

Fig 16 Areas of tranquillity early 1990s (Council for the Protection of Rural England). The shaded areas are those of tranquillity and unshaded ares are those of greatest disturbance.

most barn owls would be released without rings.

Following research by the BTO it was found that captive-bred barn owls were more likely to die in their first year than wild-bred birds. On average only 10% of captive-bred birds and 15% of released adults survived their first year compared to 19% and 55% of those raised in the wild. In view of this information the BTO considered that the release of captive-bred birds was unlikely to be aiding barn owl conservation. During the course of my study I came across a number of owls in captivity, some of which were being used for breeding and releasing. Undoubtedly their presence in the countryside could have influenced my survey, although to the best of my knowledge no captive-bred birds feature in the distribution map.

Perhaps a more important aspect of introducing captive-bred birds into the wild is their influence upon wild barn owls that may already be present in the vicinity of the introduction. The introduction of captive-bred birds might disturb existing wild barn owl populations by competing for food and nesting places. It could be argued that responsible operators of breeding and release schemes should always check for the presence of existing wild barn owls, but historically we know that barn owls can live at low densities and may go unnoticed. We also know that when conditions are right, barn owls will return to hospitable areas unaided.

THE THIRD NATIONAL BARN OWL SURVEY 1995-97(TOMS ET AL, 2001)

During the years 1995-7, a further barn owl study was carried out in the United Kingdom but this time it was to establish the breeding population and to set a baseline for future monitoring. The methodology and detail of the survey is fully described in Toms et al (2001) and so only a brief outline is given here.

The basis of the survey involved fieldworkers visiting selected tetrads over a three-year period; twice in the first year, once in the second and twice in the third year. During the first year, fieldworkers were requested on their first visit to record all potential barn owl nest-sites during winter within their survey tetrads. These were sites that the observer thought were suitable for breeding barn owls and included farm buildings, tree cavities, bale stacks, cliff sites and nest-boxes – a formidable task, none more so than in many lowland areas of Britain where barn owls may often choose to nest in trees. During the second visit of the year, timed between mid-June and the end of August, observers were instructed to determine the occupancy of all the potential nest-sites that they had located during the winter fieldwork. There was no attempt at mapping the distribution.

Of the 1,100 survey tetrads that were chosen at random for the project, 61 received a visit from the 'Project Officer'. From those it was considered that fieldworkers were able to identify 92% of 'suitable' sites and 84% of 'possible' sites, and that no breeding barn owls were missed by fieldworkers whose squares were validated by the Project Officer. It was also considered that the results from the survey supported a high level of confidence in the abilities of fieldworkers who were provided with detailed instructions and practical training before the project started.

From this survey it was calculated that in 1995 there were 2,830 breeding pairs of barn owls in the United Kingdom, including Northern Ireland, with a confidence interval of a minimum of 1,952 pairs and a maximum level of 3,761 pairs. In the following year it was calculated that there were 3,967 pairs (minimum 2,785 pairs, maximum 5,252 pairs) and for 1997 an estimate of 3,951 pairs was presented with a minimum confidence level of 2,769 pairs, and a maximum of 5,214. The authors of this report confidently presented the results as being accurate to 'around 95%' and it was anticipated that the survey would be repeated in 10-15 years' time.

THE PRESENT

Since Colin Shawyer's survey, Tony Warburton felt that there had been a further decline in barn owl numbers and that the estimates being given in Britain during the mid-1990s were too optimistic. In reply to this Shawyer firmly estimated that by the year 2000 there would be 7,500 pairs of barn owls in Britain due to the ongoing conservation efforts that revolved around creating good feeding habitats along with the provision of nesting sites in areas free from disturbance. We have no indication as to whether that target was achieved.

As a result of the survey, the RSPB set a target increase of 50% (c 2,000) additional pairs in Britain by the year 2010, while at the Suffolk Barn Owl Seminar at Thetford on November 4th, 2006, a target population of 450 pairs for Suffolk was declared by the year 2010, suggesting an anticipated increase of around 200%. These are significant and positive figures and it will be interesting to see whether these targets are achieved.

SOURCES USED IN THIS CHAPTER

Andrews, J. 1992: Some practical problems in set-aside management for wildlife. *British Wildlife,* 3: 329-336.

Anon., 1979. Survey of elm trees in Suffolk – 1979. Suffolk County Council, Ipswich.

Ballance, D.K. 2006: *A History of the Birds of Somerset.* Isabelline Books, Falmouth.

Bennett, A. 1995: On a wing and a prayer. *Sunday Express Classic,* January 22nd, 1995: 16-18.

Bunn, D.S. Warburton, A.W. and Wilson, A.A.B. 1982: *The Barn Owl.* Poyser, Calton.

Cayford, J. and Percival, S. 1992: Born captive, die free. *New Scientist,* 1807: 29-33.

Clark, J.M. & Eyre, J.A. 1993: *Birds of Hampshire.* Hampshire Ornithological Society.

Coombes, R.A.H. 1933: Barn Owls nesting in crags high up in Westmorland. *British Birds,* 26:309.

Davenport, D.L. 1982: Influxes into Britain of Hen Harriers, Long-eared Owls and Short-eared Owls in winter 1978/19. *British Birds,* 75: 309-316.

Dennis, M.K. 1996: *Breeding Birds of Essex.* Essex Birdwatching Society.

Duckett, J.E. 1984: Barn Owls (*Tyto alba*) and the "second generation" rat baits utilised in oil palm plantations in Peninsula Malaysia. *Planter,* 60: 3-11.

Gibbons, D.W. Reid, J.B. and Chapman, R.A. 1993: *The New Atlas of Breeding Birds in Britain and Ireland: 1988-1991.* Poyser, London.

Hagemeijer, W.J.M and Blair, M.J. 1997: *The EBCC Atlas of European Breeding Birds.* Poyser, London.

Hanson, M.W. 1990: *Essex Elm.* Essex Field Club.

Harrison, G. & Harison, J. 2005: *The New Birds of the West Midlands.* West Midlands Bird Club.

Johnson, I. 1996: Pesticide poisoning of wildlife in Britain. *British Wildlife,* 7: 273-278

Lack, P. 1986: *The Atlas of Wintering Birds in Britain and Ireland.* Poyser, Calton.

Lack, P. & Ferguson, D. 1993: *The Birds of Buckinghamshire.* Buckinghamshire Field Club.

Leech, D., Barimore, C. & Crick, H. 2006: NRS Concern List – five new species added. *BTO News,* 267: 4-5.

Leech, D., Crick, H. & Shawyer, C. 2006: Barn Owls and winter weather. *BTO News,* 262: 8-9.

Martin, J.R. 1984: Results of the Suffolk Barn Owl Enquiry. *Suffolk Ornith. Group Bull.* 64: 5-11. Suffolk Ornithologists' Group, Ipswich.

Martin, J.R. 1988: Barn owl mortality during the winter of 1986/87. *Suffolk Birds 1988,* 37: 12-15. Suffolk Nat. Soc., Ipswich.

McWilliam, J.M. 1936: *The Birds of the Firth of Clyde.* Witherby, London.

Moore, D.R. 1979. Review of the Year. *Suffolk Birds 1979.* Suffolk Naturalists' Society, Ipswich.

Newton, I., Wyllie, I. & Freestone, P. 1990: Rodenticides in British Barn Owls. *Environ. Pollut.,* 68: 101-117.

Piotrowski, S.H. 2003: *The Birds of Suffolk*. Helm, London.

Piotrowski, S.H 2006: Suffolk Community Barn Owl Project. *The Harrier,* 145: 2-11.

Sharrock, J.T.R. (ed.) 1976: *The Atlas of Breeding Birds in Britain and Ireland*. Poyser, Calton.

Shawyer, C. 1987: *The Barn Owl in the British Isles – Its Past, Present and Future*. The Hawk Trust, London.

Shawyer, C. 1998: *The Barn Owl*. Arlequin Press, Chelmsford.

Stott, M., Callion, J., Kinley, I., Raven, C., & Roberts, J. 2002: *The Breeding Birds of Cumbria: a tetrad atlas of 1997-2001*. Cumbria Bird Club.

Taylor, I.R. 1994: *Barn owls; predator prey relationships*. Cambridge University Press.

Toms, M.P., Crick, H.Q.P. & Shawyer, C.R. 2001: The status of breeding Barn Owls *Tyto alba* in the United Kingdom 1995-97. *Bird Study*, 48: 23-37.

Tubbs, C. 1986: *The New Forest*. Collins, London.

Wright, M. 2001: *Survey of Breeding Raptors & Owls in Suffolk, 1995-1998*. Suffolk Ornithologists' Group, Ipswich.

Wood, S. 2007: *The Birds of Essex*. Helm, London.

In addition:

The Essex Bird Report, 1987

The Suffolk Bird Report, 1987

11 THE CHALLENGE: AN APPROACH TO CONSERVATION

'But it is the common species that keep the living world ticking over and provide most of our everyday experiences of wildlife, and I would argue that maintaining the abundance of these is as important a conservation priority as maintaining the abundance of rarities.'

Richard Mabey, *The Common Ground* (1980)

PRESENT STATUS

Under existing law the barn owl in Britain is placed on Part 1, Schedule 1 of the Wildlife and Countryside Act 1981. This means that persons who deliberately harm barn owls or steal them or their eggs from the wild render themselves liable to prosecution with special penalties. The law also restricts access to its nest-site, including photography, unless the person concerned is in possession of a special permit. Persons wishing to ring barn owls or to record the nest contents for conservation purposes must also be in possession of a government licence, and these are issued through the BTO. The barn owl was given this special protection following the severe decline of the early 1960s, although it does not protect its nest-site throughout the year, or its roost site or the areas where it feeds. The barn owl is also on Schedule 3, Part 1 of the Act, which allows barn owls to be sold or exchanged at any time, providing they have been bred in captivity and close ringed. It is also on Part 1, Schedule 9 that restricts the release of captive-bred barn owls into the wild without a licence. Some authorised release schemes are in operation but unauthorised releasing still continues here and there.

Across Europe barn owls are gradually declining and it would appear that it is the nominate race, *Tyto alba alba*, that is suffering the most. The Spanish population is, perhaps, of greatest concern because the largest population of white-breasted barn owls is found there. There are large numbers of barn owls in France but the status

In many parts of Britain the phantom of the farmyard has gone, and will never return.

of their population is unclear. Barn owls also appear to be declining in Italy but their population may now be stable at present in the United Kingdom and also in Belgium. Elsewhere, barn owls appear to be holding their own in Germany, Holland, and some of the other central European countries.

The reports from around the British Isles suggest that barn owl numbers are increasing but occasionally there are hiccoughs (see Leech et al, 2007, for example) but as long as this is not part of a long-term trend such events should not be a serious problem. However, Leech did re-affirm that the barn owl was a species of medium conservation concern and because of that it is placed on the Amber List of Birds of Conservation Concern (see www.bto. org/psob/index.htm). In Europe it is listed as a species of European Conservation Concern, Category 3, under the EU Birds Directive 1979 and is regarded as a declining (D) species. In Britain the barn owl is included on several local bio-diversity action plans but it is not, at present, on the national action plan. As a result of these listings there are now a considerable number of barn owl conservation schemes around Britain, most of which involve erecting nest-boxes in areas of suitable habitat, monitoring the breeding success of each box and ringing the young. The reason for these conservation measures is due largely to the national barn owl survey that was undertaken by Colin Shawyer in the early 1980s and, while these efforts are commendable, we must avoid too narrow an approach to conservation by concentrating solely on providing nest-boxes within areas of grassland. A wider choice of feeding habitats, including quality hedgerows and field margins, should be embraced. The question must be asked, is the present approach to barn owl conservation sustainable in the long-term?

VOLE MANIA

'Truly this species is the farmland owl' is how Dobbs in 1975 aptly described the barn owl and because of that its conservation poses many problems. It is not, for example, easily confined to specific localities such as nature reserves where its requirements may be catered for, and so I think it likely that in the lowlands of Britain we must look to farmland for its conservation, but along the way there are some issues that must be addressed. Earlier I described how Britain has been largely divided into two agricultural segments: in the north and west the land is mainly pastoral while in the south and east it is largely arable. Much of the land in the east is devoted to cereal and other crops, although now, with the view very much on reducing production, a sizeable portion of the land has been placed into various 'agri-environment' schemes which are aimed at lowering food production and creating a better wildlife environment. However, some other crops are also being grown in abundance. Now, instead of the yellow fields of wheat that once presided over the arable landscape, fields of yellow oilseed rape dominate the scene in many places during the spring, but whether the rape fields provide suitable foraging after their harvest, compared to those of wheat, remains to be seen.

We know that barn owls throughout much of Britain are largely dependent upon field voles for their survival and in the lowland areas of the British Isles, river valleys, grazing marshes and fen-land are the key areas for their present survival. However, it is important to remember that there is now good evidence to support the view that barn owls once fed upon a wider spectrum of prey than they do at present. In Ireland, where the field vole is absent, barn owls have lived for many hundreds of years on a diet of small mammals, notably wood mouse, pygmy shrew, house mouse, brown rat and, more recently, bank vole, and I have shown earlier that elsewhere in Europe barn owls are sustained on a diet of small mammals in which voles are either largely or totally absent. The important fact is that on mainland Britain barn owls now feed upon a narrower spectrum of prey than they once did and the field vole is now the dominant species. Because of that it is the target prey species in all barn owl conservation programmes and as a consequence grassland has become the prime habitat for their survival everywhere.

Shawyer remarked that although farmland of mixed habitats was important for barn owls and needed protection, he believed the fenlands of east Lincolnshire and the afforested areas of the Scottish Border country held greater numbers of barn owls because both those regions retain large amounts of grassland supporting large numbers of voles. In the lowlands of Britain, however, there should be no doubt that barn owls were once most definitely reliant upon mixed farming; Taylor found that the barn owls of mixed farming in his study area on the Scottish Borders had a more stable population, being able to switch from one prey item to another as one or other prey species became depleted. I have also demonstrated that in south-west Suffolk a switch from mixed to arable farming, along with habitat destruction and elm disease, wiped out large numbers of barn owls around 40 years ago.

The fens of eastern England do offer colonisation opportunities for barn owls because the vegetation that grows along the many drainage ditches amidst the farmlands of the fens provides homes for abundant voles. Many of these places in fenland, however, have never been homes for barn owls. Before they were drained they were wetlands and, following their drainage, they retained very few nesting places. It is good to see so many barn owls there now, but their presence there does not compensate for the loss of barn owls on farmland. The forestry plantations of the Scottish Borders and elsewhere do provide vole-rich grassy habitats and are good places for barn owls so long as barns and other buildings, such as abandoned farmhouses, are available and nest-boxes provided.

There can be little doubt that the creation of the ESAs has been important in conserving and increasing the numbers of barn owls in some places and perhaps efforts should be made to secure more of these areas on a permanent basis. We should not rely upon governmental farming policies for their long-term security. Governments have many decisions to make that affect issues other than wildlife and whilst there is no area of land, including nature reserves, that can be permanently secured for the future, they are more secure if they have some formal protection. It is likely that ESAs will become a major issue in barn owl conservation in the future and maybe governmental action of a different kind can bring about the long-term security of some, if not all, of these ESAs.

Throughout I have emphasised the importance of barn owls enjoying a wide spectrum of prey as they undoubtedly did in earlier times; this was provided by a greater diversity of habitats including hedgerows, ditches, farmyards and hay-ricks. But in the last sixty or so years lowland barn owls have moved away from those areas largely because they have become inhospitable due to intensive farming and now they are mainly restricted to low-lying grassland areas. Barn owls in Britain still face many trials, one of which concerns the flooding of their feeding habitats, either through rainfall, sea-level rise or the scheme of managed retreat when land is deliberately surrendered to the sea. During the course of the summer of 2007, heavy rainfall across many parts of Britain caused very serious flooding and much of that occurred at a time when there would have been young barn owls in the nest. It seems likely that some barn owls would have been affected by these disastrous floods although at this time it is too early to be precise. It is for this reason, and other examples of which I have presented earlier, that I believe that efforts should be made to attract more barn owls to areas where the risk from flooding is reduced.

TAKING THE HIGH GROUND

The fact that many barn owls throughout the British Isles are concentrated along river valleys and other low-lying areas has serious implications. I have previously stated that from time to time rivers flood and sometimes the surrounding land may be under water for long periods. During the course of wet winters barn owls may lose body condition due to food shortages and this may well prevent some owls from breeding. Numbers of barn owls appear to be greater in the west of Britain than in the east and I think it likely that because many barn owls in eastern England are confined to the river valleys and coastal grazing marshes, they are highly vulnerable to lower breeding rates and greater mortality because the rivers there are at risk to flooding. When this occurs, field vole populations and other small mammals, and especially shrews, are susceptible to drowning which subsequently causes food shortages. During the course of their study Derek Bunn et al noticed that when a favourite hunting area for barn owls became flooded the owls moved away. There are many other predatory creatures, such as stoats, weasels, foxes and kestrels, to name but a few, that feed upon voles and they too will be under pressure when land is flooded and so competition for food will be heightened. The matter of flooding may not be such a problem in many parts of western and northern Britain where the terrain is more undulating and where hunting grounds are more likely to be on on well drained land, but in the lowlands, where water may take longer to drain, the problems could be longer lasting and more serious.

In lowland Britain there are large tracts of farmland that could be incorporated into various environmental schemes along the lines of national parks, where landscaping and habitat diversity could be a major feature. These may not necessarily be run as national parks but they should be away from areas of flood risk and some of the 'Areas of Tranquillity' that have been highlighted by the CPRE would make ideal locations in which to site such projects. Funding along the lines of national parks is already afforded to AONBs, so perhaps financial support could be assigned to those places too?

For some time conservationists have been campaigning for reforms to the CAP, a policy that is designed to promote production through farming subsidies and market intervention. In 2003 modifications were introduced that were designed to lower production and various schemes were introduced by which if a farmer did not comply he would then lose part of his subsidy. In May 2007 a parliamentary report heavily criticised the CAP and following this the RSPB stated that the large amount of money that is presently being spent on farming subsidies should be channelled into schemes that improve the countryside. At the time of writing Birdlife International, which is comprised of representative organisations from some 42 bird conservation partners in Europe and which is active within all of the EU member states, is lobbying for a radical reform of the CAP when its budget comes up for review later this year, 2008. It pointed out the main threats to Europe's farmland birds and it expressed concern that those countries of central and eastern Europe, which have recently joined the EU and which at present have a wealth of bird life, are in danger of losing that richness unless the CAP is reformed. It was especially concerned for farmland birds and in Britain this has been a matter of ongoing concern for many years. I have no doubt that if the numbers of farmland birds, such as yellowhammer, corn bunting and skylark, for example, were restored to what they were at the time of the first national breeding atlas, there would be a knock-on effect for our barn owls. This is because the food that these birds eat, such as berries, seeds and insects, are often those that are eaten by small mammals. In addition to this, the absence of thrushes, such as blackbird, redwing and fieldfare that I have noted on farmland during the winter, is due to a lack of food in the hedgerows (where they exist); I will return to this subject.

However, this thinking does not mean that farms within these proposed areas should be run as agricultural museums but that they should concentrate on the quality of the farming as well as enhancing the landscape and its natural features. There is a raft of farming incentives for farmers to participate in if they wish to receive subsidies, but to obtain them there is a myriad of qualifications they must comply with. These are far-ranging in their requirements and can be found in a collection of 'guides' whose contents together far exceed those of this volume! There is a need to simplify the qualifications for farmers to receive those grants and perhaps funds could be made available to encourage more people to work on the land that would involve re-instating some traditional farmland practices?

HEDGEROWS

Earlier the importance of hedgerows was pointed out in not only providing a greater diversity of small mammals but also as a means of allowing them to colonise the countryside. In recent decades a great deal of emphasis has been placed on encouraging hedges to be left uncut during the important nesting period for songbirds. However, hedge management is just as critical for barn owls because the buds of species such as hawthorn, hazel and bramble, for example, develop in very early spring and if they are cut off, even if the guidelines designed to protect nesting songbirds are observed, few or no fruits will appear later in the year to support small mammals during the autumn, winter and through into spring when barn owls themselves are building their strength for the coming breeding season. Thus, in order to encourage good populations of their prey species, the success of our farmland barn owls will be enhanced if more care and consideration is given to hedgerow management through the year. Recently incentives have been put in place to encourage farmers not only to plant hedgerows, as they did during the Enclosure Period, but also to cut them in rotation. Even so, I see that many continue to be poorly trimmed in spring and autumn thus removing the prospect of any fruits appearing. If they were managed in a sympathetic manner to the requirements of small mammals then well-maintained hedges, along with the marginal strips of grassland that are now retained on a number of farms, would provide a wide band of prey.

It is not just hedge-cutting that is important, for unless hedges have some firm structure small mammals will find them inhospitable. There can be little doubt that the ancient craft of hedge-laying is of great consequence because it creates good density, thus providing greater cover for small mammals and birds and it may allow more sensitive trimming of the growth, thus encouraging greater fruiting. In recent years there has been a revival in the art of hedge-laying but this interest needs to be intensified. With so much money now being injected into environmental farming, perhaps some could be 'set-aside' for professional hedge-layers? Opportunities should abound for young, intelligent people who are not necessarily academically inclined. There is a need for a greater understanding of how hedge management affects the density of small mammals and its consequential effect upon barn owls. Working alongside botanists, there is a need to establish how the blossoming of hedgerow plants and shrubs are affected by cutting in the early part of the year, and to offer advice to farmers and local authorities as to the timing of the cut to benefit small mammals.

The benefits of leaving grass corridors has also received attention in recent years and all of the proposals, which are based upon farmers leaving wide strips of rough grassland approximately 3-5m wide around their field edges, are to be encouraged. These not only provide foraging areas for barn owls, they may allow any owls that are seeking a territory to colonise the countryside, provided they can find a suitable territory.

In addition to these areas of grassland, there is much else that can be done to increase the numbers of small mammals. Verges, ditches and headlands should not be cut too short, particularly during the crucial summer months when barn owls need food for their young, and also during the winter months when they may find it difficult to catch enough prey to sustain them. Often, the most effective way to manage those marginal habitats is to do nothing, except perhaps for some light mowing or grazing from time to time but very often verges and field margins are cut very short and provide inadequate cover.

However, while road-side verges, ditches and drains have an important role to play in providing food for barn owls, there is a danger in encouraging barn owls to areas where there are risks.

NEST-BOXES

It became abundantly clear to me during the early stages of my study that in Suffolk barn owls were heavily reliant upon trees for nesting and as a consequence I became convinced that putting up nest-boxes in the right place would be increasingly important to ensure the barn owl's survival. Just over twenty years later, use of nest-boxes are being strongly promoted.

There are many designs for barn owl nesting boxes 'on the market' and I have no further recommendations although I do have some comments that I feel are relevant. Nest-boxes are designed as much for the eye of the maker as they are for the target species, and so whatever design is chosen, and wherever it is located, a box should be designed ideally to provide a dark and secretive chamber within it. We know that in Britain barn owls tend to stay faithful to their nest-site for perhaps the duration of their lives and a safe and quiet environment is necessary. They are essentially cave dwellers and whilst we cannot provide caves, a barn or other large building is the nearest equivalent. If that cannot be provided, and we should remember that barn owls in many parts of Britain have lived in trees for hundreds of years, then a quiet and safe box, even if it is an outside location, should be the ideal to aim for. I shall outline how a tea-chest sized nest-box should be adapted and how other boxes could be designed in a way that may provide a favourable environment.

Before it is secured to the box, an entrance hole should be cut into one corner of the box-front (Fig. 17) of no more than 12-14cm square. Before the front is secured, however, a partition the height of the box should be fitted. This should be fixed 16-18cm away from the side of the box and extend around two-thirds of the way inside. Consequently, when the front is secured then the partition and the side of the box should form a 'tunnel' that the owls can, upon arriving at the entrance, walk along before entering the darker nesting chamber, which is hidden away on the other side of the partition. Barn owls are secretive birds and they might well prefer this type of construction, which may also help to exclude other species such as jackdaws, which Shawyer found to be a problem. Chris Mead expressed concern that the introduced Egyptian goose, a species that is increasing its numbers and range, might well take over the nesting cavities of barn owls, so a box such as this might also serve to deter them.

It may be useful to provide some sort of access to the nesting

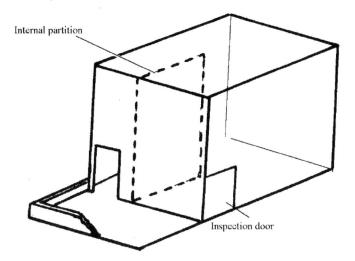

Fig. 17 Suggested nest-box design for barn owls. The box should be approximately 60cm deep and 40cm high and wide. The internal partition, which should be as high as the box, should extend approximately $^2/_3$ of the way inside.

chamber, such as a door or removable panel, so that licensed nest-box recorders or bird ringers can gain access. Before putting the box up, add a platform to the front for the parents to alight upon, and for the owlets to begin safely exploring their environment, because if any of the young fall to the floor and fail to climb back to the nest, the parents usually ignore them. Ian Anderson tells me that in their Oxfordshire scheme (see below) they only use boxes with holes at least 18"(45cm) above the box floor so as to ensure that the young owls cannot gain access to the outside before they are strong enough to get back in again. Although these boxes can be bulky and are generally intended for interior use, in some places, such as private estates and some of the more remote farmlands, they could also be erected in trees although the addition of roofing felt is advisable.

It may be that an external box, mounted on a tree for example, might be more appropriate than an indoor box and the 'A' shaped design that Colin Shawyer has illustrated may well be suitable. Whatever design of tree-box is chosen, it needs to be sited at a height that will afford it some measure of security. Fifteen to twenty feet is a good height, with fastenings to either the tree

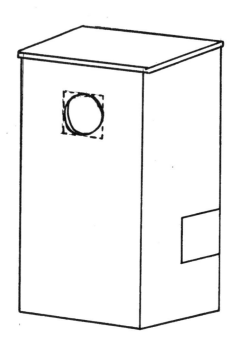

Fig. 18 Suggested design for an upright nest-box. Designed mainly for external use but it could also be used on semi-internal sites such as open barns. If the hole was created in one of the top corners, then an internal partition could be created such as in figure 8.

trunk or to the actual branches of the tree, preferably near to the bole. No perch is necessary, although barn owls will often rest on a nearby branch before entering. It is most important, however, that the approach to the box should be clear; the owls will usually approach at a low altitude before flying vertically up to land at the nest entrance hole.

I can also suggest a large 'tit type' box of similar dimensions but this should be constructed vertically (Fig. 17). A hole of around 10-12cm in diameter should be cut in the front and, although the size might seem inadequate, barn owls are able to enter and leave their nests through a remarkably small entrance. The partition that I described earlier could also be installed but the entrance hole would then need to be placed in either the top left or right hand corner to accommodate it.

The choice of where to place the nest-box is an important matter to consider but assuming that a tea-chest type box is going to be used, then this is best placed in an enclosed building that has an entrance hole in the gable end near to the apex of the roof. The typical 'owl window' that once upon a time used to be built into barns is a superb entrance and if one could be accommodated, then this should measure around 30cm by 14cm. Many years ago these upright rectangular holes used to be incorporated into many barns when they were being built. Whether they were intentionally put in to allow access for barn owls or whether they were provided for ventilation is a matter for conjecture. Owl windows should not be too elaborate or wide and a perching place on the outside of the building is not desirable as this might encourage pigeons and the like. In some places, such as Suffolk and Essex especially, there are weather-boarded barns and the removal of a plank, or section of plank, is often adequate to allow access. Inside the building, it might be better to site the box away from the entrance and as high up in the darkest corner as possible. Alternatively, boxes can be placed against the entrance hole so that the owls have access to the nest-box only and not the building's interior. Nest-boxes may also be sited in modern, open-design barns but it might be necessary to fix a wooden support to the box that can then be tied to the metal trusses of the barn. Church towers could also be used and there are many references in the old literature of barn owls using them, but understandably there is reluctance to allow birds access due to the mess they make. In such circumstances it is possible to site a nest-box inside a tower but in a position where it does not allow the owls access into the building itself (see above).

There is ample evidence that the provision of artificial nest-sites does assist barn owls to either consolidate their position or help them establish themselves in areas where they are absent. The provision of more than one box should be considered in some places because outside of the nesting period, male and female owls tend to roost apart. During the early part of the nesting season, the pair, as I described earlier, spend most of the time together and so the need for a reasonably sized box is important. Later, when the young grow large and boisterous, they tend to take up most of the room inside the nesting chamber and that is when the female also needs a quiet spot to herself. It is possible that three or four nest-boxes spaced out in one area, rather than just one, are more likely to encourage barn owls to breed in some localities. This strategy may be more important in areas where owls are present but they are breeding at low density. The idea of creating nesting sites for barn owls is not a new one and in 1932 Copinger-Hill reported that at Buxhall, in Suffolk, nest-boxes had been erected, one of which had been occupied by a kestrel and five young, whilst another was the home of barn owls.

NEST-BOXES AND CONSERVATION

In one area of Britain (south-west Lancashire) 105 boxes were erected between 1972 and 1975 and subsequently 14 of these were used for nesting. That was a good success rate (13%) in relation to the number of boxes that were provided. More recently, Duckels reported that in 2002 there were 40-50 pairs usually breeding in this scheme and that because of the success of the project, it had received national recognition. Following on from this, Colin Shawyer has reported on various nest-box programmes that are operating in the fenlands of eastern England and other places, such as southern Scotland with great success.

In West Oxfordshire Ian Anderson tells me that the Friends of Wychwood Barn Owl Project is making steady progress in helping to restore the number of barn owls in that part of the county. Like a number of others, this project is community-based and involves a group made up of the members of the Wychwood Project and the Friends of Wychwood. The scheme is sited within the boundaries of the old Royal Hunting Forest of Wychwood, which stretches from Chipping Norton in the north, to Burford in the west, Woodstock to the east and the River Thames to the south. Through the barn owl and its needs, the whole scheme is designed to provide the members with a better understanding and appreciation of the interaction between the local environment and the landscape. Like many of these schemes, this one has a good scientific base and through a local qualified bird ringer a substantial amount of data involving breeding success and ringing is gathered and then channelled into the BTO's data banks. To date the scheme has seen a slow increase in barn owl numbers and results indicate that in 2005 an excellent number of young were raised and 134 were ringed. The downside is that like many parts of Britain, 2006 was infinitely poorer and only 9 young were ringed. The diet of Wychwood's barn owls is largely unknown, although there appears to be a tendency, as there is throughout most parts of Britain, for field voles to dominate the diets although quite recently, when one of the boxes was inspected, ten freshly killed wood mice were found as a store for the incubating female.

The Suffolk Community Barn Owl Project was instigated in 2006 with the prime purpose of increasing the number of barn owls. Originally launched under the umbrella of the Suffolk Ornithologists' Group, the project became jointly managed with the Suffolk Wildlife Trust in 2007, and in the fullness of time, maybe most if not all barn owl box projects will form a similar partnership. Up until February 2007 the project had erected 150 nest-boxes and had also taken on the responsibility for a further 90 and although the scheme is presently focussed around the north-eastern parts of the county, Steve Piotrowski, the project organiser, has informed me that the intention is to have a wide spread of barn owl boxes throughout the county. With an agreed target of 450 pairs by the year 2010, might we eventually see barn owls returning to those parts of Suffolk where they have been absent for so long? I hope so.

As I stated in my introduction, my interest in barn owls has its roots in the Stour Valley, between Suffolk and Essex, and so I am pleased to see that David Wilken, a farmer from Little Clacton in Essex, has a fine barn owl conservation project underway. It started on his farm in the autumn of 1997 with two boxes and by the following spring 2 chicks were found in one of them. This was an encouraging start and later, after putting up more boxes, 4 breeding pairs had raised 16 owlets by the end of 1998. The scheme progressed so that by the year 2002 there were 80 nesting boxes in north Essex in which 20 pairs of barn owls had produced 97 owlets. The project has now been extended along the Stour Valley and currently David has 250 boxes covering north-Essex and south-Suffolk. By the year 2006 there were 43 pairs which is excellent progress and he feels that in 'north-east Essex and south Suffolk the outlook looks bright, but that could change very quickly so we must continue to do what we can to preserve this beautiful bird'. He feels that grazing marshes, water meadows and river valleys are important and that 'Nest-boxes will continue to be a lifeline in their breeding success in the future and who can tell what impact climate change may have on us all?'

Indeed, but looking to the long-term, we do not know if all or indeed any of these schemes are going to be in existence in say, 100 years time, and so consideration needs to be given to the future role of trees in barn owl conservation. This is particularly relevant to lowland Britain where the future of elms needs to be thought through. There are many parts of the countryside where elm hedges are still present and if, as Rackham has suggested, the elms recover at some stage in the future, then this needs to be taken into consideration. At present elm disease is still with us and any saplings that grow to a reasonable size soon succumb. When the disease has eventually run its course, however, then many will flourish and grow into magnificent trees – as long as the saplings are not destroyed. Black poplars should also be considered as possible nesting places, especially as river valleys are one of this tree's favoured habitats. The protection and management of oaks is an extremely important issue and the craft of pollarding (see below) has an important role to play in the barn owl's future.

Elsewhere the future of nest-sites needs to be looked on from a different angle. So many old buildings in northern and western Britain have fallen into disrepair, been subject to disturbance, demolished or been converted for domestic use that there now exists a shortage of nest-sites in many places. In Gisburn Forest Lancashire, Derek Bunn's study came to a sad end due to nest robbing. His nest-sites were sited in old cottages and the like on Forestry Commission land and although nest-robbing was the prime reason for the cessation of his study, vandalism of the nest-boxes and general disturbance, even from birdwatchers, became a serious problem as more and more people gained access to a previously remote area. Many old buildings that were present in the forest during his study were destroyed by the Forestry Commission because they became unsafe for humans. Derek spent many hours, alone at night, watching the owls and he made many marvellous discoveries about their behaviour, but he considers that it would be unwise to spend lonely nights in that area now. Coupled with that, he is unaware of any barn owls there at present anyway. Along with the declining numbers of buildings that are now available in the British Isles, one wonders what effect the conversion of so many farm buildings will have in such places as France and Spain, where barn owls are also declining?

WOODLAND

Interest in woodlands has heightened in recent years and the idea of creating new woods and enlarging existing ones has attracted a lot of attention. Nevertheless, many new woodlands are being planted on farmland without, it would appear, consideration being given to the presence of barn owls. With planning, however, it might be possible to create a woodland environment that will

Barn owls may also hunt along wooded rides, and the careful placing of nest-boxes within new woodlands may help to encourage a diverse range of owl species.

accommodate barn owls because in its formative years woodland creates rich undergrowth that attracts small mammals. As the trees grow, however, the herbaceous plants are shaded out and many small mammals either disappear or become impossible for a barn owl to catch. When new woodlands are developed or existing ones enlarged, there exists an opportunity to attract barn owls by creating wide rides along which they can hunt. The provision of nesting boxes is likely to act as an inducement for them to take up residence, while boxes of different designs might well attract a diversity of owls if the area is large enough. A woodland habitat that includes good ground cover, along with open areas such as those found in parkland is an attractive habitat for barn owls. With some light coppicing in the more enclosed areas providing open spaces in which mice and voles may live, these are ideal haunts for owls. However, the woods do have to be substantial in size to create this environment.

The ancient art of pollarding is a way forward and could be introduced into these woods and indeed elsewhere. This form of management, that involves 'topping off' young trees at a height that makes the new growth unreachable by deer, can have great long-term benefits if the correct species of tree is used. Oak is the classic tree for pollarding and many of our greatest oaks are those that were pollarded over three to four hundred years ago. A visit to Staverton Park in Suffolk is well worthwhile. There, hundreds of ancient pollard oaks have, over the centuries, developed wonderful nesting holes and crevices within which barn owls find their homes. From time to time I see a revival of this ancient and beneficial craft and this, I believe, is a positive way with which to secure a long-term future for our barn owls, and not only in eastern England.

GOLF COURSES

One of the most popular sports in Britain today is golf. At present golf courses cover around 145,000ha of land, which is more than 0.5% of the land surface of Britain and which is the same area as all the Wildlife Trust and RSPB reserves put together. What is more, this area is increasing although not at the rate it was just a few years ago. Various parts of a golf course are subject to different cutting régimes and there are areas where the grass is allowed to grow. These areas, 'the roughs', are places where small mammals may live and it has been estimate that the total golf course roughs in Britain equated to 80% of the Wildlife Trust reserves. This is a tremendous amount of land that could be rendered suitable for small mammals if it were managed sympathetically. Golf courses have much to offer in terms of barn owl conservation because many are undisturbed at night, leaving owls to exploit them at the time when they do not conflict with man's interests.

RESEARCHING THE BARN OWL

During the course of this book I have highlighted certain aspects of the barn owl's biology that we need to know more about. Certain areas require further investigation to complement the excellent pioneering work that Derek Bunn and his colleagues undertook on this fascinating and at times elusive species is a credit to the amateur naturalist. Indeed, it could be argued that although we now have a large number of professional naturalists working for a whole raft of organisations, the need for amateur ornithologists to

A continuous programme of plotting the barn owl's distribution may well be more important than trying to assess how many there are. Young ornithologists have a valuable role to play in understanding the requirements of Britain's barn owls.

become involved in barn owl conservation is now more than ever. Today, the demands that are being put upon the professionals to produce results are greater than they have ever been, but where professionals may not have the time or opportunity for the necessary research, amateur ornithologists may well be able to fill in the gaps. There is much that they can achieve without involving themselves in nest-recording or ringing, for although both of those disciplines are important, they may not be attractive to everyone.

There is a need to evaluate which is more important: trying to establish the barn owl population in Britain or trying to establish its distribution? Some would no doubt argue that establishing the population is the more important, but I would argue that determining its distribution will tell us more about how our barn owls are progressing than establishing how many there are. Iain Taylor was in two minds over this, for he considered that establishing the population was important in some, more local studies, but felt that establishing the range and distribution was more important if there were conservation concerns. He is probably right in his assumption but I am of the opinion that as time progresses it will become more important to monitor the distribution than it will be to count the population because it will oscillate from year to year.

I am also of the view that barn owl enthusiasts cannot work alone in the matter of conservation. For some years now ornithologists have worked alongside mammalogists in seeking to establish what our barn owls are eating (David Glue, a research biologist working for the BTO, was one of the first to integrate owl studies with mammalogy in Britain) and this link needs to be continued and strengthened. Perhaps botanists could also be involved because they could give guidance on the timing of hedge-cutting and what plants would be best in a particular habitat which appeals to barn owl prey? Once upon a time, when ornithology appears to have been more integrated into the natural history movement, naturalists of various disciplines would come together to share knowledge and experiences, but for some time now bird studies appear to have become largely divorced from the natural history scene, although both the RSPB and the BTO have made great efforts in recent years to address this problem, and they are to be commended for that.

Whilst remembering that there is no substitute for study and direct observation in the field, there are some exciting aspects of modern technology that may well bring a new dimension to owl studies. It could be that by using technology, together with fieldwork and research, we may learn even more about the barn owl's status and requirements in Britain. Naturalists now have the ability to be able to identify land cover types from data obtained from satellites. Using satellite global positioning systems, observations of barn owls could be recorded in the field and their location plotted along with nest and roost sites. Some of the sophisticated night-sights now widely available could also be employed. The use of land cover maps should enable surveyors to identify those areas where barn owls are most likely to be found but where they have yet to be located. In other words, it would enable barn owl conservationists to go directly to those places that hold similar habitat qualities to those that already hold nesting barn owls. This would save a lot of time and resources. However, the system would have to be secure.

Barn owl workers have a perennial problem: all owls, and none more than the barn owl, have incredible hearing and to obtain meaningful records and observations it is nearly always necessary to work alone and as silently as possible. With two or more people working in the field this is virtually impossible and in their monograph Derek Bunn et al described the problems of watching barn owls from a hide 25m away. 'Even at this distance note-making is difficult, the slight clicking from some ball-point pens or the crinkling of some paper being sufficient to attract the bird's attention – and unwrapping one's sandwiches in complete silence can be a major problem!' The subject of personal safety needs to be fully addressed before venturing out alone at night. Derek Bunn tells me that he often returns to Gisburn Forest to watch and study birds, but even if barn owls were present he would not consider sitting out alone throughout the night to watch and study them because he considers the area unsafe. The role of landowners with safe and secluded land within which there are breeding barn owls will be important in the future for those who wish to study these fascinating but exasperating creatures who will always hear the careless fieldworker approaching and depart long before he can declare that 'there are no barn owls here'.

As I write the concluding sections to my history, preparations are well in hand for the forthcoming Bird Atlas 2007-11 that is being organised by the BTO, Birdwatch Ireland and the Scottish Ornithologists' Club. With this mammoth project ornithologists, both professional and amateur, will have the opportunity to record what is happening to our barn and other owls throughout the years of the Atlas. Let us hope that by the end of the project we will have a greater understanding of the distribution of our barn, and other, owls throughtout the British Isles so that meaningful conservation measures can be introduced where necessary.

SOURCES USED IN THIS CHAPTER

Bunn, D.S. Warburton, A.W. and Wilson, A.A.B. 1982: *The Barn Owl.* Poyser, Calton.

Copinger-Hill, H. 1932: Observations. *Trans. Suffolk Nat. Soc.,* 2: 94.

Dobbs, A. (ed.) 1975: *The Birds of Nottinghamshire.* David & Charles, Newton Abbot.

Duckels, A. 2002: The Barn Owl in South-West Lancashire. *Coastline, Summer*: 3. Sefton Coast Partnership.

Hagemeijer, W.J.M and Blair, M.J. 1997: *The EBCC Atlas of European Breeding Birds.* Poyser, London.

Leech, D., Barimore, C., Crick, H. & Shawyer, C. 2007: Monitoring Barn Owl populations. *BTO News*, 268: 14-15.

Martin, J.R. 1984: Results of the Suffolk Barn Owl Enquiry. *Suffolk Ornith. Group Bull.* 64: 5-11. Suffolk Ornithologists' Group, Ipswich.

Mead, C.J. 2000: *The State of the Nations' Birds*. Whittet Books, Stowmarket.

Rackham, O. 1994: *The Illustrated History of the Countryside*. Weidenfeld and Nicholson, London.

Seymour, J. 1988: Nestbox studies of Barn Owls. *BTO News*, 155: 5.

Shawyer, C. 1987: *The Barn Owl in the British Isles – Its Past, Present and Future*. The Hawk Trust, London.

Taylor, I.R. 1994: *Barn owls; predator prey relationships*. Cambridge University Press.

Tobin, B. & Taylor, B 1996: Golf and Wildlife. *British Wildlife,* 7: 137-146.

12 WHAT FUTURE FOR THE BARN OWL?

'The value of human life is, I think, rather more than a few protected species. I can't see this halting the development and nor should it.'

The comments of a senior civil servant, that were reported in the *Daily Telegraph* 20/10/2002, regarding the proposal to develop a disused airfield where barn owls were nesting.

Extinction is a strong word that has a disturbing finality about it but it is a word that has been used by some conservationists when contemplating the barn owl's future. Extinction of the barn owl *T.a.alba* seems unlikely, although it does seem possible that certain island races might come under severe pressure in the future and indeed some of these could become extinct, so there is plenty of opportunity for further research there before they do. One of the biggest threats to barn owls in western Europe, and particularly in the British Isles, is the diminishing size of their living space and this is an issue that will grow in importance.

URBANISATION

On July 13th, 2004, plans were announced to build over one million new homes in England and four areas in the south-east were singled out to receive 200,000 of them by the year 2016. These were the London – Stansted – Cambridge corridor, Milton Keynes/South Midlands, Ashford in Kent and the Thames Gateway corridor, which threatens, eventually, to eradicate the relic population of barn owls on the Thames marshes. In March 2006 the government of the day published further figures to indicate that England needed 5 million homes over the ensuing 20 years, of which 1.5 million were needed to meet record levels of immigration. The projection was based on the 2001 census (Table 21) which indicated new households were being formed at a rate of 209,000 a year, compared with projections of 189,000 in 2004 and 153,000 in 1996. Shortly after this, government advisers estimated that the East of England would have to build the equivalent of a city the size of Birmingham by 2021 to meet the

The open countryside is a diminishing habitat for the barn owl.

demand for new homes. While these figures are projections, they do give an indication of how trends are moving in south-east England, and especially in those counties to the immediate north and north-east of London, although nowhere is safe from development.

No new towns have been started since the development of Milton Keynes 40 years ago. Built between London and Birmingham, it was Britain's last new town, replacing three of the former towns and 13 villages that were there originally. Of all the new towns Milton Keynes is the largest and covers an area of around 9,000 hectares and this is increasing. It has a present population of around 250,000 which, according to the planners, is set to expand and may double by around 2036. Elsewhere, other new towns, such as Basildon and Harlow in Essex, for example, are set for 'regeneration' and the size and populations of these towns are also set to increase over the next 20 or so years.

If these building programmes go ahead in England, the

infrastructure needed to support them will be substantial. Roads, schools, shops, work-places, offices and many more ancillary buildings will need to be provided, and all of these developments will need to be supported by energy and water. It is not surprising, therefore, that in October 2003 Thames Water stated that they wanted to build a reservoir near Abingdon in Oxfordshire and that they were considering flooding nearly four square miles of farmland. This proposal is just one of seven reservoirs being considered across the country, although the Environment Agency stated that reservoir developments were far down their list of priorities. If the projected housing does become a reality in the south-east of England, and if the area continues to suffer water shortages as it has done in recent summers, then the need to create reservoirs will increase and so will the pressures on our farmland wildlife. Apart from the Oxfordshire example, there are other places in southern England that may be targeted for new reservoirs such as near Great Bradley in Suffolk, a site that was mooted in the early 1980s to supply water to the fast growing population in that region, and elsewhere near Canterbury, in Kent, a region that often suffers from water shortages during long, hot dry spells of weather. All of these sites could well bring problems for those barn owls living in their vicinity, although I suspect that their plight would be regarded as mitigated by provision of homes for water birds and species such as osprey, otter and water vole.

The growth of air travel is an important factor to be considered and despite opposition it seems likely that the expansion of Stansted Airport, including a second runway, will proceed. On May 21st, 2007, a governmental white paper was published that was designed to reform the planning laws by enabling planning procedures to be relaxed, thus allowing developments, such as airports, to proceed quickly and more easily. Stansted Airport in Essex is just one airport in Britain clamouring for the attentions of the highly mobile human population, and if we consider that in East Anglia alone there at least two other airports looking to expand, Southend and Norwich, then it is likely that the growth of airports, and all that goes with them, are set to have some considerable impact upon the terrestrial environment irrespective of its possible impact upon the climate. The RSPB also expressed concern at the publication of this white paper and at the proposed expansion of Lydd Airport near Dungeness, in Kent. Whilst this development may not have direct implications for barn owls if it goes ahead, the resultant spread of disturbance on the nearby Romney Marsh area may well have.

In Suffolk, it has been reported that the Suffolk Structure Plan Review Consultation Draft of 1998 made provision for 48,700 new dwellings in the County between 1996 and 2016, and a further draft of the plan made provision for a further 5,000 homes. Richard Stewart considered that current 'green-field' sites on the edge of Ipswich were already under threat from proposed housing development. From my fieldwork I am of the firm opinion that it was this factor that caused the 3-4 pairs of barn owls on the southern outskirts of the town to disappear during the 1990s, and further pressure on green-field sites on the edges of many towns and villages in Suffolk will come in the future as it will elsewhere.

In Europe, new towns, including those in Britain, are brought together under the umbrella of the European New Towns Platform (ENTP), which is the European network within the EC representing new towns across Europe from nine countries. The ENTP stretches from Pulawy in Poland to Torfaen in Wales and from Almere in Holland to Barcelona in Spain. Clearly, with the founding of the ENTP in 2001, new towns will feature highly in the future of the EC.

Recently a report from the United Nations population division stated that human migration is now at its greatest level ever and it predicted that at the time of writing until the year 2050, at least 2.2 million migrants will arrive annually into the rich world. These migrants will originate from Africa, Asia and the Middle East where rising populations will prompt tens of millions of people to migrate to Europe and North America. The report further predicted that the world population will increase by 2.5 billion by the year 2050 when the total will stand at around 9.2 billion. It appears that predictions from this department of the United Nations have usually been accurate and the calculation that Britain's population will rise from 60 million to around 69 million by 2050 must add further concern for our countryside. However, the report does state that populations will fall in countries such as Germany, Italy and more especially in Bulgaria, Ukraine, Russia and Poland. In the future it may be possible to increase barn owl numbers in some of those countries, although if this does happen it is unlikely that the white-breasted race will benefit.

So far I have not ventured far into Europe, for my chief concern has been for the barn owl in the British Isles. However, it is impossible to discuss Britain in isolation and at some stage in the future it may be necessary to manage Europe's barn owls on a comprehensive scale. The EC is a vast organisation comprising a range of countries with different backgrounds and with vested interests. At the start of this book in 2003, there were just 12 member countries but on its completion there were 27, with a further 3 Candidate Countries and a number of other countries also wishing to join. As these new nations adjust to the benefits they may well receive by joining the EC, there is likely to be a knock-on effect for the environment. For example, concerns have already been expressed about the construction of a four-lane motorway from Warsaw in Poland to Helsinki in Finland and this could well have implications for the barn owls in Poland. The concern for some bird species on mainland Europe is so great that recently the RSPB has made a significant and far-reaching decision to purchase a tract of land in Poland to protect the aquatic warbler's habitat from development. This extraordinary and bold step demonstrates the concerns that are now being expressed for the future of some species in Europe.

FARMING

At the time of writing the British government has relinquished a substantial part of its farming rebate in return for reforms to the European Common Agricultural Policy (CAP); at present it seems that the reforms will definitely go ahead. The surrender of at least £7 billion to the CAP is to allow more money to be given to eastern European countries for them to modernise their farming practices. It remains to be seen whether these will help or hinder barn owls in Eastern Europe or indeed in Britain.

As this report draws to a close, it is becoming clear that the lifespans of some of the 'agri-environment' farming schemes will draw to an end during the course of the next decade or so – perhaps sooner, and this came to be on September 26th, 2007, when the agricultural ministers of the European Union announced, to the consternation of the conservation movement, that the 'Set-Aside Scheme' was being suspended for one year in an attempt to counter-act soaring wheat prices. The suspension of this scheme will bring a great deal of land back into cultivation. Whether this scheme will be re-instated remains to be seen but there must now be concern for other agri-environmental schemes in the future. Many of those schemes have now been closed to new applicants, while the need to produce food to feed a growing population in Britain, Europe and worldwide, on an ever-shrinking amount of farmland, will dictate

Table 21
Population trends in England & Wales 1891 - 2001

	Persons 1901	1931	1951	1991	2001	2031 (projected)
England & Wales	32,557,843	32,468,567	43,763,031	50,748.000	52,084.500	60,088.000
East Anglia						
Cambridgeshire	200,680	139,238	166,887	510,600	553,600	
Isle of Ely		62,809	89,049			
Essex	1,062,645	1,487,246	2,044,964	1,249,100	1,312,700	
Suffolk	361,900	401,114	442,561	649.100	669,400	
Norfolk	467,754	453,747	548,062	754,300	797,900	
sub-total	2,092,979	2,404,916	3,291,523	2,514,649	2,111,823	
Remaining Home Counties						
Hertfordshire	239,760	326,217	609,775	984,300	1,034,900	
Berkshire	283,531	307,615	408,284	n/a	n/a	
Surrey	718,549	957,894	1,602,483	1,023.300	1,059,500	
Kent	935,144	1,097,283	1,564,324	1,285.800	1,331,100	
Buckinghamshire	173,061	250,334	386,291	455.700	479,100	
Bedfordshire	174,972	205,211	311,937	355.900	382,100	
Middlesex	810,306	957,649	2,269,315			
sub-total	3,335,323	4,102,203	7,152,409			
London	4,536,541	3,591,071	3,347,982			
London (inner)				2,599.300	2,771,700	
London (outer)				4,230.000	4,416,400	
sub-total	4,536,541	3,591,071	3,347,982	6,829.300	7,188,100	

The populations of some Home Counties, notably Surrey, Kent, Essex and Middlesex have changed over the years as parts of those counties were absorbed into Greater London especially after the 1974 boundary changes what happens to our farmlands in the future. It is to be remembered that it is just under a hundred years ago that many of our farmlands were brought back into production after a period of some forty or fifty years of low productivity and I have no reason to suppose that this will not happen again. In addition to this we cannot rule out the possibility of a national emergency at some stage in the future. If intensified farming does recur it seems unlikely that habitats will be destroyed on a senseless and wholesale basis as they were during the post-war decades. The conservation movement has fought long and hard to show that very little, if any, benefits arise from such actions. It is also unlikely we will return to a landscape heavily polluted by agricultural pesticides, although it seems probable that rodenticides will continue to exclude barn owls from our farmyards. Rats, it seems, will never be tolerated, but in the wider countryside perhaps the method of rodent control (to be described later) that is now being exercised in the Middle East could be replicated here?

The polarisation of farming in Britain today means that in general, cattle and sheep are farmed mainly in the north and west and arable farming has tended to be focussed upon the south and east, and I feel this has influenced some people's thinking in the way that we help our barn owls. It is important to appreciate that the approach to barn owl management taken in the Borders Region of southern Scotland, for example, is unlikely to be suitable for barn owls in East Anglia, or indeed throughout many parts of southern England. The studies of Bunn et al and Iain Taylor were conducted in areas where grassland is an important habitat for barn owls, and there seems little doubt that their studies have influenced the way of thinking, with regard to barn owl conservation, throughout the British Isles. I am of the view that in many other places we must look at providing prey that is more compatible to the dominant habitats, such as the largely arable farmlands of East Anglia for example, where mice and shrews are more likely to be the main prey species along with voles in the marginal grassland areas. At present most of the barn owls in southern Britain are confined to the river valleys and coastal grazing marshes, thus feeding largely on field voles, and for reasons that I will explain shortly, it may not be ideal to allow this to continue. There is a need for a long-term detailed study of barn owls on traditional lowland farmland, such as the one that Taylor carried out in his Scottish study, although finding sufficient owls at present on arable farmland to carry out such a study might prove difficult, as might accessing some tree-nests. Here the use of mini-cameras might be useful.

COASTAL GRAZING MARSHES, FENLAND AND RIVER VALLEYS

We know that in many parts of Britain the majority of barn owls live along river valleys, in claimed fenland and in coastal areas, and I have expressed concern that, although it is important to retain those areas as prime places for barn owls for the present, we should prepare other places to accommodate them in the future, and I give the following reasons why.

In fenland, problems are looming because for many years the East Anglian Fens have been progressively drying out, as a consequence of which the peat has shrunk and eroded and so the under-lying chalk is beginning to show through. The fens are gradually becoming unsuitable for farming and because of this the process has started to return large parts to their former wetland status. The Great Fen Project is dedicated to restoring large areas of farmland to a wetland comprising open water, reed beds, grassland and woodland on land between Huntingdon and Peterborough. In May 2007 3,200 acres of farmland were purchased for this project, which is half of the land needed to join Woodwalton Fen and Holme Fen nature reserves. The project aims to restore the area to wetland status within 50 years by which time it is estimated that the peat soil will have completely eroded. However, crucial to this will be the acquisition of farms so they can be flooded, which will be achieved when the current tenancies end or if the farmers can be persuaded to change their method of making a living.

Apart from the creation of wetlands, which the National Trust and RSPB are also actively involved in creating, there is a constant reminder from recognised authorities that future sea-levels will rise substantially in the future and that consequently low-lying areas, particularly in eastern England, will be under increasing threat from flooding (see Fig. 19 for example). At the launch of the World Wide Fund for Nature report in October 1998, it was predicted by English Nature (now Natural England) that 13,000 hectares of shoreline along the east coast of England would be lost to the sea by the year 2018. That report, which was written in conjunction with the Wildlife Trusts, said that this is already happening in Essex and accordingly it stated that in 20 years time 'the sea will be about 12 centimetres higher than now in South-east England, but in 50 years time it is expected to be 50 centimetres higher – more than 18 inches'.

Looking at the problem on a much longer time-scale, in April 2004 a climate study was published in the journal *Nature* by a team from the University of Reading and the Meteorological Office, which stated that in their view the Greenland ice-sheet could melt in 1,000 years time unless action is soon taken to reduce carbon dioxide levels. They stated that without this action the sea-levels would eventually rise by up to 23 feet and this will cause disastrous floods. They further believed that unless action was taken to halt the heating of the environment by the year 2100, the progress of the ice eventually melting would be irreversible due to a rising temperature over Greenland.

Like most predictions concerning the natural world, there is always some controversy; there are those who have an alternative view and believe that this is a gross exaggeration of the situation. The arguments continue but they do not change the accepted overall view that south-east England is slowly sinking and that for whatever reason the climate is warming and the sea-level is rising. The consequences are that this will affect many low-lying areas such as river valleys, fenland and the coastal areas. The long-term implications for those barn owls inhabiting those areas are therefore potentially serious. The mean sea-level at Sheerness in Kent is used by the Environment Agency as one of its indicators of change and since 1850 the level has risen at the rate of 2.2mm per year, while further north, at Aberdeen in Scotland, the level has risen just 0.7mm.

Other events threaten our coasts such as the huge tidal wave that swept down from Norway some 5,000 years ago. This was a result of an underwater landslip, and which covered parts of east Scotland up to a height of 100 metres. Just as threatening was the event in January 1607 when a huge flood engulfed large parts of Somerset and the coastal areas of South Wales. The area that was particularly affected was what we know as the Somerset Levels, an area that was claimed from the sea many years ago and which today is an important area for nature. Like the East Anglian and Lincolnshire Fens, the Somerset Levels require constant draining to prevent them from flooding, although it is now thought by some leading geologists that this flood was not the result of high tides and storms but rather of a tsunami, similar to the one that devastated large parts of Asia in December 2004. The flooding of the east coast in 1953 is a recent reminder of what can happen to such places as the low-lying areas of eastern Britain, and particularly to those in south-eastern England.

In the meantime, due to the present and anticipated rise in sea-level, flooding of the East Anglian coastline is already beginning to happen. Schemes are being created to deliberately flood parts of the coast to alleviate flooding pressures on other parts of the coastline. At Abbotts Hall in Essex, just to the south of Colchester, 84ha of arable land was flooded in October 2002 to allow it to eventually revert to salt-marsh. In this report it was stated that over the next 15-20 years 13,000ha of salt-marsh will need to be created and this will entail flooding much of the coastal landscape. Measures do need to be taken to alleviate the risk of coastal flooding but there is a danger that once the attractiveness of this venture is seen as a means of increasing some uncommon coastal plants and animals, or providing a refuge for other species, including wetland birds, the plight of the barn owl may well be overlooked. Only time will tell, but the concept of managed retreat is here to stay, for in March 2004 it was announced that a further 115 hectares of coastal wetland is to be created at Wallasea Island in Essex by flooding more farmland. This area was chosen to replace two lost areas of wetland after nearby port developments in the 1990s, and will serve as a nature reserve which it is hoped will not only be a wintering home for wading birds but also a means of flood defence that will take the pressure off the existing flood defences, especially at Burnham-on-Crouch (the flooding of the island took place in July 2006). In Sussex the creation of 46ha of intertidal mudflats is set to take place over the next few years on the lower reaches of the Cuckmere valley. More recently, the Environment Agency announced startling and radical plans to allow the flooding of a relatively large and undisturbed part of Norfolk during the course of the next 100 years. Addressing the situation, the chief executive of the agency, Lady Young, stated that, following research by Natural England, it was very likely that a large part of the Norfolk Broads would be lost to the sea, although Natural England pointed out that allowing this to happen was just one of four possibilities to alleviate the pressure of coastal flooding in that region. It was also believed that if this area was flooded, it would become a huge wetland for wildlife.

However, it is not just in Britain that rising sea-level has aroused concerns. In Holland plans are in place to flood 1,500 acres of farmland on the banks of the Western Schelde estuary and return them to the sea. It appears that since 1960 two thirds of Zeelands

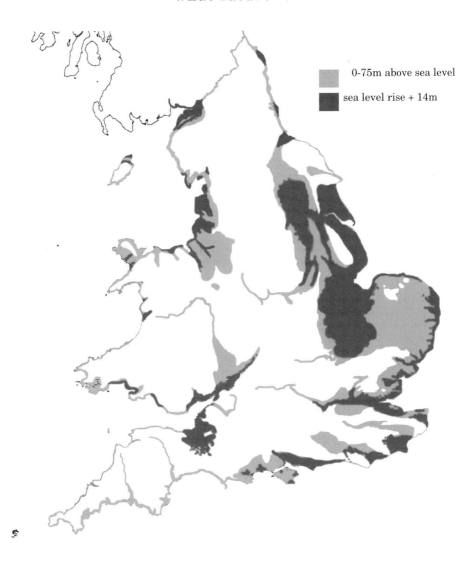

0-75m above sea level

sea level rise + 14m

If the sea level continues rising at the present rate large areas of south and east England especially will become inundated. Particularly vulnerable are the East Anglian and Lincolnshire Fens and the Somerset Levels. Elsewhere large parts of the eastern and southern coastlines are also susceptible to flooding.

wetlands have been lost to agriculture. Significantly, one leading Dutch wetlands expert believes that farmland is less valuable, ecologically, than wetlands.

The seemingly attractive idea of flooding farmland to create wetland areas for wildlife, whilst at the same time creating managed retreat areas to try and prevent coastal erosion and flooding elsewhere, involves flooding farmland that may be frequented by barn owls. It could be argued that before land was claimed from the sea, many coastal areas were flooded from time to time but then the situation was different because barn owls were not as reliant as they are now upon the low-lying coastal and riverside habitats for their survival. It will not be just the coast that feels the effect of flooding – the rising sea-level will infiltrate the countryside along our river systems. Perhaps future barn owl conservation strategies should feature higher ground, such as the 'East Anglian Heights', although that too has problems?

It not just wildlife that will be affected by the rising sea-level because according to a report issued by the Department of Trade and Industry in its 'Foresight' programme, at present 1.6 million people are at risk from flooding and by the year 2080 between 2.3 and 3.6 million people will be vulnerable. Therefore, buildings for housing and industry are more likely to be carried out on higher ground, away from the high-risk coastal areas and river valleys, and so conflict is likely to arise between conservation of wildlife and the need for housing.

A sign of the acceptance that flooding is likely to have an effect upon coastal wildlife was expressed in 2004 when concern was raised for the future of the RSPB's flagship reserve at Minsmere. During the winter of 2003-4 the north wall of the reserve was breached by the sea and in the light of the increasing number of storms in the North Sea together with rising sea-level, the Environment Agency prepared some possible options for the reserve which included either holding the present line of defence or abandoning it and retreating to higher ground. An indication of how serious the society viewed the long term situation can be assessed by a statement in which it said that they wished to see the reserve protected for as long as practically possible. The society has also expressed similar concern for its reserve at Strumpshaw Fen on the Norfolk coast, while on the Suffolk coast they are already constructing reed-beds inland to protect the bittern's dwindling coastal habitat.

THE FUTURE OF NESTING SITES

The availability of suitable nesting places is a long-term problem that will not be resolved easily. As Taylor pondered, it does seem likely that the conservation of barn owls in Europe and North America will depend upon the long-term management of nest-sites, involving the maintenance of traditional sites and the provision of new ones. There are, at present, a number of barn owl conservation programmes involving nationwide organisations and local communities. Most of these revolve around the provision of nest-boxes and improving the feeding habitats. Not all of these schemes will survive over the next 10-20 years and those that do may not attract the same enthusiasm that presently exists. In the long term, and here I am talking of beyond the year 2100, we cannot guarantee that the current interest in the barn owl will be maintained.

It is not only the loss of elm that has to be dealt with. Virtually everywhere large trees are under assault from development and from removal for health and safety reasons. Electricity suppliers are concerned that if large trees are left in the countryside, they may be blown down in strong winds and will bring down power supply lines. Apart from this, the general public is not tolerant of large trees for a variety of reasons and this is a problem. There has to be an end to the premature destruction of trees just because they are old and decaying as they have an important wildlife value not just for barn owls but for many other species. A way has to be found to preserve these 'stand-alone nature reserves' in the wider countryside without landowners facing the fear of litigation when an old tree falls and causes damage or injury. Perhaps we need more dedicated areas where these trees can live out their full lives or be allowed to stand even when they are dead?

The lack of suitable buildings is posing a problem because many have either been demolished or have been converted to housing or offices. Even in East Anglia, where I have previously stated that barn owls do not depend upon barns for nesting, the scarcity of such buildings means that opportunities for nest-boxes are becoming fewer and fewer, although to some degree this can be compensated for by placing nest-boxes on trees. For some people this might appear to be a problem but when planning proposals to convert barns and other country buildings into dwellings are presented to local authorities, the presence of barn owls should, ideally, be notified to the local authority. Provision for the owls can then be made ideally away from the conversion in the form of nest-boxes either within alternative buildings or in trees.

The provision of nest-boxes is undoubtedly helping to bolster the barn owl population, but when boxes are sited on poles in the fens and other open areas, problems may arise. There can be fierce competition between barn owls and other bird species, particularly jackdaws, but with some modifications, such as an interior partition (see Fig 17), the problem might be solved – unlike barn owls, jackdaws might not be inclined to enter such an enclosed space. Care must be exercised with exposed boxes, however, because in very hot weather the temperatures may rise, causing the owls to suffer from dehydration, while conversely in very cold temperatures barn owls may die from hypothermia. It seems preferable to site outside boxes in sheltered positions where possible. This is particularly important in high risk areas where the boxes might be subjected to vandals, nest-robbers, egg thieves and general disturbance, including disturbance from birdwatchers who sometimes gather in the vicinity of a nest-site to watch barn owls come and go.

It could be argued that the prediction that the sea-level will rise, eventually engulfing many low-lying areas, is alarmist and has little relevance to the conservation of barn owls, but history tells us that overwhelming floods do occur and all the evidence points to this happening again. It may also be argued that the issue of urbanisation of the countryside is also alarmist but all the evidence points towards this happening on an ever increasing scale.

In July 2004, the government announced that the housing budget would rise from £5,900,000,000 that year to £7,200,000,000 2007-08. On top of that there would be a new Community Infrastructure Fund of £150,000,000,000 by 2007-08 which would provide transport and other infrastructure around new housing developments. Is it unrealistic to suggest that a small portion of that amount should be spent on environmental projects that protect sensitive species of the open countryside?

THE POWER OF THE BARN OWL

Although my views on Britain's barn owls might appear to be pessimistic, there is hope for the species if the will is there. In the previous chapter I stated that the barn owl was now an influential species in political and conservation terms and nowhere is this more apparent than in the Middle East where a barn owl conservation project has brought the nations of Jordan, Israel and the Palestinian

Authority together to promote the use of barn owls and kestrels as biological pest controllers in agriculture on both sides of the Jordan River. I am grateful to Dr Yossi Leshem, the project leader for Israel and the Director of the International Centre for the Study of Bird Migration, for providing me with the details of the project.

To elaborate, the project started in the Hula Valley in 1982 to combat the damage that small mammals were having on crops and although it was initially successful, it foundered due to the use of rodenticides which affected the owls. In 1983 the project was moved to the Kibbutz Sde Eliyahue because of its large organic farming scheme and its willingness to participate.

Due to the popularity of the scheme there are now around 700 barn owl nest-boxes in place along with around 130 boxes for kestrels. This pairing is thought to be ideal because the barn owls hunt nocturnally and the kestrels take over during daylight. Small mammals can be a considerable pest in this region and in 2006 the diet of barn owls in one area of the Jordan Valley, was found to be largely comprised of house mice, Tristram's jird, rats, shrews and then birds. It appears that voles are not important in the diets and because of this, food is available on a consistent and regular basis, that is, there are no peaks and troughs as there are with vole-dependent owls in many parts of Europe. Consequently there is no periodic large-scale mortality as happens when vole populations crash.

This unique and interesting project not only involves naturalists from countries that are in a political and sometimes violent 'hot-bed', it also seeks to promote the participation of school children from different backgrounds, and to this end in 2007 the Kfar Ruppen School in Israel announced it was keen to find a partner school in Jordan to build on the relationship. Equally important is the willingness of the Jordanians to participate because for Muslims barn owls symbolize bad luck, and so it is very interesting to hear that once the benefits of barn owls over chemical pesticides was recognized by just a few of the farmers, others then followed suit. The project now ponders whether it will be the barn owl and not the dove that will eventually bring peace to the Middle East! The project is aimed at assisting with regional cooperation involving Israelis, Jordanians and Palestinians, and it will hopefully encourage the progress of the 'Corridor of Peace and Prosperity', the Japanese sponsored new initiative for regional economic cooperation.

Is there anybody out there?

Earlier I made the point that at some stage in the future aspiring young ornithologists may take up the study of the barn owl – perhaps in the spirit of Bunn et al? Hopefully they will realise that the study of owls does not rely solely upon nest recording or ringing, although both of those disciplines are very important. These studies will need to be integrated into a wider study embracing behaviour, habitat studies and other related matters such as pellet analysis and longevity.

It is, I believe, important for the professional bodies to encourage and guide amateur ornithologists in this, for both parties have much to gain. In recent years especially, there has been a vast volume of scientific documentation that makes little or no impression upon the layman, indeed there is a great danger that this approach could divorce one from the other. Throughout my study I have read a plethora of scientific material that I believe is either meaningless for many amateur ornithologists (and I suspect for some of the professionals) or whose purpose is obscure. The important dietary study by David Glue (1974) remains one of the most useful pieces of literature for the barn owl student, not only because of the information contained within it but because of its easy-to-read and informative manner. There is a need for good scientific papers relating to various aspects of barn owl ecology and biology that will interest the amateur and not 'turn him off' or only confuse him. Information must be presented in a user-friendly manner if the conservation movement is not to distance itself from the volunteers, whatever our faults, because there are signs that this is beginning to happen. Marren (2002) was forthright in his views when he stated 'Even so, nature conservation remains a rather inclusive activity with an off-putting bureaucrat's language. Most of its many publications offer only a partial view, or are forbiddingly technical. After half a century the industry still lacks an informed, popular literature'. Apart from this, I believe that amateur naturalists can speak out independently on important issues where, perhaps, professionals may feel themselves constrained.

'Particularly in Europe, the Barn Owl and man are closely linked in many ways. There can be no question of the popularity and attraction of the Barn Owl to the general public, nor indeed is there much doubt that the agricultural community recognize Barn Owls as valuable components of the countryside, with a very positive contribution to make in the overall regulation of the numbers of harmful small rodents. Farmer, financier, industrialist and conservationist must combine in efforts to provide a secure future for this elegant owl, so much a feature of our farmscape'

Eric Hosking
Eric Hosking's Owls (Pelham Books, 1982)

SOURCES USED IN THIS CHAPTER

Bunn, D.S. Warburton, A.W. and Wilson, A.A.B. 1982: *The Barn Owl.* Poyser, Calton.

Marren, P. 2002: *Nature Conservation*. Harper Collins, London.

Pitches, A. 2004: Minsmere under threat. *British Birds,* 97: 484-488.

Stewart, R. 2001: *The Millennium Atlas of Suffolk Butterflies.* Suffolk Naturalists' Society, Ipswich.

Tabor, R. 2003: Turning the tide for saltmarshes. *British Wildlife,* 15: 10-19.

Taylor, I.R. 1994: *Barn owls; predator prey relationships.* Cambridge University Press.

SOME OBSERVATIONS OF BARN OWLS IN HAMPSHIRE

DURING THE 1930s BY F. GIBSON PHILLIPS

INTRODUCTION

Following the death of the late Eric Hosking, I came into possession of a box full of newspaper cuttings and other snippets of information concerning owls that Eric had collected over the years. At the bottom of the box was a small sheaf of type-written papers simply headed 'BARN OWL'. The name of the author was not typed on the collection, although Eric had written in pencil the name 'Frank Phillips'. It subsequently appears that Frank Phillips was a naturalist and wildlife photographer who had a number of articles and photographs published in magazines such as The Field. Most of his field-work appears to have taken place in Hampshire and there is no mention of who he was working with. To the best of my knowledge, he did not write any books and neither did he publish these notes and so, in tribute to him, I publish them here. The notes were made in 1939, just before the Second World War.

I have made great efforts to try and establish whether Frank Phillips is still alive but to no avail. I have also made efforts to try and locate any members of his family who might still be alive, but that has also been without success. I therefore trust that by publishing these extremely interesting and methodical notes, made in the field when the countryside was much more of a welcome place for barn owls than it is today, I shall neither offend Frank Phillips, his memory, or indeed any members of his family that may still be alive. I am grateful to Derek Bunn for assessing these notes and for agreeing with me that they should be published. It is an excellent model for any aspiring owl student to follow. They are presented unabridged and grammatically uncorrected and as near to the manner in which they were written.

1939 BARN OWL
A. UP TO HATCHING

1. DESCRIPTION OF SITE ETC

The owls were nesting in a hollow elm tree in the middle of a ten-acre field which was always occupied by about twenty cows. The tree was about a hundred yards from farm buildings at the end of a village and the owls were therefore quite accustomed to people and animals moving in the vicinity of the nest. The ground was of a marshy nature, the north-west side of the field being bounded by a tributary of the Itchen. On the other sides it was bounded by roads from the village which lay on rising ground to the South. The countryside for a distance of about half a mile round the nest was either arable and pastureland or marsh, with a few isolated trees and the usual hedgerow. A fairly large wood lay some three quarters of a mile to the east.

2. Description of Nest

The nest was about seven feet from the ground in the hollow trunk of the old elm tree, no branches of which were lower than about fifteen feet. There were two holes – the result of the breaking off of branches – one at each end of a cavity some five feet long and three feet wide. The floor was level and covered with a thick carpet of old, disintegrated pellets (the farmer said that the nest had been in use every year for the last twenty two years). There was a fair amount of foliage above the level of the nest.

3. Incubation and Hatching

The nest was found on the 15th April and contained one egg which one of the birds was incubating while the other roosted at the other end of the nest. The owls took no notice of my looking in and had to be lifted with a walking stick in order to see what she was sitting on. It was impossible to say, from the appearance of the birds, which was male and which female, and this distinction was only possible from observation of their habits. Further visits were paid to the nest at intervals but it was often impracticable to examine it properly, owing to the difficulty of removing the bird even with the aid of a walking stick. On the 29th April, however, it could be seen that there were then four eggs. Accurate observation of the hatching was again impossible but on the 25th May the nest contained four owlets the last of which was just leaving the egg. There appeared to be a difference of three or four days in the ages of the young birds, but this estimate is based only on the size etc. of them at that time. This makes a difference of about twelve days as between the ages of the oldest and youngest.

3. The Hide

The erection of the hide was begun on the 26th May and was completed on the 31st. The front of the hide was six feet from the hole on which we had decided to work (the other hole was blocked). While the hide was being built one nbird remained in the nest brooding the young and on one occasion, while we were actually working beside the nest, the (presumably) cock bird returned to the nest with food. It took this into the nest and emerged some ten seconds later without it. Observation from the hide was begun on the night of the 2nd June.

Summary of Observations from Hide

1. Type of food

As the nest was situated in the open it was easy (particularly on moonlit nights) to see exactly what food was being brought to the nest. An examination of the pellets and contents of the nest was also periodically carried out (as well as was possible). The relative quantities of the different types of food were approximately as follows:

Rats	60%
Mice and Voles	5%
Miscellaneous	15%
made up of the following:	
Stoats	2
Weasels	1
Slow worms	4
Grass snakes	1
Shrews	2
Young rabbits	1

Young birds (principally thrushes or blackbirds) were also occasionally brought back - - it was judged about one every four or five days. No trace of any other kind of food other than that given above could be found during the whole of our observations.

Bringing of Food

For ten or eleven days after observation was begun both birds often visited the nest but the cock's visits soon became less frequent and after 23rd June it was not seen at all. In the early stages both birds left the nest some half hour after sunset to hunt. One or other would then return at half-hourly intervals with food for the young, though on several occasions they returned together, the cock leaving almost immediately but the hen remained to feed the young. After midnight neither bird entered the nest for an hour and a half to two hours, although they were frequently heard in the immediate vicinity. Subsequent observations away from the hide, showed that they were accustomed to feed themselves during this period. For about two hours before dawn visits to the nest with food again took place at about half-hourly intervals. After the cock had lost interest in the nest, the hen alone fed the young with much the same frequency.

Procedure at Nest

The usual procedure of the parents when bringing food for the young was first to perch on a bough ten feet above the nest and there change its prey from its talons to its beak. It would then sit looking round for periods varying considerably from a few seconds to a quarter of an hour. The bird was observed in this in this position a considerable number of times and it was always in exactly the same place, almost to a matter of inches. It then flew straight to the nest (far more audibly than when hunting). It seemed, from the volume of their hissing, that the young birds were quite unaware of the nearness of the owl until its talons were actually scratching on the bark, for the steady but subdued hissing, which did not cease for more than a few seconds at a time during the whole of our nocturnal observations, only at this point increased sufficiently to warrant the assumption that they were more than usually excited. Once outside the nest there was no delay in entering (provided, of course, that the owl had not been disturbed by a recent change of occupation in the hide; for in this case it would often give an enquiring glance at the hide). Usually, however, as soon as it alighted it immediately thrust its head and shoulders into the hole and dropped lightly down to the floor of the nest – a distance of about nine inches. The vocal enthusiasm of the young was then tremendous, but as the food was administered it subdued to a satisfied 'bubbling'. While the owlets were still very young the parent remained in the nest for some minutes tearing up the food (which was heard from the hide) and, presumably, generally superintending the feeding. After the 12th June her stay in the nest became noticeably shorter and after the 16th she was never in the nest for more than a few seconds at a time during the night. It seems, therefore, that the young were able to attend to their own feeding when about twenty four days old. When leaving the nest the owl would frequently stand in front of the hole for some minutes looking round, before flying off.

In addition to this general procedure for feeding the young there are three further points :-

On a few occasions (though it was certainly unusual) the owl flew direct to the nest with food under the talon and changed it to its beak outside the nest.

When just about to enter the nest she frequently emitted a noise which was never heard on another occasion – a brief and subdued clucking twitter.

When the young were forty to fifty days old food was quite often taken into the nest while still alive.

Apart from feeding of the young a good deal was seen of the owl during the night for she would often perch on any branch of the tree, on the hide or outside the nest, or fly about from one to another. She would then perch, either on a branch or outside the nest hole to consume the results of her recent hunting. She was observed to eat a short-tailed field vole as follows. Flying down with it in her left talon she immediately turned her back on the nest-hole and looked at it closely in an almost human speculative attitude, evidencing at once that the food was not intended for the young. Picking up the vole in her beak by the back of the neck, she stood up still and straight and looked steadfastly into the distance for quite ten seconds. Then quite suddenly, she lifted her head and, with four or five continuous gulps, swallowed the vole completely in the total time of no more than three seconds. Neither a noise from the hide nor the touching off of a flash bulb made her look round and she remained looking in the same direction (i.e. away from the hide) for some seconds before she flew away.

None of the young were seen outside the nest until they were fifty-five to sixty days old. In this connexion there were some remarkable facts. On the 25th May there were four recently hatched young in the nest but a fortnight later one was missing, while by the end of June the number had been reduced to two. The nest was in the middle of a field which was strictly private owing to its containing cows in calf. Moreover the house of the village policeman overlooked the field and he was quite sure that no one would have gone to the nest and removed any of the young. On the other hand it seems inconceivable that they could have left the nest on their own*.

On 13th July one of the young was seen outside of the nest for the first time. It had some difficulty in climbing the nine inches to the top of the hole but it immediately went in again and practised the climb several times until it was quite competent. It then began the climb up the side of the hole and sit on the top. This manoeuvre also it repeated several times going right back into the hole on each occasion. It then took to climbing right round the hole and sitting on the top or just outside for longer periods. Whenever food was brought it would either rush back into the nest before the parent actually perched and wait for the latter to come in, or tear it from her beak as it dived into the hole.

Both young were at this time still white and downy but a fortnight later most of this had disappeared and were just like small thin and larger-eyed editions of their parents. They were now able to flutter though they never strayed more than two or three yards. At the age of about eleven weeks they seemed almost fully developed and self-reliant but still made frequent use of the nest by day and night. The development of their voices was quite recognisable, a gentle hiss developing perceptibly into a harsher and more screech-like note.

*The disappearances of young barn owls from their nesting place has been reported by several authors and cannibalism is one of the reasons that has been given for this.

C SUMMARY OF OBSERVATIONS OF HUNTING HABITS

1. THE COCK

The habits of the cock, in the early stages of the nest, were almost exactly the same as the hen's. The same localities were visited and the same type of food was brought to the young. However, he soon lost interest in the nest and then appeared to move to another locality. At all events, he was never seen anywhere in the vicinity of the home tree and it was a matter of conjecture as to whether Barn Owls seen elsewhere in the district were the cock or not. Therefore our observations are, of necessity, confined to one bird which, we assumed was the hen. But for the short time that both birds were about, they were frequently seen hunting together in the same corner of field or at the same ricks, but we never saw any signs of conscious co-operation between the two. They both seemed to carry on their hunting regardless of the activities of the other, although they would frequently perch in the same tree, and when they both had food, fly back to the nest together. In every respect it was impossible to tell which bird was which when away from the nest, so similar were their actions.

Therefore the following observations are applicable to either bird.

2. THE HEN

We found that the bird had a very definite system in its hunting. Certain spots were never visited whereas other places were apparently favourite hunting grounds. The surrounding country fell more or less into the following divisions.

a. The ten acre field where the nest was.

b. The water meadows with the Itchen and its tributaries to the north.

c. The farm yard and barns and village to the south and west.

d. Two more fields and the woods to the east. (The woods had an open glade about ¾ of a mile to the east of the nest.)

The procedure on leaving the nest was as follows. The owl would first sit outside the nest and look around the nesting field for anything up to ¼ hour. It would then set off to hunt. It always proceeded to a small group of willows by the stream to the north where it would perch for a time and make one or two flights out over the marsh keeping to the hedges, ditches etc; It would then proceed in a circular tour round the road and houses to the and so on round to the south and the farm yard and the barns. A considerable amount of time would be spent at the farm, where it would perch on the roof of the barns etc. and wait for the rats and mice to run. A whole night was spent here.

The night was fine with a good moon and it was possible to see the bird at anything up to about seventy yards. It was found that it visited this locality about once every three quarters of an hour though sometimes it would be considerably less. On arrival, it would fly around the barns in its usual way, checking, swinging round to re-examine a spot when it thought it saw anything or heard a rustle. Sometimes it would make a kill at this time, dropping onto the ground and killing with talons under drooping wings, though usually it would perch on the roof of one of the buildings and wait for the rats and mice to run out into the open. When perched, waiting she would always keep dead silent, never screeching or anything like that. She would sit, staring down, her head turning about as she looked in different directions, sometimes bending forward to stare particularly hard when anything caught her attention. When a rat or mouse appeared, she would fly off and drop on it as he ran, killing as usual. There was very little routine or system followed at these buildings. Once the owl had arrived there she would fly around in a more or less haphazard way and perch wherever she felt inclined at the moment. Where the system lay was in the way she arrived at the spot regularly, always coming in from the same direction and always leaving in the same way. I found however, that once a kill had been made, the bird nearly always returned in a fairly direct line to the nest. Of course, if she came to a hedge along which she was accustomed to hunt and it was leading in the right direction she would follow it in the usual way and I have, while waiting to see the bird hunt, seen her coming along the usual way with food already caught but she always branched off when near the nest and flew back direct.

When flying back with food, I often noticed that the owl flew quite high, sometimes quite a hundred feet up when coming from a considerable distance but almost always at least twenty five feet up. This of course is in direct contrast to the method when hunting when the bird usually keeps about five to ten feet up.

The method of killing the pray is of interest and I saw it best at Hungerford a year or so ago. It was a winters night, with a full moon and I was siting under a rat infested rick. I was on the north side in the shadow but, being winter the moon was very high in the sky, and the shadow only extended about eight feet out. Beyond that it was brilliant moonlight but of course I was very nearly invisible. A barn owl hunted there regularly, arriving every half hour or so, coming along the hedge. She would fly around the rick once or twice and perch in the trees by the lane twenty feet or so behind the rick, or sometimes even on the rick itself. Here again she would wait sometimes for as long as ten minutes without making a sound and I often thought she had gone. Once, after about five minutes of silent waiting, a rat ran from the rick just beside me. I was watching the rat rather than looking for the owl, but before the animal had gone more than ten feet I caught sight of the owl. She had just flown from the top of the rick and was gliding off after the rat. She caught up with it, passed it and then swung up and over, closed its wings, and dropped from a height of about ten feet, landing on the rat with both talons. She made a really loud thud as she struck. She was therefore facing me as she landed, and I had a fine view of her only fifteen feet away. She gripped the rat with both feet and fluttered her wings over it, letting them droop and trail on the ground. It was a splendid sight. The bird then took not the slightest notice of the victim. She just stood there and waited for the creature to die. This it did after about a minute, but it wriggled about a good bit at first and squeaked. Once the owl bent its head down and did something to it with its beak but I could not see clearly what it was. She then flew off with the prey in the talon. The bird always carries the food in the talon over any distance transferring to the beak on branches near the nest or as I have seen another owl at Winchester do regularly this year, transfer it in full flight. When carrying food the flight is much more ragged. The bird does not take any pains to fly quietly but just flaps along with larger and more decisive wing beats. When carrying a full grown rat or anything of that nature the flight is very laboured and I have seen a bird barely able to rise with the weight. At the nest it was possible to here a swishing noise from the wings as much as nine or ten feet away through when hunting, such care is taken and the wings are moved with such a light, sensitive touch that scarcely any sound is made.

After leaving the barns etc: the bird would sometimes proceed along the fields or again along the river and water meadows to the wood and open glade. I often saw her hunting in the glade but of course when it was dark it was impossible to see in the wood and I have only heard the bird in it. The glade consisted of an open patch of grass, long with nettles, about 200 yards long by 100 wide. There were a number of chestnut trees here and the bird was often seen here, but, being about ¾ of a mile from the nest it was not very often visited and then only spasmodically. She would quarter this glade dozens of times, going round under the chestnuts back and forth from side to side. I never knew her to perch here. She always kept on the move and seemed to rely more on finding the mice by covering a lot of ground than by waiting for them to appear in a likely spot. This was the most interesting place to watch her, for she was always in sight and usually would fly back and forth for half an hour or more without finding anything. The prey caught here was usually small, mostly short tailed field voles or mice. When we saw the bird leave this glade with food it was possible in the car to get back to the nest before she arrived and to check up on the prey when she got there, having settled in the hide a good minute before she got there but one had to move! This shows that the bird does not travel very fast even when coming almost straight home. It was always possible when there was a moon to see exactly what the bird was doing and almost always possible to identify the food.

As regards calling when hunting, I have never been able to decide anything definite. The voice does have a very marked effect on the prey. I have noticed this when sitting under my haystack. When an owl called the rats would usually freeze where they were but there were always a few who would bolt back to the rick and take cover. They would then keep quiet for about a couple of minutes but soon were making as much rustling and squeeking as ever. I am sure they were rather curios as to what the noise might be rather than actually frightened for when the rats had been really scared, as for example by me, it took quite half an hour for them to come out again. Of course the barn owls cry is a dreadful sound and no doubt the rats were greatly startled by it but as is the case when one is startled by a train whistling, they soon forgot it again. It is equally certain that the owl has no intention of frightening its prey. Such reasoning would denote an intelligence of an introspective and conscious type rather than the simple objective reaction to external stimuli that is normally shown. As with nearly all birds, its behaviour is governed by simple reflexes. It sees a rat so drops on it etc: it is too much to believe it capable of the complicated mental process involved in working out in its own mind the probable effect on the mind of a rat that a screech would have. It may be that an individual bird might find out by the old method of trial and error that a screech often makes a rat show itself by bolting etc: but this is unlikely. I think the bird is merely giving vent to its own feelings. It may give an exultant screech when it sees a mouse and so petrify the creature so that its capture is certain but I feel sure the owl has no such intention. I should think that the haphazard screaming cries given at odd intervals must do more harm than good from what I have seen of the reaction of the rats. Similarly, I don't think the bird flies so noiselessly in order to approach its pray unheard, but rather so that itself may here without being worried by the swishing of its own wings. I am certain that hearing is as important as sight to the bird when hunting but I do not think it ever actually attacks prey unless it can see some sign of movement. I have watched an owl sitting on one side of a barn and have seen it turn round at the sound of a squeek from the other side and fly round, but unless the prey was in sight it would never drop into the grass on the off chance. I am also certain that they work very much by sight. By that I mean sight alone.

I saw an owl flying over a large expanse of grass in Avington Park in August. It was flying along when it suddenly looked down circled round three or four times and then perched. This was in the quite early evening when I was on my way to put up hides. I was astonished to see a barn owl sitting in the middle of an open space like that, so I get out the old telescope and watched it. [I have two authoritative witnesses to vouch for this too.] The bird was standing by a molehill and the mole was working inside. I could see the earth being moved about by the animal within. It stood by this mound for a full five minutes, watching. At last the mole either came to the surface or was near to it for the owl suddenly stuck out its talon and grasped the unfortunate creature and flew off with it. We knew where this bird had a nest with four almost fully-fledged young so went to it and there sure enough found a mole still warm. [I have noticed that if an owl can get mice etc: it very rarely eats moles or weasels etc: but leaves them untouched in the nest.] It is certain that the bird could not hear the mole scraping for it was flying too high. It must have seen the ground moving and come down to investigate. Hearing is very important for first drawing the bird's attention to prey but what I have seen this is no good unless backed up by sight as well.

3. TIMES OF HUNTING

Hunting used to start some half hour after sunset and go on without a break until dawn. They found food both for young and themselves in this time but they were never about in daytime at all. I think a few observations about other nests I have watched would not come amiss so I shall deal with them in bulk under various types of hunting rather than under each separate bird

4. AT NESTING TIMES

This is the time when the most discrepancies in the normal time of hunting may be observed. Normally with all the birds they are as above but everything works backwards sort of style when there are young. There was a nest in the park this year [the mole one] where the parent used to start hunting about six o'clock even in bright sunlight. Of course she was grand to watch. As far as could be ascertained she adhered to the same routine in daytime that she did in the night. She had a favourite glade some what like the Easton one and every evening she would hunt in this for two hours or more. If one went to this glade any evening between 6.30 and 7.30 one could be absolutely sure of finding her there. As far as I could ascertain she hunted solidly all the night as well. But as a rule would not come out in the mornings or afternoons though I have seen her once about 8 a.m. A third nest down near the river and lakes had a pair that used to take fish. I was never able to see them do so but have found the remains of fish in the nest. They seemed to be fairly small, not more than eight inches in length. This bird used to hunt a bit more frequently in the early evening than mine but she was not so early as the park one.

The stony lane one [half a mile from home but a rotten site.] used very rarely to come out in the day, but she nearly always seemed to get mobbed. [The others never were.] In all cases of early hunting I never saw the slightest sign that they were hampered by the light. It did not seem to have the slightest effect on them, and I have often seen the Park bird flying with its face right to the sun without the slightest inconvenience.

5. YOUNG BIRDS

These seem to be about at all times of the day or night. They rarely seem to know what to do with them selves and appear to be rather pottering round than hunting. It is, I believe the generally accepted theory that the parents drive the young birds off as soon as they can look after themselves but I have never seen anything to support this myself. The tawny owl that I worked this spring had one youngster and he is now [October] still in the company of his two parents and may be heard calling with them every night. This would appear to illustrate that these young at least are not driven out. I am quite sure of this fact as I have been out regularly ever since he flew and have followed his history most carefully. I think it more probable that the young, once leave the nest tend to move off on their own rather than to be driven off. Unless there are definite observations to support the theory of driving out I am not prepared to accept it.

6. MIGRATIONS

It has been my experience that these birds do not migrate through young birds on leaving the nest may travel some distance to find a territory of there own. A youngster has recently arrived here and calls from the roof above my window each night [a curious hissing, a bit more developed than when in the nest but not a proper screech yet.] I saw him about in the daytime at first apparently hunting, but he has not been seen in the day of late. This probably implies that he has got to know the country fairly well and has found somewhere to roost This movement of young birds cannot be classed as migration however.

7. FURTHER HUNTING TIMES

Hunting in winter etc: will be dealt with later under general observations. This seems to cover hunting procedure well, but I shall doubtless think of further points as I go along.

D A TYPICAL NIGHT IN THE HIDE

Being the observations on the 27th June 1939.

9.18. Arrived in hide. It is a fine fresh evening, still quite light as the sun has barely set. There has been no sight of the owl as yet. The young, now about 35 days old are hissing steadily; a continual persistent noise, always keeping about the same amount of volume.

10.5. The hen left the nest. No sign of a second bird has been seen of late, so suppose this one must be the hen. She scrambled out, the young making a slight crescande of hissing as she did so, and stood outside, looking all around the field for about three minutes. She looked up at the sky almost as though she were trying to decide if it would fain. She was probably letting her eyes become accustomed to the brighter light outside the nest. She always waits a good time when she first comes out. She flew straight off from the nest away to the north west and has probably perched on the willows to the north. As usual while sitting outside, she gave one or two very faint screaming calls, almost under her breath.

10.17 Called once from the direction of the village.

10.30. She has just perched on the bough above and to left [east] of hide. I heard her talons scratch. It is still to light and too much breeze to hear her wing beats yet

10.35. Still on the bough. I can see the shape of the prey under her talon.

10.38 She flew down, with prey in beak. She perched on top of the nest hole, right up at top and looked all round, tremendous hissing from young. Old bird answered with twitter call and scrambled down side of nest hole, and stopped on right of it. She then looked at the hide. Food young rat. Turned and scrambled into nest. Terrific noise from young. Changed to bubbling after about 60 seconds. Two minutes later hen came out. She stood for about 10 seconds. And then flew off towards east this time.

11.0. I can now see more by the moon than by daylight. It is approaching a full moon and gives a good light.

11.10. Arrived at nest, flying straight in and dived almost at once Inside, pausing to regain her balance only. Food looked small. Usual terrific hissing.

11.12. Hen left nest and is now sitting on the usual bough to left. She seems interested in the cows who are restless tonight.

11.28. Hen left bough and flew off over hide towards willows. The young have been hissing steadily all the time she has been on bough but she has not answered them at all.

12.0. Hen still away. I have heard her calling, the long drawn out

Screaming one from time to time, mostly from the direction of the village and farm buildings. The hissing from the young has died down a bit now beginning to become more insistent

12.15. The hen is sitting on the usual bough. I heard her wings

Beating, a soft swishing sound as she arrived and her talons scratch. She arrived a minute or two ago. She has called the soft twittering call twice so far. The young I think heard these calls for they are hissing very loudy.

12.18. Now on top of the hide.

12.19. Still on hide. I have heard the twittering call very distinctly.

12.21. Flew on to nest. Food was a fairly small rat. She took it down in her talon and stood outside, looking at the hide and all around the surrounding countryside. I fired flash as she was doing this [Movement of head subsequently shown] She then looked at the hide and after a bit picked up the rat in beak and prepared to enter nest. I fired a second flash just before she went in.[I used to work with two flash reflectors, two bulbs in each and sometimes with two more single ones as well. I had two double and one single this night. I think it is a good scheme to have several, as it illuminates changing bulbs and enables a series to be obtained. I took three of her swallowing but only the one had   little movement. Each reflector only coast me 2/6 to have made.

12.27. Hen left again.

12.30. Back on bough with food.

12.34. Seems to have eaten food herself.

12.40. She has moved twice to other branches and has now
flown off in direction of farm.

1.53. Returned to favourite bough and ate moor food. She
only stopped a minute or so. Young still hissing
steadily.

2.37.Hen arrived at the nest with a bird of sorts. It looked
all legs. Might have been almost anything. The bird
when returning over the fields to the east frequently
disturbs a pee-wit. It would seem that she probably has young although it is pretty late for them. She changed it to her beak on the bough above nest and dived straight in on perching with-out any twittering or anything, so did not get a really good view food.

2.38. Hen came out again. The hissing has continued with-out any bubbling. It would seem that they have not been fed this time.

2.46.Back on bough again. Flew almost at once to nest carrying a young rat in talon. Perched on left of hole this time. Rat did not seem to be quite dead. Bird gripped it very hard and looked at it intently. Picked it up in beak and sat up very straight. Rat seemed dead then. Fired flash. When I could see again she had put it back under talon and was gazing at flash reflector very suspiciously . Picked up rat again and flew up to top of hide. A few tinny sounds as she tapped the reflector with her talon or beak. [She quite often does this.] She did not attack it but merely investigated. She then flew back down again and I noticed the noise the wings made while she was fluttering just before perching. The pray was in the beak, and she turned right round with her back to the nest and lowering her head, gazed at the lens. I had had these displays of uncertainty before and knew she never minded what happened, so I fired off another flash. She took no notice and then went on into the nest. She emerged again in about four minutes, looked at the reflectors in a very speculative way and flew off in direction of the willows behind the hide.

3.10. It is now getting quite light again and the moon is going behind the trees.

3.17. Returned with quite a large rat. Had it in talon and transferred to beak directly and went into nest.

I fired the last flash as she did so. I could this time hear the sound of tearing flesh quite distinctly

3.24. Left again. The young have been bubbling a lot, and

are now not hissing nearly so much.

3.30. Back on favourite bough. She sat here and called the   screaming cry under her breath a number of times.

3.45. Flew to the nest. As far as I could see she had no prey during this last visit. She perched outside for about two minutes and then went on inside. The young hissed louder but it soon died down again. She did not appear again and at 4.15. I was relieved.

GENERAL OBSERVATIONS OF EASTON BARN OWL

METHOD OF HOLDING PREY

The various methods by which food was held are of interest. These are derived primarily from the photographs, which show the grips very well. When carrying food in the beak it is nearly always held by the back of the neck but when the prey is brought back alive, as when the young are getting larger, it is often held very carefully by one ear. I have a print that shows this beautifully but it is a rotten photo of the bird.

The main interest lies in the talon grips. The bird seems to always have two claws each side of the victim. In the print where the bird is looking at the hide it can be seen that the end of the claw that bears the sharp point [technical term unknown I fear] is bent round so that the sharp points are imbedded in the victim's vitals. An examination of almost any print showing the plain talon will show that the talon itself is curved round so that when standing the bird is right up on the point of the claw. Therefore when seizing a victim, the talon goes fight round the creature and penetrates the soft underneath side of it. In the print that shows the bird with young rat in beak, looking over the shoulder before entering hole, there are two marks on the lower part of the abdomen of rat which I think are the marks of the claws. [I should appreciate a second opinion on this by the way.] Judging from these marks it would appear that the talon penetrates almost straight up, which is not what one would think from watching the bird drop on top of its prey.

The owl also usually grips the pray by the shoulders, one talon each side of the fore-legs. I have noticed this from the hide as well as from the print showing it. I also have another print that shows it but it has a light fog on the bird. [These negs can be sent along if of any interest.] Of course, when killing the pray in the first places the owl cannot be sure of getting this grip and seizes the first spot available. [Hence wounds on lower abdomen.]

2. REVERSIBLE BACK CLAW

A comparison of the prints with food in talon and those of bird just standing etc: will show many different positions of the back claw. I think actually that the claw that moves its position is the off-side front one, the real back one staying behind all the time. In the print of the bird swallowing, there are two to the front one to the back and one to the near side while in the one with the bird standing at the entrance looking to the side, all three claws are to the front and only the one back one straight to the back.

ACKNOWLEDGMENTS
Over the years I have been grateful for the help and encouragement of so many people. Dr. Geoff Heathcote patiently guided me through my formative days as an aspiring author while the late R.B. (Bob) Warren was particularly helpful during the Suffolk Barn Owl Survey. He was a remarkable man and a first class ornithologist. I am pleased that when Bob was in his seventies I was able to show him his first long-eared owl. I also thank Jean and Ken Garrod, Mike Marshall, Robin Biddle, David Bakewell, Mrs M. Dyke, B.Ranner, C. Buttler, M. C. Keer, Philip Murphy, S. Bishop, R. Cottrill, J. Goddard, J. Mansfield and J. H. Woolfries for providing many of the records to my Suffolk survey, while Neil Mahler was unknowingly instrumental in prompting me to publish my work. I hope it justifies his enthusiasm.

Various organisations have assisted me and I especially thank the Suffolk Naturalists' Society who supported the Suffolk Barn Owl Survey from the beginning. I also extend my appreciation to the Suffolk Biological Records Centre (SBRC), and to the Suffolk Ornithologists' Group (SOG). I thank its president, Steve Piotrowski, along with John Grant, for their interest and kind support. I also acknowledge the help of the Suffolk Wildlife Trust (formerly the Suffolk Trust for Nature Conservation).

The Royal Society for the Protection of Birds (RSPB) has been helpful in a variety of ways and I thank Chris Durdin at their Norwich Office. I am grateful to Lord Cranbrook for putting me in touch with John Duckett and his work on barn owls in Malaysian oil palm plantations. At the British Trust for Ornithology (BTO) Carole Showell, their librarian, welcomed me on my visits. I also acknowledge the assistance of Dawn Balmer, Sue Adams, Jacquie Clark and Simon Gillings of the BTO, along with Prof. Graham Martin in allowing me to use the map from the late Ian Prestt's survey from Bird Study. Several years ago David Glue published a number of interesting and useful owl papers and I thank him for his interest and allowing me to re-produce his 1974 paper also from Bird Study on barn owl diet. Elsewhere Alisdair Love was most helpful in allowing me to draw upon his pellet analysis from Essex and I thank him and his fellow authors for allowing me to re-produce the distribution map with regard to pellet samples across Britain, while at Wiley-Blackwells Publishing I thank Sally Byers and Penny Baker. In Norfolk John Goldsmith provided useful correspondence and also gave me permission to use the data from the barn owl diet study he undertook with John Buckley.

In my forward I pointed out the importance of the planners in securing the barn owl's future and Suffolk County Council was very helpful to me in many ways. I also appreciate the help from Essex County Council with my elm enquiries. Nicola Franklin at the Council for the Protection of Rural England (CPRE) provided assistance and I thank the CPRE for allowing me to reproduce their 'Tranquility Map'.

I thank Colin Shawyer for his assistance and for his kind permission to re-produce the map from his survey. I appreciate the kindness of Dr Oliver Rackham for permission to quote from the History of the Countryside and to re-produce his regional map from the New Naturalist volume, Woodlands. Richard Mabey was kind in allowing me to quote from the Common Ground. In Suffolk Barbara and John Mellor made me welcome at their farm at Saxmundham.

I thank Tim Hodge, of the Kent Ornithological Society, who provided me with the records of 'dark-breasted barn owls' and to Simon Wood who kindly provided a draft on barn owl for The Birds of Essex. David Ballance also kindly provided me with a draft of barn owl prior to the publication of his Birds of Somerset. I am most grateful for the help that has been afforded to me in West Oxfordshire by Ian Anderson and The Friends of Wychwood Barn Owl Project, a community based scheme which is designed to encourage people from the local community to get involved in barn owl conservation. In Hampshire I thank Richard Williams, of the Hampshire Observer, Clive Chatters, of the Hampshire Wildlife Trust, Alison Deveson, of the Hampshire Field Club, Alan Cleavers of the Hampshire Chronicle and Gill Jones and Richard Cartridge of BBC Radio Solent, for helping me in my attempts to track the whereabouts of Frank Gibson Phillips, or members of his family. I thank Gerry Allen, and Bob Leslie for providing office support, and Joan Humm who has kindly read the manuscript and made valuable comment. I particularly thank Bob Yexley of the Codair Group for his kind support.

The name Hosking is synonymous with barn owls and therefore I am sad that neither Dorothy or Eric are alive to see this book published. However, I am especially pleased to be able to express my sincere gratitude to their son David for his kindness, help and encouragement and for allowing me to use quotes from his father's books. When I first muted the idea of writing a book on barn owls Eric very kindly wrote a splendid foreword which, although it was written in the 1980s, I have no hesitancy in including it now. Eric is a part of the barn owl's history in Britain and his comments in that foreword are as relevant today as they were then.

The present day interest in Britain's barn owls started in 1982, with the publication of The Barn Owl. I am particularly grateful to have the opportunity to thank my friend and correspondent of many years standing, Derek Bunn, and to acknowledge all of the great work that he and his fellow authors, Tony Warburton and Roger Wilson, have made to our knowledge of this most fascinating of bird species. I thank them for allowing me to quote from their book, while Derek's help and encouragement was particularly heartening to me when progress was difficult. I am also grateful to him for reading the entire manuscript and for making valuable comment, while I am delighted that he agreed to write an accompanying preface to Eric's foreword.

In Germany I thank Peter Schell, while in Australia I appreciate the support from Alan Parker. I also thank Marius Nieuwenhuis and Mike Neish for their help in various matters.

In the United States James Steed provided assistance from the Smithsonian Institution. So often we hear of conflict from the Middle East and so I am grateful to be able to draw attention to the good work that is being under-taken there by the Society for the Protection of Nature in Israel, and I acknowledge help from Michelle Levin and Don Alon, Director of the Israel Ornithological Center. A great deal of the enthusiasm which is being fostered for the barn owl in the Middle East is being conducted by Dr. Yossi Leshem, Director for the International Center for the Study of Bird Migration, Latrun. In Palestine Imad Atrash, the Executive Director to the Palestine Wildlife Society, has, together with Yossi and Don, provided a project which is helping to draw together people from different religions and backgrounds.

I sincerely thank Annabel Whittet for her help, guidance, editing expertise and patience in taking on my book and turning what I envisaged to be a regional contribution into something a little different!

To my wife Tina I owe a great deal. Through difficult times she has given me her undivided support and most importantly she has given me her time and help unselfishly. She has read the entire manuscript (several times!) and has provided many useful comments. In addition to that, her observations and assistance in the field have been a tremendous help, and it is largely through her that I am now able to present my views upon the future of the barn owl. If I have overlooked the help of anyone then I sincerely apologise, while any errors are, of course, all my own work.

Abbreviations mentioned in the text

BTO   - British Trust for Ornithology
CPRE - Council for the Protection of Rural England
EC   - European Community
EU   - European Union
SNS   - Suffolk Naturalists' Society
SBRC - Suffolk Biological Records Centre
RSPB -   Royal Society for the Protection of Birds
SCC   - Suffolk County Council
ESA   - Environmentally Sensitive Area
MAFF - Ministry of Agriculture, Fisheries and Food.
AONB - Area of Outstanding Natural Beauty
SSSI   - Site of Special Scientific Interest
CAP   - Common Agricultural Policy

INDEX